TEACHER'S GUIDE

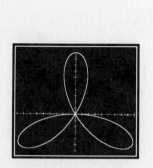 # Calculus

Graphical, Numerical, Algebraic

Addison-Wesley Publishing Company

Menlo Park, California • Reading, Massachusetts • New York • Don Mills, Ontario
Wokingham, England • Amsterdam • Bonn • Sydney • Singapore • Tokyo
Madrid • San Juan • Paris • Seoul, Korea • Milan • Mexico City • Taipei, Taiwan

ISBN 0-201-86307-3

4 5 6 7 8 9 10-ML-98 97 96

CONTENTS

CHAPTER 1 Prerequisites for Calculus

1.1 Coordinates and Graphs in the Plane

Objectives

- Determine and set appropriate viewing windows for indicated points and complete graphs of linear, quadratic and cubic equations.
- Estimate graphically and confirm algebraically the coordinates of the intercepts and any high and low points of a graph.

Key Ideas

Cartesian coordinate system

Intervals

Viewing window

Graphs of equations

Complete graphs

Teaching Notes

The standard viewing window is $[-10, 10]$ by $[-10, 10]$. Open and closed intervals are used to document the dimensions of the viewing window and the domain and range of functions in future sections. Whether by interval notation or set builder notation, this section provides the opportunity to set standards of punctuation and grammar for documenting intervals. As you attempt to find a complete graph of an equation, begin with the standard viewing window and change xMin and yMax values as needed. Students need to know the impact that changing the viewing window has on the representation of the graph. The xScl and yScl values are indicators of the scale of the viewing window. Students should beware of *fat* axes that are caused by setting xScl and yScl too small.

Students are expected to draw on previous knowledge in finding the complete graphs of lines, quadratic, and cubic equations. The viewing window must suggest all the important features of the graph. The reading gives the features expected to appear in the complete graphs for the assignment.

Agreement on drawing graphs: The phrase *sketch a graph* will mean to use pencil and paper; GRAPH will suggest (but not necessarily require) the use of a grapher; *graph* and *draw a graph* will mean to use a method of your choice. This terminology is consis-

1

tent throughout the text and should be used in your lectures, class presentations, and testing.

Notes on Examples

- Example 4. When using TRACE to support algebraic computation of the intercepts, the graph may or may not give the exact values. TRACE along the graph and watch the screen coordinates as you cross the axis.
- Example 6. If the standard viewing window does not give the complete graph, exploration using the TRACE feature will provide clues. TRACE and observe the screen coordinates.

Notes on Exercises

- Exercises 21–34. Students may choose to use the Zoom In and Out and Box features of the graphing utility. The directions ask the student to use the graph to estimate the intercepts. Agreements on accuracy and exactness are found in Section 1-5. A solution with an error of at most 0.01 is sufficient.
- Exercises 23–28. A quadratic equation program or polynomial solving feature can be used to confirm the values of the x-intercepts.
- Exercises 29–30. These are odd functions with symmetry about the origin. Have students take notice of the behavior of these graphs. Even and odd functions are discussed in detail in Section 1-3.
- Exercises 35–36. The discrete nature of graphing calculators allows for the setting δx and δy to produce friendly windows. The setting of δx and δy can be done by programming or it may be a feature built into the graphing calculator.
- **Cooperative Learning:** Exs. 35, 37–40.

Assignment Guide

Exs. 1, 4, 5, 8–11, 14, 15, 18, 19, 21, 24, 25, 28, 29, 31, 32.

1.2 Slope, and Equations for Lines

Objectives

- Write the equation of a line given specific information and sketch a complete graph.
- Find the distance from a line to a point not on the line.

Key Ideas

Slope

Equations of lines

Absolute value

Distance on the coordinate plane

Distance from a point to a line

Teaching Notes

There is a thorough development of the different forms of equations of lines. The concept of slope is used to develop the point-slope, slope-intercept, and general linear equations of lines. A discussion of the slope of horizontal lines (zero) and vertical lines (no slope) should be connected to the discussion of parallel and perpendicular lines.

Common Errors

In calculating slope and distance given two points, students often make errors when substituting into the formulas and in doing arithmetic calculations involving negative signs.

Before students begin calculating slope or distance by using two points, have them plot the two points and visually estimate the slope or distance, then compare the estimate with their derived answer.

The same strategy can be applied to graphing a line given its slope-intercept equation or its x- and y-intercepts. Students should first visualize the line in terms of its slope and/or intercepts and then confirm this with a graphing utility.

Notes on Examples

- Example 7. The slope of the given line is 1. A slope of 1 produces an angle of inclination of 45 degrees. Another avenue of attack to this problem is finding the isosceles right triangle. The hypotenuse is the distance from the point to the line.

Notes on Exercises

In the exercises for which students are asked to find the equation of a line, no instructions are given as to which form the answer is to take. An assessment of the algebraic skills of your students may dictate how much algebraic manipulation you wish them to use and in what form(s) the final equation answer is acceptable.

- Exercises 49–51. These are written in intercept form. Exercise 51 shows that an equation with x-intercept a, and y-intercept b can be written in this form.

- Exercises 53–62. An algebraic procedure for finding the distance from a point to a line is as follows:

  Step 1. Find the equation of the line perpendicular to the given line through the point.

  Step 2. Find the coordinates of the point of intersection of the given line and the line found in step one.

  Step 3. Find the distance between the two points.

  Be careful in using a graphing utility to draw a picture of perpendicular lines. Because of the scaling, the representation on the screen may not appear accurate. Squaring the viewing window of the grapher will produce a more accurate picture of the graph.

- Exercise 73b. The intersection of the lines is at $(-40, -40)$. The viewing window should contain the complete graphs of all three lines including the x- and y-intercepts.

- Exercise 80. This a challenge exercise.

- **Cooperative Learning: Exs. 67–70, 80.**

Assignment Guide

Day 1: Exs. 2, 3, 5, 8–10, 12, 13, 15, 18, 20, 21, 24, 25, 28, 30–33, 36, 37, 41, 43, 46, 48.
Day 2: Exs. 53, 56, 58, 59, 62, 63, 66, 73, 76, 78.

1.3 Relations, Functions, and Their Graphs

Objectives

- Identify a relation or function from a graph or equation and determine its domain and range.
- Identify and describe symmetries in graphs and equations and relate those symmetries to those of even and odd functions.
- Use the sum, difference, product, and quotient properties to write and evaluate the composition of two functions.
- Interpret and find formulas for piecewise defined functions.

Key Ideas

Relations and functions

Identifying the domain and range

Tests for symmetry in graphs

Even and odd functions

Library functions

Piecewise defined functions

Composition of functions

Teaching Notes

Agreement on the domain of a function: If the domain of a function is not stated explicitly, then assume it to be the largest set of x-values for which the equation gives real y-values. If we wish to exclude values from the domain, we must say so.

In the exploration of functions, the vertical line test is used to help students recognize relations which are functions.

Exploration 1 introduces parametric mode of graphing a function. Parametric equations are covered in Chapter 10, but there are examples, exploration activities and problems in selected exercises throughout the textbook that use parametric equations to develop and demonstrate concepts and solve problems.

The library function absolute value is used to introduce graphs and the notation of piecewise functions. In exploring these graphs with the TRACE feature of the grapher, students will find it beneficial to set the dimensions of the viewing window appropriately.

Students will find the complete graphs of absolute value, greatest integer, square root, reciprocal, and piecewise defined functions in the exercises. Students are expected to draw on previous knowledge in finding the complete graphs of these functions. Some discussion may be needed on what important features are expected to be shown in the complete graphs of these functions.

The connection between the symmetries and the definition of even and odd functions is made in Exploration 3. The addition, subtraction, multiplication, division, and composition of even and odd functions are reserved for the exercise set in Section 1.7.

Common Errors

A common error with parametric graphing is confusing the range valves of t with the range values that govern the size of the viewing window. The scale factors of the viewing window do not have an effect on the way the graph is drawn. The t step does affect the way the graph is drawn.

Notes on Examples

- Examples 4 and 8. The ability to generate a graph instantly and independently from any analysis is a powerful tool. On the one hand, a graph can strongly suggest any number of facts which we can then verify algebraically. On the other hand, a graph can be used to support conclusions we have already reached analytically. These two ideas, "determine graphically, then verify analytically" and "determine analytically, then support graphically," are major themes that will occur throughout the text. The instructor can begin laying the foundation for these ideas by a careful exposition of Examples 4 and 8. Example 4 shows how a grapher can aid us in determining the domain and range of a function. In Example 8 we can see from the graph that the minimum value of the function is 4 and that the function can be defined in a piecewise linear fashion. The example then proceeds to verify these facts.

Notes on Exercises

The documenting of the domain and range is asked for in several problems. Example 11 gives samples of documenting the domain of several functions that contain restrictions. See the agreement on the domain of a function. Exercises 21–26 have no restrictions on the domain and should be documented as such.

- Exercises 13–30. Students should enclose algebraic expressions in parentheses when they are part of radical, quotient, or rational expression. Exercise 13 should be keyed $y = 2 + \sqrt{(x-1)}$. Exercise 19 should be keyed $y = 1/(x-2)$.

- Exercise 29. This exercise can be changed algebraically to $(x+1)/x$. Exercise 30 can be changed algebraically to $(x^2 + 1)/x^2$. The ability to recognize that these expressions can be rewritten is useful since they will reappear in derivative and integration exercises (also exercise 77e).

- Exercises 55–56. Use the TRACE feature of the grapher to find the hidden part of these graphs that coincide with the x-axis.

- Exercises 69–72. See the note in Teaching Notes on library absolute value function.

- **Cooperative Learning:** Exs. 84–86.

Assignment Guide

Day 1: Exs. 1–4, 6, 9, 13, 16, 18–21, 24, 25, 27–29, 32–42, 44, 49, 50.
Day 2: Exs. 51, 54–56, 58, 60, 61, 67, 69, 72, 73, 76, 78, 81.

1.4 Geometric Transformations: Shifts, Reflections, Stretches, and Shrinks

Objectives

- Determine the graph of a function by applying geometric transformations.
- Describe and analyze the sequence of geometric transformations needed to obtain the graph of a function.

Key Ideas

Geometric transformations

Teaching Notes

In graphing a series of geometric transformations, set the mode of the grapher in sequential rather than simultaneous plotting. Sequential mode allows students to see the transformations appear one at a time in the order they are entered into the calculator.

The focus of the text is applying geometric transformations to the parabola $y = x^2$. Exploration 6 is a step-by-step presentation of completing the square. Completing the square is a critical procedure to analyzing the transformations of a parabola. Students can check if they have completed the square correctly by entering the equations in the form $y = ax^2 + bx + c$ and $y = a(x + h)^2 + k$ into the grapher. The desired result is one graph directly over the other. Two distinct graphs in the viewing window imply an error.

Conclusions drawn from analyzing parabolas in the form $y = a(x + h)^2 + k$ need to be transferred and altered to parabolas in the form $x = a(y + h)^2 + k$. Note that one is a function and the other is not.

Common Errors

Students sometimes make errors in the order in which they apply geometric transformations. In general, the composition of transformations is not commutative. When a sequence of transformations includes a vertical or horizontal stretch or shrink or a reflection with respect to the x- or y-axis, the order in which the transformations are applied may cause a difference in the final graph.

Notes on Examples

- Examples 3 and 6. The effect of the geometric transformations on the graphs of simple functions is illustrated in the examples. In Example 3, the point is made that a horizontal and a vertical shift can be made in either order to achieve the same result. In Example 6 reversing the order of the stretch and the shift has a very different effect.

Notes on Exercises

- Exercises 15–24 and 49–68. Per agreement in Section 1.1, the instructions to students are to use pencil and paper to sketch the graph and then support the answer with a grapher.

- Exercises 63–68. In supporting sketches of the graphs, complete graphs can be seen in the standard viewing window. In parametric mode, let X1T equal the equation, and Y1T equal T. Minimum setting of a Tstep of 1 with Tmin = −6 and Tmax = 6 will produce complete graphs of the parabolas. In function mode, two equations need to be entered to produce a complete graph.
- **Cooperative Learning:** Exs. 57–58, 69.

Assignment Guide

Exs. 1, 2, 4, 6, 7, 9, 12, 13, 15, 18, 20, 21, 23, 25, 26, 29, 32, 37, 39, 43, 44, 57, 59, 62.

1.5 Solving Equations and Inequalities Graphically

Objective

- Solve equations and inequalities using algebraic and graphical techniques.

Key Ideas

Solving equations graphically with ZOOM

Agreements on accuracy and exactness

Polynomials

Solving inequalities graphically using ZOOM and TRACE

Combining graphical, algebraic, and numerical methods

Six steps for solving a problem

Equations and inequalities with absolute values

Teaching Notes

To solve an equation means to approximate all real solutions with an error of at most 0.01 or to give the exact solution. This agreement will work well most of the time. Exceptions may occur when solutions are very large or very small.

The Rational Zeros Theorem assumes the coefficients of the polynomial are integers. Students should be cautioned about using the theorem when a polynomial contains non-integer coefficients. The goal of this section on solving polynomial equations is for students to make the connection between the algebraic and graphical techniques of finding solutions. Students are encouraged to find the exact solutions algebraically when feasible and then to confirm them graphically or by the use of a polynomial-solving feature. There are problems that do not have an algebraic solution or if they do, finding them involves a great deal of work. The power of the graphing utility allows students to find solutions to these problems by graphing and applying ZOOM and TRACE. A strategy for solving an equation using ZOOM and TRACE is the following:

1. Rewrite the equation so it is equal to zero.
2. Find the complete graph.
3. ZOOM and TRACE for the x-intercepts.

Common Errors

In solving inequalities that involve multiplying or dividing both sides by –1, students often forget to reverse the inequality sign.

Notes on Examples

- Examples 1 and 2. These examples illustrate the ZOOM and TRACE method for approximating a root.
- Example 3. The Rational Zeros Theorem is used to find a rational root of a cubic polynomial. A quick inspection of the graph enables us to eliminate every candidate except the actual root.

Notes on Exercises

- Exercises 1–8, 11–16. Solving an equation means finding all its real number solutions. There are exercises that have only one or no real solutions.
- Exercises 57–66. The six-step procedure for solving a problem is used.
- Exercise 61f. The answer is not an integer, and therefore not a solution to the coin problem.
- **Cooperative Learning:** Exs. 65–66.

Assignment Guide

Day 1: Exs. 1, 2, 6, 9, 11, 13, 16, 17, 21, 24, 25, 29, 36, 37, 39, 42,44, 48.
Day 2: Exs. 54, 57–59, 61, 63, 65, 66.

1.6 Relations, Functions, and Their Inverses

Objectives

- Determine the algebraic representation and the geometric representation of a function and its inverse, and be able to tell if a function is one-to-one.
- Manipulate and interpret the equation and geometric representation of a circle.

Key Ideas

Equations for circles in the plane

Inverse relations and inverse functions

Exponential and logarithmic functions

Special bases for logarithms

Teaching Notes

The symmetry of a function and its inverse about the line $y = x$ motivates much of the critical thinking about inverses. When using a grapher to confirm the graphical representation of a function and its inverse, enter the line $y = x$ with the two functions and square the viewing window. This will allow easier recognition of the reflection about the line of symmetry. Important concepts for students to understand about functions and inverses are (1) their composition yields the identity function, $f(f^{-1}(x)) = f^{-1}(f(x)) = x$, and (2) the relationship between the domain and range.

The text introduces exponential functions on an informal basis. It is important to explain to students that a^x is simply *a raised to the power of x* and that a must be positive when we allow the exponent x to be an arbitrary real number. To enter a^x for calculating a value or for graph, key in a^x.

Students will find complete graphs of exponential and logarithmic functions in the exercises. They are expected to draw on previous knowledge in finding the complete graphs of these functions. Some discussion may be needed on what important features are expected to be shown in the complete graphs and the domain and range of these functions.

Common Errors

Remind students that the $^{-1}$ in f^{-1} is not to be interpreted as an exponent. That is, $f^{-1} \neq 1/f$. The notation f^{-1} is simply a symbol used to name the inverse relation of f.

Notes on Examples

- Examples 1–3. These examples should be tied in with Explorations 1 and 2 which discuss how circles can be graphed on the calculator.
- Example 6. The inverse of a linear function is calculated. A discussion of Exploration 5 provides a nice follow-up.

Notes on Exercises

- Exercises 17–20. *Sketch a graph* means to use pencil and paper.
- Exercises 21–22. Students should use a grapher. The graphs are obtained by simultaneously graphing two branches of the curves, as in Exploration 2.
- Exercises 27–32. Students are not asked to find the inverse but only to determine which of these functions have inverses that are functions.
- Exercises 33–44. Students are asked to find $f^{-1}(x)$. The two-step method for finding the inverse is: (1) interchange x and y, and then (2) solve for y.
- Exercise 43. This exercise can be rewritten as $y = 2 - 5/(x+3)$.
- Exercise 44. This exercise can be rewritten as $y = 1 + 5/(x-2)$.
- Exercises 45–63. The change of base formula is useful in being able to confirm the graph of a logarithmic function with a grapher. Exercise 45 should be keyed $y = 2 \log (x-4)/\log 3 - 1$ or $y = 2 \ln (x-4)/\ln 3 - 1$.
- Exercises 63–66. Solve the equation means to find all real roots. You may choose to use either algebraic methods or the ZOOM and TRACE features of the grapher.
- **Cooperative Learning:** Exs. 67–69.

Assignment Guide

Exs. 1–9, 12, 15, 17, 20, 22, 25, 27, 28, 33, 36, 38, 40, 43, 45, 48, 51, 53, 56.

1.7 A Review of Trigonometric Functions

Objectives

- Convert between radians and degrees and find arc length.
- Find values for the six trigonometric functions and explore trigonometric identities.
- Generate the graphs of the trigonometric functions and explore various transformations upon these graphs.

Key Ideas

Radian measure

Six basic trigonometric functions

Graphs of trigonometric functions

Odd versus even functions

Geometric transformations of trigonometric graphs

Trigonometric formulas

Inverse trigonometric functions

Teaching Notes

There are decimal approximations to irrational numbers that appear frequently in evaluating trigonometric functions of selected angles. Students should be familiar with these numbers. In Exploration 1, have students take note of the angles as they appear as x- and y-values using the TRACE feature.

$$1/\sqrt{2} = 0.7071067812 \qquad \sqrt{3}/2 = 0.8660254038 \qquad \sqrt{3} = 1.732050808$$

$$\sqrt{2} = 1.414213562 \qquad 1/\sqrt{3} = 0.5773502692$$

Students are expected to draw on previous knowledge in finding the complete graphs of trigonometric functions. For a graph of a periodic function to be complete, it must show at least one period.

The Pythagorean and double-angle identities are important in solving integration problems. One of the Pythagorean identities is developed in the text. The others are left to students in the exercise set as problems 63 and 64.

Common Errors

Common errors in working with trigonometric functions involve the setting of the radian or degree mode of the calculator. Students need to pay attention to the mode in which they are working to avoid bizarre computations and graphical results.

Notes on Examples

- Examples 1 and 2. These two examples concern the conversion between degree and radian measure. Calculus students need to become comfortable with using radian measure.

- Examples 3–5. The definition of radian measure is reinforced.
- Example 12. This example confirms that the function $f(x) = \sin x + \cos x$ is a sinusoid. The graph of this function was previously discussed in Exploration 5. The calculation makes use of the angle sum formula for $\sin(A + B)$. The angle sum formulas, (6), are two of the most important trigonometric identities.

Notes on Exercises

- Exercise 37. The cotangent function has no amplitude. The range is $(-\infty, \infty)$.
- Exercises 43–52. Note agreements on domain, accuracy, exactness, and solving an equation. Students should find all real solutions.
- Exercises 53–56. Reference 1.6 Exploration 1 and 1.7 Exploration 1. Exercise 55 should be keyed X1T = 3 cos T + 2, Y1T = 3 sin T – 3.
- Exercises 71–74. These exercises involve an exploration of shift formulas.
- Exercises 75–76 Students should calculate exact values. Note that the answers are the same on both exercises because of a cofunction relationship.
- Exercises 87–90. The exercises are explorations into the addition, subtraction, multiplication, division, and composition of even and odd functions.
- **Cooperative Learning:** Exs. 85, 87–90.

Assignment Guide

Exs. 2, 3, 6, 8, 9, 12, 13, 15, 18–22, 27, 28, 31, 33, 35, 38, 40, 43, 47, 67, 75, 81.

CHAPTER 2 Limits and Continuity

2.1 Limits

Objectives

- Define and calculate limits for function values.
- Use the concept of limit to test functions for continuity.

Key Ideas

Numerical limits to values of functions

Informal definition of limit

Properties of Limits

Right-hand limits and left-hand limits

One-sided limits and two-sided limits

Teaching Notes

The compound interest problem on pages 105 and 106 is an excellent way to intuitively introduce the concept of limit. An informal definition of limit is given at the bottom of page 106 followed by some examples of limits. In the margin of page 105, use caution when presenting *How the Balance Grows* with a graphing utility. Some hand-held graphing utilities will give strange results for the formula $S_k = 100(1 + 0.06/k)^k$ if k takes on values of 1.0×10^6 or more.

Be sure to point out that the concept of limit and the definition of limit will be examined more precisely at the end of Chapter 2. In this section, informal language is used to preserve student interest and keep the topic focused. While the concepts are introduced informally, it is very important to discuss all of the theorems. Theorem 4 is of particular importance in the development of the concept of one-sided and two-sided limits.

Graphing calculators are particularly useful in the study of functions, but they cannot be used for proofs. It is essential that viewing-window graphs be complete. Examination of functions near particular points may be accomplished using the Zoom-in feature of a graphing utility, but caution should be exercised in relying only upon the

12

view of the function as shown by the grapher. Exploration 4 should be done in class to demonstrate the appropriate use of a graphing calculator.

Common Errors

In Exploration 2 and in problem 1 of Exploration 3, it is important that the teacher know how to set a *friendly window* in a graphing utility so that removable discontinuities will appear as a *holes* in the graph of the function.

Notes on Examples

- Examples 1 and 2. These examples are traditional limit problems.
- Example 3. This example makes use of Theorem 1 to calculate limits. If you have access to a graphing utility that has a table-building capability, use a numerical approach to develop an intuitive understanding of limit. Stress the importance of confirming all graphical solutions by algebraic methods.

Notes on Exercises

- Exercises 27–32. These exercises are appropriate for applying the table-building capability of many graphing utilities to solve problems.
- Exercises 38 and 40. These are excellent exercises for presentation in class for whole group discussion.
- Exercises 43–47. These exercises provide a strong foundation for problems to be presented in later sections of the textbook. They are important for students who are planning to take the Advanced Placement Calculus examination.
- **Cooperative Learning:** Exs. 74–77.

Assignment Guide

Exs. 8, 13, 17, 25, 30, 38, 40, 45, 49, 58, 61, 64, 67, 71, 75.

2.2 Continuous Functions

Objectives
- Define continuity and apply the tests for continuity for functions.
- Write composites of continuous functions.

Key Ideas

Definition of continuity

The Continuity Test

Discontinuities

Algebraic combinations of continuous functions

Composites of continuous functions

Important properties of continuous functions

The Max-Min Theorem for continuous functions

The Intermediate Value Theorem for continuous functions

Teaching Notes

A simple demonstration of continuity is to take a pencil and trace the graph of a function over any interval without lifting the pencil from the paper. Be careful to distinguish between continuity at an interior point in an interval (which involves a two-sided limit) and continuity at an end-point (which involves a one-sided limit).

The continuity test (and the equivalent test on the same page) must be understood by students before they can be successful in this course. The test for continuity and the test for differentiability (covered in Chapter 3) are the basis of calculus.

Different types of discontinuities are stated on page 119. It will be worthwhile to illustrate each type of discontinuity with a graphing calculator or by a chalkboard sketch. Names for the different types of discontinuities should be used in a consistent manner throughout the course. The text uses:

removable discontinuity

jump discontinuity

oscillating discontinuity

infinite discontinuity

When graphing piece-wise functions like the one in Exercise 16, some graphing utilities allow you to keep the calculator in connected mode and use Boolean logic tests to cause the different pieces of the function to be displayed without connecting them. One particular way to graph the functions in Exercise 16 is to enter:

$$Y_1 = 1/(X < 0)$$
$$Y_2 = \sqrt{(1 - X^2)}/(0 \le X)(X \le 1)$$
$$Y_3 = (X - 1)/(X > 1)$$

Note that this function happens to be continuous everywhere.

Common Errors

Graphing utilities sometimes connect the two branches of the graph of a function like $f(x) = 1/(x + 1)$, suggesting that the function is defined and continuous for every value in the domain, including $x = -1$. To avoid this *spike* or *phantom asymptote* in the display of the graph, many graphing utilities allow you to change the connected mode to a dot mode format for the display of such functions.

Notes on Examples

- Examples 3–8. These examples may require a discussion with students if they have not used a graphing approach in previous course work. Students who have used a graphing approach to functions should be able to move quickly through this material.

- Examples 12 and 13. These involve the concepts of maximum and minimum using a graphing approach.

- Example 14. This example illustrates a function that can have neither a maximum or minimum value.

- Example 15. This example involves finding a zero of a function using a graphing calculator. In Exercise 47, students are asked to determine the solution to $f(x) = 0$ with an error at most 10^{-8}. You may need to explain the concept of finding a zero with an error at most 10^{-8} when discussing Example 15.

Notes on Exercises

- Exercises 1–14. Assign these exercises to cooperative groups for presentation in class.
- Exercises 17–38. Use these exercises for written work.
- Exercises 49–56. These exercises can also be used for class or small-group discussion.
- **Cooperative Learning:** Exs. 53–56.

Assignment Guide

Exs. 1–6, 8, 14, 21, 26, 30, 33, 38, 41, 45, 47, 53, 55, 56.

2.3 The Sandwich Theorem and $(\sin \theta)/\theta$

Objective

- Define and apply the Sandwich Theorem.

Key Ideas

The Sandwich Theorem

Applications of the Sandwich Theorem

Teaching Notes

This is a very short, but important, section of Chapter 2. A formal proof of the Sandwich Theorem is found in Appendix 2 for those teachers who wish to present it to the class. For most students, the formal proof will not be necessary. A geometric representation (graph) and a numerical representation (table of values) of the theorem will allow students to understand how the theorem works.

The Sandwich Theorem in action is best demonstrated by using the illustration given in the top margin on page 128 for

$$y_1 = (\sin \theta)/\theta$$
$$y_2 = \cos \theta$$
$$y_3 = 1$$

Exploration 1 allows students to review some useful trigonometric identities in the context of limits. It may be necessary to refresh students' memories on these identities.

Common Errors

When doing the problems of this section with a graphing utility, be sure that RADIAN MODE is selected.

Notes on Examples

- Examples 1 and 2. These should be done graphically and then confirmed algebraically. The algebraic confirmations rely on Theorem 6.
- Example 3. This example relies on a simple trigonometric identity. You will probably want to work through this problem with students.

Notes on Exercises

- Exercises 1–16. Students who need a review of the basic properties of limits will need to work many of these problems.
- Exercises 17–30. Use these exercises to review basic skills relating to limits.
- **Cooperative Learning:** Exs. 20–22, 30.

Assignment Guide

Exs. 2–16 (even), 17, 19, 20, 22, 23, 26, 29, 30.

2.4 Limits Involving Infinity

Objectives

- Demonstrate what it means for the values of a function to approach infinity.
- Demonstrate what it means for a function $f(x)$ to have a limit as x approaches infinity.

Key Ideas

Functions with finite limits as $x \to \pm\infty$

Properties of finite limits as x approaches infinity

Limit $f(x) = \infty$ or limit $f(x) = -\infty$

End behavior models

Polynomial function end behavior

Polynomial end behavior model

Horizontal and vertical asymptotes

Asymptotic behavior of rational functions

Rational function end behavior

End behavior asymptotes

Changing variables with substitutions

Teaching Notes

The mathematical meaning of the symbol ∞ should be understood in the context of the phrase "$x \to \infty$", meaning that in a function of x, the x value *increases without bound.*

Encourage students to learn the important definitions in this section and summarize other important facts in their notes.

A major theme in this section is *end behavior modeling* for several different functions. Theorem 11 holds for polynomial end behavior modeling. Exploration 1 helps students to understand the meaning and concept of end behavior modeling. Students should be encouraged to express their understanding of end behavior model in their own words both for class discussion and for inclusion in their notebooks.

A discussion of horizontal and vertical asymptotes is a large part of this section. Three types of rational functions should be demonstrated.

1. the numerator and the denominator have the same degree

2. the degree of the numerator is less than that of the denominator

3. the degree of the numerator is greater than that of the denominator

Students should be able to use graphs to deduce properties of these functions and should confirm the results algebraically.

When exploring the end behavior of functions like those described in Example 15, be sure to set the X-scale = 0 on your graphing utility. Sometimes students fail to change the X-scale from a value of 1, or some other small number, and this results in a graph with a *fat axis* on the x-axis. Setting the X-scale prevents this from happening.

Notes on Examples

- Example 1. This example is used to explore the notion of the function approaching both positive infinity and negative infinity.

- Examples 2 and 3. These are used to illustrate the behavior of a constant function as x approaches infinity.

- Examples 4–6. These examples are used to explore the properties of finite limits as x approaches infinity. Be sure to do Example 6 with students. It is a revisitation of a similar one given in Section 2.3 on the Sandwich Theorem, this time using the following sequence for graphing purposes:

  $y_1 = (\sin x)/x$

  $y_2 = -(1/x)$ and

  $y_3 = 1/x$

  The oscillation that occurs about the x-axis decreases in amplitude as x approaches infinity.

- Examples 8 and 9. Polynomial end behavior modeling is shown through these examples.

- Examples 11–14. These examples provide an opportunity to demonstrate the end behavior modeling for rational functions. The asymptotic behavior of these functions is explored using a graphing utility. In Example 14, the line $y = x + 4$ is usually called a *slant asymptote*. In this textbook, it is called the end behavior asymptote.

- Example 15. The Exploration Bit on page 142 suggests that this example shows a creative way to see the limits at infinity using a graphing utility. First, use the viewing window suggested in Figure 2.43 and then use the viewing window [−1000, 1000] by [−2, 2] to see a picture of the graph. In this window, use the TRACE feature and trace to the far right and then to the far left. Observe the values of y at the bottom of your graphing calculator screen as you do this tracing. (The value of y will approach 1.)

Notes on Exercises

- Exercises 1–30. The theme for these exercises is to do algebraically and support graphically.
- Exercises 67–74. Some of these functions will appear again in Chapter 7.
- **Cooperative Learning:** Exs. 67–74.

Assignment Guide

Exs. 1, 5, 8, 12, 15, 20, 23, 28, 30, 33, 37, 41, 46, 49, 58, 60, 66, 69, 74.

2.5 Controlling Functions Outputs: Target Values

Objectives

- Use a graph to determine how to control the variable x in order to keep the function $f(x)$ within some predetermined target value.
- Use algebra to confirm how the variable x should be controlled in order to keep the function $f(x)$ within some predetermined target value.

Key Ideas

Controlling linear, quadratic, radical, trigonometric, and rational functions

Controlling function outputs as $x \to \infty$

Teaching Notes

The emphasis in this section is upon building the basic foundation for the epsilon-delta notation of limits. Graphing techniques are used to introduce the concept of target values, while algebraic techniques are used to confirm the results from the graph. Students need to have a thorough understanding of the explorations and examples in this section so that the more difficult concept of epsilon-delta notation can be understood in the section that follows.

The basic idea for the teacher to get across is that we can control the function values $f(x)$ to be around a target value y_0 by controlling the values of x. That is, by restricting x to a sufficiently small interval about x_0, we can force the output value $f(x)$ to fall within the target interval. Exploration 1 on page 144 is a good example to introduce this basic idea. The teacher should be sure to do the linear function example and the square root example in class.

Symmetric intervals are used for both control and target intervals about x_0 and y_0 because of their role in the epsilon-delta definition of limit. A symmetric interval is one whose center (midpoint) is the target value x_0 or y_0. If a nonsymmetrical control interval about x_0 is determined by graphical or algebraic means, we *shorten* it to a symmetric interval by taking a radius equal to the smaller of the distances from x_0 to the endpoints.

The use of epsilon-delta notation in investigating the fundamental concept of limits is a difficult topic to teach and a difficult topic for students to learn. The material in this section provides a firm foundation for understanding epsilon-delta notation.

Selecting appropriate viewing windows for a graphing utility is very important for illustrative purposes with the examples. If your graphing utility has the capability of producing vertical and horizontal lines, these lines are very effective in establishing parameters graphically for investigating intervals about x_0, which can be controlled in order to fall within a target range.

Common Errors

Students sometimes do not understand that the control interval about x_0 does not *necessarily* have to be symmetric about x_0, even though the target interval is always given to be symmetric about y_0. A graphical representation of the examples in this section followed by confirmation by algebraic methods will help to alleviate some potential problems with this concept.

Notes on Examples

- Examples 1, 3, and 4. These examples should be used as illustrative examples in class after Exploration 1 has been completed by students. A graphing utility that has the capability to draw horizontal and vertical lines will help you to reproduce the viewing windows as shown in Figure 2.46 for Example 1, Figure 2.47 for Example 3, and Figure 2.49 for Example 4. After working through Exploration 1, cooperative groups of three or four students can work through the examples so you can walk around the classroom and provide instruction as necessary.

- Examples 3 and 4. The principle of local straightness for a function in these examples is introduced intuitively through the idea of controlling the target values. The table for Example 4 shows how to find the interval about x_0 for a rational function on the left side and the confirmation of the interval on the right side. Many students usually need a review of the algebraic process by which these intervals are determined for rational functions.

- Examples 5 and 6. These examples are excellent application problems for the controlling target value concept. Students should truly appreciate the power of a graphing utility for these examples.

- Example 7. Be sure to use the Zoom-in or Solve feature of the graphing utility to show the target intervals and then show the confirmation of the interval between 0.49 and 0.51 by algebraic methods.

Notes on Exercises

- Exercises 1–22. Use these exercises to review precalculus topics and material in Chapter 1.

- Exercises 24–28. These exercises involve finding an interval within a specified parameter for trigonometric functions.

- Exercise 58. This exercise can be used as a follow-up to Example 6.

- Exercises 59–62. Students should find these exercises interesting. They provide a connection between the concept of limit and the concept of target values.

- **Cooperative Learning:** Exs. 57, 59–62.

Assignment Guide

Exs. 1–23, 26, 28, 30, 31, 34, 36, 38, 41, 44, 46, 47, 51, 54, 57, 59, 62.

2.6 Defining Limits Formally with Epsilons and Deltas

Objectives

- Define limit.
- Test the definition of limit by application.
- Find deltas for given epsilons.

Key Ideas

The definition of limit

Testing the limit definition

Finding deltas for given epsilons

Locally straight functions

How to prove limit theorems

The relation between one-sided and two-sided limits

Definitions of one-sided and two-sided limits

Limits involving infinity

Teaching Notes

The discussion on the definition of limit is an excellent way to preface the definition of limit. Be sure to make the connection between the formal definition of limit and the intuitive examples used in the previous section.

The importance of Exploration 1 cannot be underestimated. The applications of the limit definition to a constant function $f(x) = k$ and the identity function $g(x) = x$ are two of the most important in calculus.

The connection of the formal definition of limit to right- and left-hand limits is presented on page 158 and the definitions of limits *of* and *at* infinity are presented on page 159. These definitions are sufficient to form a basis for the several formal limit definitions found in subsequent chapters.

Notes on Examples

- Example 1. This example is a test of the definition of limit. A simple linear function is used to keep the calculations simple. Notice that the definition of limit does not ask for a "best" δ, just one that will work.
- Example 2. A graphing calculator is necessary to work this example. Use the viewing window version of the limit definition; that is, $[X_{min}, X_{max}]$ about x_0, and $[Y_{min}, Y_{max}]$ about L. For this example, use $[0.485, 0.515]$ by $[1.98, 2.02]$ for the initial viewing window.
- Examples 3 and 4. These examples show how to find values of $\delta > 0$ algebraically in the same way that the concept of target values was presented in Section 2.5.
- Example 5. This example uses a ZOOM-IN procedure to test local straightness for a part of the rational function $f(x) = x/(x^2 - 1)$. Capture the graph of this function in the window $[1.98, 2.02]$ by $[0.65, 0.68]$ and then trace on the function to a pixel

point slightly above the line $y = \frac{2}{3}$. Save the coordinates of the point in memory or record them as (x_1, y_1). Next, trace a pixel slightly below the line $y = \frac{2}{3}$ and save these in memory also or record them as (x_2, y_2). Now compute the slope of the line connecting the two pixel points. Then we use that slope value to tell us what δ must be for any small ε.

- Examples 6 and 7. These examples show how to apply the formal definitions of limit using algebraic methods. They should be discussed in class.

Notes on Exercises

- Exercises 1–10. Use these in class as oral problems.
- Exercises 11–20. Algebraic methods are used to find solutions.
- Exercises 21–24. The formal definitions of limit involving infinity are used to find solutions.
- Exercise 46. This can be worked as an illustrative example in class.
- **Cooperative Learning:** Exs. 42, 44–46.

Assignment Guide

Exs. 1–10, 12, 14, 19, 25, 31, 35, 37, 38, 43, 45.

CHAPTER 3 Derivatives

3.1 Slopes, Tangent Lines, and Derivatives

Objectives

- Estimate the slope of a curve at an indicated point.
- Use the definition of the derivative to find the slope of the tangent line to a point on a curve and determine the equation of the tangent line.

Key Ideas

Average rate of change

Defining slopes and tangent lines

The derivative of a function

Connections between differentiable functions and continuous functions

Differentiability on a closed interval—one-sided derivatives

Teaching Notes

The definition of the derivative of a function is presented in this section. The definition is motivated by the problem of defining and calculating the slope of a tangent line to the graph of a function.

Students should learn to calculate derivatives using the definition. This should probably be done in two stages: first, calculate the derivative at a particular point $x = c$, then generalize the process to calculate the derivative $f'(x)$ at the generic point x. Note that the alternative formula (2) for the derivative at a point is included in the proof of Theorem 1. The different notations for the derivatives should be discussed.

Exploration 3 concerns the derivation of the formula for the derivative of $\sqrt{x}$. This formula is needed in a number of exercises prior to section 3.7 where the power rule for the fractional exponents is proved. The derivation requires the technique of rationalizing the numerator which may be unfamiliar to some students.

In those examples where the equations of tangent lines are calculated, be sure to have the students graph the function together with its tangent line. Zooming in at the point of tangency demonstrates that the tangent line is a good local approximation to the function, anticipating the ideas in section 3.8.

22

Common Errors

When calculating derivatives from the definition, errors are commonly made in evaluating and simplifying the numerator of the difference quotient. Emphasize the use of parenthesis in evaluating the expression $f(x+h) - f(x)$. When $f(x)$ is a polynomial or rational function, h is always a factor of the simplified expression.

Notes on Examples

- Examples 3, 4, and 5. The derivative $f'(x)$ is calculated from the definition.
- Examples 6 and 7. Instances of functions which fail to be differentiable at a point are provided. The definition of one-sided derivatives should be discussed prior to these examples.

Notes on Exercises

- Exercises 1–4. The scales and actual functions used are as follows.
  (1) x and y scales = 1; $y = -x^2 + 4x$ (2) x and y scales = 1; $y = x^3 - 3x$
  (3) x and y scales = 0.5 ; $y = \sin \frac{1}{3}\pi x$ (4) x scale = 1; y scale = 0.5; $y = \sin x/x$
- Exercises 5–6. The equations for these exercises are in Section 3.6, Exs. 85 and 86.
- Exercises 17–20, 29, 30. See Teaching Notes on Exploration 3.
- Exercise 22. The formula can be simplified algebraically before finding the derivative.
- **Cooperative Learning:** Exs. 35–38.

Assignment Guide

Exs. 1, 4, 7, 8, 10, 11, 14, 15, 17, 20, 22, 23, 25–27, 29–32, 34.

3.2 Numerical Derivatives

Objectives

- Approximate derivatives numerically.
- Construct graphs of derivatives using numerical approximations.

Key Ideas

The NDER procedure

Graphs of numerical derivatives

Intermediate value property

Instances when the derivative does not exist

Teaching Notes

Some graphing calculators have built in routines that can numerically approximate derivatives. If a grapher does not have this capability, $f'(a)$ can be closely approximated by the symmetric difference quotient

$$\frac{f(a+h) - f(a-h)}{2h}$$

taking h to be sufficiently small. In fact, this is the formula often used by graphers for this routine. The user inputs the value of h.

The text denotes an approximation to $f'(a)$ obtained by any of the above means by the symbol NDER $f(a)$. Of course, NDER $f(a)$ depends on the method used and the value of h. For most of our purposes setting $h = 0.01$ produces sufficient accuracy, so the text takes this as the default value of h. The students should be cautioned that NDER $f(a)$ will sometimes return an extraneous value when f is not differentiable at $x = a$.

The graph of the relation $y = $ NDER $f(x)$ with $h = 0.01$ will, in many instances, closely approximate the graph of $y = f'(x)$. If the grapher does not have this built in capability, we use

$$\text{NDER } f(x) = \frac{f(x+0.01) - f(x-0.01)}{0.02}$$

for the numerical graph of $f'(x)$. Later on the graph of NDER $f(x)$ will provide graphical support in any number of differentiation and integration problems. At this stage it is a valuable conceptual tool since it allows the students to see the graph of $f'(x)$ without knowing the formula for the exact derivative.

Common Errors

In some cases it is possible for NDER to produce inaccurate or even wrong results. Students must take care in interpreting numerical results.

Notes on Examples

- Example 1. The numerical solution for the slope calculated in Example 2 of 3.1 is given. When $f(x)$ is a quadratic polynomial, NDER $f(a)$, as defined by the symmetric difference formula, always gives the exact value of $f'(a)$.

- Example 3. The function is entered
  $y = (2^{\wedge}(x+1) - \sin((x+1)/(x-2)))/(x^{\wedge}3 - 2*x+7)^{\wedge}(1/3)$

Notes on Exercises

The knowledge of how the calculator stores and retrieves information, what arguments are necessary for an operation, the available options on how to enter data, and the procedure for graphing piece-wise defined functions can save the student a great deal of time and energy in working these and future exercises. It is worth the time and effort to investigate the options available on the calculator.

- Exercises 25, 26, 43. Remind students to set their calculator in radian mode when the computations involve the differentiation of trigonometric functions.

- Exercise 26. The suggested viewing window is $[-5, 5]$ by $[-0.1, 0.5]$.

- Exercises 35–37, 39, and 40. These exercises involve graphing piece-wise defined functions. The techniques for doing this may need to be refreshed.

- **Cooperative Learning:** Exs. 42–43.

Assignment Guide

Exs. 1–3, 5, 6, 11, 12, 18, 25, 28, 35, 39, 43.

3.3 Differentiation Rules

Objective

- Use rules of differentiation to calculate derivatives.

Key Ideas

Differentiation rules

Second and higher order derivatives

Teaching Notes

By the end of this section students will be able to calculate the exact derivatives of polynomial and rational functions. Differentiation results can be confirmed by graphing $y = \text{NDER } f(x)$ and the calculated $y = f'(x)$ in the same viewing window. The two graphs should be the same. Learning the differentiation rules and their correct use is essential for all that follows, including the applications of derivatives and the antidifferentiation process.

Exploration 4 makes the point that there may be more than one way to calculate a derivative. This may mean that the answers obtained will have different forms. Students need to know this when they check their answers with the solutions given in the back of the textbook.

Common Errors

Many errors occur using the rules of differentiation, both in applying the rules and in simplifying the answer. In the Quotient Rule a common mistake is to interchange the terms in the expression $v(x)u'(x) - u(x)v'(x)$ in the numerator of the derivative. Also, mistakes often occur in simplifying this expression because of the minus sign.

Notes on Examples

- Examples 3 and 4. These examples show the process for finding points where horizontal tangents to a graph occur.
- Example 6. In discussing this example mention that when the Quotient Rule is used it is normally desirable to leave the denominator in the answer in factored form.

Notes on Exercises

- Exercises 27–30. The expressions can be simplified before differentiating.
- Exercises 31–32. These should first be rewritten as quotients.
- Exercises 35–38. The derivative of $\sqrt{x}$ is given in 3.1, Exploration 3.

- Exercises 47–56. These problems require using NDER $f(x)$. Except for Ex. 49, the algebraic rules for finding these derivatives have yet to be developed in the text.
- Exercise 63. Since the Chain Rule has yet to be introduced, the denominator of $f'(x)$ has to be expanded before the student can find $f''(x)$.
- Exercises 67–68. These require an understanding of the rules and the proper use of notation.
- **Cooperative Learning:** Exs. 80, 85.

Assignment Guide

Day 1: Exs. 1–3, 6–8, 11–13, 16–19, 22, 23, 25–27, 29, 30, 33, 37.
Day 2: Exs. 41, 44, 46, 48, 49, 67, 68, 71–74. 78, 79

3.4 Velocity, Speed, and Other Rates of Change

Objective

- Apply derivatives to applications in straight line motion and other rates at change problems.

Key Ideas

Free Fall

Average velocity

Instantaneous velocity

Speed

Acceleration

Other Rates of Change

Derivatives in economics

Estimating one of f' or f from the other

Teaching Notes

The main topic of this section is the motion of a particle along a straight line and primarily free fall motion. The novelty introduced here is the method of simulating particle motion on a grapher using the TRACE key. The text refers to this as *linear animation* and describes the idea in Exploration 1.

In free fall, if $s(t)$ is the height of the object above the ground at time t, then by graphing the parametric equations $x(t) = c$, $y(t) = s(t)$ (c a conveniently chosen constant) with suitable ranges and a suitable t-step, the pixel illuminated in the TRACE mode simulates the particle. Since t represents time, as t increments, the motion of the pixel along the vertical path simulates the motion of the particle. The idea extends to motion of a particle along any path in the xy-plane that can be represented parametrically.

Significant is this section are the definitions of velocity, speed, acceleration and rates of change defined in other contexts, notably marginal cost and marginal revenue. These definitions are relevant to any number of applications occurring later in the text.

Common Errors

In straight line motion problems, students sometimes do not correctly interpret the *sign* of a computed velocity or acceleration. For example a student may not realize that an answer of "–5 ft/sec" is equivalent to "5 ft/sec downward".

In applied problems, students will sometimes use the wrong units of measure in their answers, or omit the units of measure altogether.

Notes on Examples

- Example 6. The vertical path of the rock is plotted together with the graph of the rock's height as a function of time. The maximum height of the rock and the time it returns to the ground can be seen using either graph, then confirmed analytically. Students will need guidelines on how to choose appropriate graphing ranges for t, x and y in problems of this type. Exploration 2 applies these techniques to a horizontal motion problem.

Notes on Exercises

- Exercises 1–6. Use Exploration 2 as a model for these problems. The calculations in parts **b** and **c** can help to determine the appropriate viewing window for parts **a, e** and **f.**
- Exercises 11. For the moon, [0,350] by [0,70000] would be an appropriate viewing window.
- Exercise 36. The equation is $s(t) = -6(t - 2.5)^2 + 50$
- Exercise 37. The equation is $s(t) = 6(t - 1.5)^2 - 10$
- **Cooperative Learning:** Exs. 36–37.

Assignment Guide

Exs. 1, 2, 4, 7, 8, 10, 14, 15, 17, 18, 21, 22, 27–30, 35.

3.5 Derivatives of Trigonometric Functions

Objective

- Use the rules for differentiating the six basic trigonometric functions.

Key Ideas

The derivatives of the six basic trigonometric functions

Simple harmonic motion

Teaching Notes

The rule for differentiating $\sin x$ is proved directly from the definition using the two fundamental limits

$$\lim_{h \to 0} \frac{\sin h}{h} = 1 \text{ and } \lim_{h \to 0} \frac{\cos h - 1}{h} = 0.$$

The rule for $\cos x$ is derived is a similar manner and is left as an exercise (31). The instructor could point out the importance of the angle sum formulas for $\sin (A + B)$ and $\cos (A + B)$ in these derivations.

The rules for differentiating the four other basic trigonometric functions are shown easily by using the identities and the rules for differentiating sine and cosine. Example 3 shows the derivation of the rule for $\tan x$. The others are left as exercises (46–48). The instructor could point out the symmetry in the six differentiation formulas. In any of these rules, if you replace each function with its cofunction and change the sign of one side, you obtain the corresponding rule for differentiating the cofunction.

Common Errors

Students sometimes forget or misapply the basic trigonometric identities. The instructor may need to review the reciprocal, Pythagorean, angle sum and half-angle identities.

When working with trigonometric functions, a few tips can help avoid problems using the graphing calculator. Radian mode should be the default mode. Secant, cosecant and cotangent are entered using the reciprocal identities. An expression like $\cos^2 x$ is entered $(\cos x)^2$.

Notes on Examples

- Example 1. The Product Rule and Quotient Rule take on added significance with these new rules.
- Example 2. Simple harmonic motion is discussed.

Notes on Exercises

- Exercises 34–37, 40–42. In these exercises take note of the restriction on the domain. The solution(s) must fall within the given interval.
- **Cooperative Learning:** Ex. 45.

Assignment Guide

Day 1: Exs. 1, 2, 4, 7–9, 12–15, 17, 19, 22, 24, 25–28.
Day 2: Exs. 31, 34, 38, 39, 42, 46, 47.

3.6 The Chain Rule

Objective

- Students will differentiate composite functions using the Chain Rule.

Key Ideas

The Chain Rule

Differentiating integer powers of differentiable functions

The "outside-inside" rule

Derivative formulas that include the Chain Rule

Teaching Notes

The text takes the traditional approach for teaching the correct usage of the Chain Rule. First, students are taught to differentiate $y = f(g(x))$ by setting $u = g(x)$, calculating the two derivatives $f'(u)$ and $g'(x)$, then applying the Chain Rule to obtain $y' = f'(u)g'(x) = f'(g(x))g'(x)$. The process is then shortened by dispensing with the u and simply referring to $g(x)$ as the *inside function*. The abbreviated process is called the *outside-inside* rule for employing the Chain Rule. The latter is purely mechanical and should be mastered by every calculus student.

Common Errors

In applying the outside-inside rule to differentiate $f(g(x))$, a common mistake is to omit the factor $g'(x)$ in the answer.

Notes on Examples

- Examples 6–8. These three examples illustrate the outside-inside rule.
- Examples 1 and 2. Along with Exploration 1, these examples are meant to motivate the idea behind the Chain Rule.

Notes on Exercises

- Exercises 65–70. These exercises require evaluating the derivative of the composite function at a particular point. Examples 3 and 4 serve as models for these calculations.
- Exercises 75 and 76. These two exercises anticipate related rate problems in Section 4.6.
- **Cooperative Learning:** Exs. 80, 83.

Assignment Guide

Exs. 1–3, 5, 9, 13, 15–17, 20, 27, 30, 35, 38, 41, 44, 53, 54, 59, 61, 65, 72, 78.

3.7 Implicit Differentiation and Fractional Powers

Objectives

- Find the derivative using implicit differentiation.
- Find the derivative using the power rule for fractional exponents.

Key Ideas

Graphing curves of the form $F(x, y)$

Implicit differentiation

Tangents and normal lines

Fractional powers of differentiable functions

Points of nondifferentiability

Teaching Notes

The instructor should first spend some time with an informal discussion about functions implicitly defined by a relation $F(x, y) = 0$. Examples should use relations $F(x, y) = 0$ which can be graphed on the graphing calculator, either in parametric mode or in rectangular mode, by graphing the separate branches in the same window.

Implicit differentiation is a powerful and important technique. It is used in applications and in deriving rules for differentiating inverse functions. The four steps for the computational process appear at the top of page 240.

Common Errors

Mistakes commonly occur when a student differentiates an expression $F(x, y)$ implicitly. For example the Product Rule must be used to differentiate the term xy. The instructor should explain the difference in the two power rules:

$$\frac{d}{dx} x^n = nx^{n-1} \text{ and } \frac{d}{dx} y^n = ny^{n-1}y'$$

Notes on Examples

- Example 1. The slope at a point on the unit circle is found by implicit differentiation. Challenge students to find the answer using analytical geometry.
- Example 3. The relation can be graphed by solving for y and graphing the two branches in rectangular mode. Gaps may appear in the graph near the two points where there are vertical tangents.

Notes on Exercises

- Exercises 29–34. These exercises require finding the second derivative by implicit differentiation. Example 4 shows the techniques for doing this.
- **Cooperative Learning:** Exs. 53, 59–60.

Assignment Guide

Day 1: Exs. 1, 4–9, 12, 13, 15–17, 19, 20, 22, 24, 27, 28.
Day 2 Exs. 29–31, 34–36, 38, 40, 41, 46, 51.

3.8 Linear Approximations and Differentials

Objectives

- Investigate the linearization of a function at a point.
- Estimate change in a function value with differentials.

Key Ideas

The standard linear approximation of a function at a point

Estimating change with differentials

Formulas for differentials

Teaching Notes

Exploration 1 is a good starting point for this section. If a function f is differentiable at a point x_0, then the graph of the function and the graph of the tangent line at $(x_0, f(x_0))$ will appear on the grapher to coincide when we ZOOM in close enough to the point of the tangency. The equation of the tangent line written in functional form

$$L(x) = f(x_0) + f'(x_0)(x - x_0)$$

is called the *linearization of f at x_0*. For x close to x_0, $L(x)$ will be a good approximation to $f(x)$ since the error $f(x) - L(x)$ will be small relative to the magnitude of $x - x_0$, in fact

$$\lim_{x \to x_0} \frac{f(x) - L(x)}{x - x_0} = 0.$$

In (1), we denote $dx = x - x_0$ and define the *differential of f at x_0* to be $df = f'(x_0)\, dx$. For dx small, df will be a good approximation to $\Delta f = f(x_0 + dx) - f(x_0)$ since

$$\lim_{dx \to 0} \frac{\Delta f - dx}{dx} = 0.$$

Emphasize to the students that df is a function of two variables x_0 and dx. Whereas $L(x)$ approximates the value $f(x)$, $df = L(x) - f(x_0)$ approximates the *change* in the value of f, $\Delta f = f(x) - f(x_0)$. The two approximations differ by the constant $f(x_0)$ and have the same error.

Common Errors

When estimating a function value using a linear approximation, students will sometimes confuse the correct value of x that needs to be substituted into $L(x)$. For example, to approximate $\sqrt{0.9}$ using $\sqrt{1 + x} \approx 1 + \frac{x}{2}$, the student may incorrectly substitute $x = 0.9$ rather than $x = -0.1$.

Notes on Examples

- Example 1. This example and Exploration 2 concern the linearizations of $f(x) = \sqrt{1 + x}$ at the points $x = 0$ and $x = 3$. Completing the tables of values in Exploration 2 (2) will show how surprisingly good these approximations are when Δx is sufficiently small.

- Example 2. This example and Exploration 3 discuss the standard linear approximation $(1 + x)^k \approx 1 + kx$, for x near 0, and its generalization to $(1 + f(x))^k \approx 1 + kf(x)$, provided $f(x)$ is small near 0.

Notes on Exercises

- Exercise 23a. Students may choose to convert to fractional exponents and simplify before entering expression into the calculator.

- Exercises 31–44. The formulas needed are in the exercises. The appendix contains a list of standard geometric formulas. The students may need to review the most important ones.

- **Cooperative Learning:** Exs. 23–24, 48.

Assignment Guide

Day 1: Exs. 3, 5–7, 11–14, 17–19, 20, 25, 27, 29, 30.
Day 2: Exs. 31–35, 37, 41, 43, 51, 52, 55, 60.

CHAPTER 4 Applications of Derivitives

4.1 Maxima, Minima, and the Mean Value Theorem

Objectives

- Determine the local extrema of a function.
- Determine the intervals where a function increases or decreases.

Key Ideas

Maxima and minima

The First Derivative Theorem

Rolle's Theorem

The Mean Value Theorem

Teaching Notes

The first section of Chapter 4 is critical to the study of the applications of a derivative. Students need to understand the language of calculus, so emphasize the terminology of this section. Since confirmation of what is seen in a viewing window comes from analysis, it is important to incorporate into the calculus previously acquired algebraic skills.

The section presents two tests which are fundamental to analyzing a function and sketching its graph. These are the First Derivative Theorem for locating relative extrema (Theorem 1), and the First Derivative Test for increasing and decreasing functions (Corollary 1 of the Mean Value Theorem). It is vital that students begin to refine their curve sketching techniques by learning to interpret these tests. Stress that it is the analysis of the first derivative and (later on) the second derivative which establishes all the important features suggested by the graph on our graphing calculator and confirms that we are seeing a complete graph.

Spend some time discussing the Mean Value Theorem, its hypotheses and conclusions. The significance of the Mean Value Theorem is that it allows us to deduce properties of a function from its derivative.

Common Errors

In applying the First Derivative Test for increasing and decreasing functions, mistakes can be made solving the inequality $f'(x) > 0$, either by factoring $f'(x)$ incorrectly or by an incorrect sign analysis. Graphical confirmation should enable students to detect such mistakes.

Notes on Examples

- Example 1. Change the viewing window to [–2, 4] by [–7, 22] to show a complete graph of $f(x) = x^5 - 5x^4 + 5x^3 + 20$. Emphasize the derivative's role, along with the tools of algebra, that establishes the completeness of the graph. Regarding Theorem 1, stress that the condition $f'(c) = 0$ does not guarantee that f has a local extremum at $(c, f(c))$.

Notes on Exercises

- Exercise 9. Graph each polynomial along with its derivative and begin to make connections between y and y'.
- Exercise 14. Our graphing utility will return fractional powers of negative numbers only when the exponent has the form $\frac{1}{n}$ where n is an odd integer. In this problem, $(x-2)^{2/3}$ needs to be entered as $((x-2)^{1/3})^2$ or $((x-2)^2)^{1/3}$
- **Cooperative Learning:** Exs. 53–55.

Assignment Guide

Exs. 1, 4, 8, 9, 12–14, 17, 19, 22, 23, 25, 27, 37, 38, 43.

4.2 Predicting Hidden Behavior

Objectives

- Determine the concavity of a function and locate the points of inflection by analyzing the second derivative.
- Use the First and Second Derivative Tests for determining the local extrema of a function.
- Determine the complete graph of a function by analyzing the first and second derivatives.

Key Ideas

The First Derivative Test

The Second Derivative Test

Points of inflection

Complete graphs

Teaching Notes

Further tests for curve sketching are presented in this section: the First and Second Derivative tests for local extrema and the second derivative tests for determining concavity and points of inflection. By the end of this section students should be able to sketch complete graphs of the functions given in the exercises. In this regard, concepts like domain, range, intercepts, symmetry and asymptotes may need to be reviewed here. On page 286 there is a four step summary for applying the derivative tests which the students may find helpful.

After this section is finished, continue to include at least one or two curve sketching problems in each assignment until Chapter 4 is completed. This will help reinforce the techniques learned and connect these techniques with the optimization problems in sections 4.3 and 4.5.

Common Errors

Some students identify the point(s) for which $\frac{d^2y}{dx^2} = 0$ as point(s) of inflection. The students need to be reminded that a *change* in concavity must exist in order for a function to have an inflection point.

Notes on Examples

- Example 8. Graphing utilities afford students and teachers the opportunity to make connections between y, y', and y'' before formal methods of calculating derivatives have been established. Making these connections reinforces the concepts of differential calculus .

Notes on Exercises

- Exercises 33–36. These are rectilinear motion problems. Use Example 7 as a model. Linear animation modeling for this type of problem is described in Exploration 2 Section 3.4.
- Exercises 47–49. These exercises require students to create graphs of functions which have specified features.
- Exercises 51–54. Linearizations of functions at points of inflections are of special interest since they have an extra degree of accuracy.
- **Cooperative Learning:** Exs. 56–59.

Assignment Guide

Day 1: Exs. 2, 3, 7, 9, 15, 19, 25, 27, 29, 33, 45–49.
Day 2: Exs. 51–54.

4.3 Polynomial Functions, Newton's Method, and Optimization

Objectives

- Apply previously established curve-sketching techniques to polynomial functions.
- Use Newton's method to approximate the zeros of a function.
- Develop a strategy to solve maxima or minima problems that model real situations.

Key Ideas

Polynomial functions

Newton's method

Optimization

Teaching Notes

This section presents some specialized results for the analysis and graphing of polynomial functions. Included is a review of the Fundamental Theorem of Algebra and the result that complex roots of real polynomials occur in conjugate pairs.

Newton's method is presented since it is a fast, efficient way to approximate roots of differentiable functions. Exploration 3 gives an outline on how Newton's method can be programmed into the grapher. This offers students and teachers the opportunity to investigate the programming features of their graphing utility. Most manuals feature Newton's method as a sample program.

Students traditionally have difficulty with optimization problems, particularly with the formulation of the function to be optimized and the determination of its domain. In this regard, stress the six step "Strategy for Solving Max-Min Problems" given on page 300.

Common Errors

In optimization problems, students may overlook endpoints as possible candidates for optimal values or find solutions which are outside the domain of the input variable.

Notes on Examples

- Example 3. This example can be used to illustrate the six step procedure for solving an optimization problem.

Notes on Exercises

- Exercises 23–36. In a number of these graphing problems the roots of $f'(x)$ of $f''(x)$ will have to be approximated. The instructor should specify (or reiterate) guidelines for the required accuracy. Calculating the x-values of local extrema and points of inflection accurate to two decimal places would be appropriate.
- **Cooperative Learning:** Exs. 62, 67–69, 71.

Assignment Guide

Day 1: Exs. 2, 3, 5, 7, 9, 11, 12, 33, 37, 38, 40–43.
Day 2: Exs. 47, 48, 51, 52, 60, 64.

4.4 Rational Functions and Economics Applications

Objectives

- Sketch complete graphs of rational functions.
- Solve optimization problems that occur in industry and economics.

Key Ideas

Complete graphs of rational functions

Optimization examples from industry

Cost and revenue in economics

Modeling discrete phenomena with differentiable functions

Teaching Notes

The first step in graphing a rational function is to determine all the asymptotes and end behavior models. A complete graph should include all vertical, horizontal and slant asymptotes and these should be properly labeled. Asymptotes and end behavior models are defined in Section 2.4, and a review of these concepts would be helpful here.

When the rational function has the form $f(x) = p(x)/h(x)$, where deg $p \geq$ deg h, it is useful for the above analysis to rewrite $f(x)$ in the form $f(x) = q(x) + r(x)/h(x)$, where deg $r <$ deg h, using long division of polynomials. The latter form is also easier to differentiate. Make sure the students know how to make this transformation.

A five-step summary of the techniques for graphing rational functions is found on page 308. Remind students that when the graphing calculator is in connected mode, the vertical asymptotes appear in the display when the function is graphed.

Common Errors

Students often write asymptotes as numbers rather than equations. Require students to write and label asymptotes correctly.

Notes on Examples

- Example 1. A complete analysis of graphing a somewhat complicated rational function is given. A chart summarizing the key features of the graph is found on page 307. Explaining how the chart is formed may help students to develop proper techniques for this kind of analysis.

Notes on Exercises

- Exercises 1–24. In many of these problems the rational function to be graphed has the form $f(x) = p(x)/h(x)$ where deg $p \geq$ deg h. First rewrite the formula for $f(x)$ using polynomial division.
- Exercise 35. Showing that $L^2 = 2x^3/(2x - 8.5)$ can be quite laborious. However, it provides an excellent review of geometric and/or trigonometric relationships.
- Cooperative Learning: Exs. 35, 38, 43, 47, 49.

Assignment Guide

Exs. 3, 5, 15, 21, 27–29, 33–35, 37, 42.

4.5 Radical and Transcendental Functions

Objectives

- Analyze and graph functions whose expressions involve radical, trigonometric, logarithmic, or exponential functions.
- Solve maxima or minima problems that model radical, trigonometric, logarithmic, or exponential functions, using numerical derivations if necessary.

Key Ideas

Radical functions

Transcendental functions

Teaching Notes

This section examines the graphs of radical functions, cartain trigonometric functions and exponential and logarithmic functions. Since the derivative formulas for exponential and logarithmic functions are not developed until Chapter 7, the analysis of those graphs requires the use of the numerical derivative feature of the grapher.

Graphing radical and trigonometric functions provides a good test for the student's conceptual understanding of the first and second derivative tests since the formulas for $f'(x)$ and $f''(x)$ have a different *look*. The same is true for optimization problems involving these functions.

Common Errors

In graphing or optimizing problems involving trigonometric functions, alternative solutions to $f'(x) = 0$ or $f''(x) = 0$ are often overlooked. The periodic nature of the trigonometric functions must always be kept in mind in these problems.

Notes on Examples

- Exploration 2. Determining a complete graph of $f(x)$ involves many of the concepts and graphing techniques discussed up to this point. A suggested viewing window for one period of the graph is $[-1.571, 4.72]$ by $[-10, 10]$. Use the BOX or ZOOM IN functions to see the behavior near the local extrema and inflection points.

Notes on Exercises

- Exercises 2, 11, 20–22, 49, 50. When using a graphing utility, functions of the form $(f(x))^{m/n}$, where n is odd, should be entered $((f(x))^{1/n})^m$.
- **Cooperative Learning:** Exs. 63, 64, 74.

Assignment Guide

Exs. 1, 7, 9, 14, 19, 23, 24, 46, 49, 58, 59, 64, 69.

4.6 Related Rates of Change

Objective

- Solve related rate problems.

Key Ideas

Strategy for solving related rate problems

Visualizing relationships on a grapher

Modeling related motion

Teaching Notes

Success in solving problems where there is not a direct functional relationship between two quantities depends on mastery of the Chain Rule and implicit differentiation. Before beginning related rates, it is important for students to review and practice these concepts, both of which are difficult for them.

The six-step procedure "Strategy for Solving Related Rate Problems" on page 328 affords students a step-by-step process to follow in order to reach the desired result. Students should also be aware of appropriate ways to support graphically (see Exercise 24). Furthermore, when the motion of a moving object can be expressed as a funciton of time, parametric mode on a graphing utility can be used to model that motion. Investigate all the features of a grapher that will help support this very difficult topic.

Common Errors

The most common student error in solving problems that involve related rates is premature evaluation or substitution. Emphasize to students that the step in which they evaluate to find the unknown rate is the final one in the 6-step instructional process.

Notes on Examples

- Examples 1 and 2. Identify and label the 6-step "Strategy for Solving Related Rate Problems" for all examples presented in class.
- Example 1. Graph dr/dt as a function of the radius r in the viewing window $[0, 10] \times [0, 1]$. Trace to support the fact that the smaller the radius, the faster the rate of change of r. Investigate the relationships in Example 1 further by following the steps outlined in Exploration 1, page 326.

Notes on Exercises

- Exercise 24. Both parts are readily solved using the techniques of this section. Beyond that, it may be instructive to have the student model this problem in the manner of Exploration 1. Assume that at time $t = 0$, the cone is full, the coffe pot is empty and the coffe begins draining.
  1. Find the volume V and the level h of the coffee in the cone at time t. Find dh/dt.
  2. Find the time t when the height of the coffee in the cone is 5 in. Find dh/dt at that moment to solve part b) of the problem.
  3. Redo 2 numerically by finding the intersection of the graph of dh/dt with the horizontal line $h = 5$ on the grapher.
  4. Find the volume V and the height h of the coffee in the pot at time t. Answer part a) of the problem. (It should be obvious that dh/dt in the coffee pot is constant. Why?)
  5. At what time t does the cone empty?
- **Cooperative Learning:** Exs. 30, 34, 38.

Assignment Guide

Day 1: Exs.1, 9, 13, 17, 20, 30.
Day 2: Exs. 3, 14, 21, 22, 24.

4.7 Antiderivatives, Initial Value Problems and Mathematical Modeling

Objectives

- Find general antiderivatives of $x^n (n \neq -1)$, $\sin kx$, $\cos kx$, and linear combinations of these functions.
- Solve initial value problems of the form $dy/dx = f(x)$, $y_0 = f(x_0)$.

Key Ideas

The second and third corollaries of the Mean Value Theorem

Finding antiderivatives

Differential equations and initial value problems

Solution curves

Mathematical modeling

Computer simulation

Models in biology

Teaching Notes

Section 4.7 introduces the operation of antidifferentiation. The process of recovering a function from its derivative is fundamental to the subject so this section should not be rushed. Note that for the time being, the general antiderivative of $f(x)$ is simply denoted $F(x) + C$. The integral notation for the general antiderivative is not introduced until Section 5.5.

The six general rules listed in Example 2 serve as a beginning for the long process of learning the techniques for computing antiderivatives. Whereas the Product Rule, Quotient Rule and Chain Rule make formal differentiation a purely mechanical process, there are no such general rules for *reversing* the differentiation process. Thus antidifferentiation is a much more difficult and problematic operation.

Common Errors

Algebraic mistakes in antidifferentiating are very common. Students should get in the habit of differentiating their answer to see that they found the correct antiderivative.

Notes on Examples

- Example 8. Introduce or revisit the list capabilities of a graphing utility to generate several solutions of the differential equation $dy/dx = 3x^2$ (see figure 4.63, page 342). Then trace to the curve that satisfies the condition of passing through the point $(1, -1)$.

Notes on Exercises

- Exercises 47 and 48. These exercises are better suited for Chapter 5.
- **Cooperative Learning:** Exs. 62, 87, 89, 91–92.

Assignment Guide

Day 1: Exs. 1, 3, 5, 7, 9, 25, 27, 33, 39.
Day 2: Exs. 11, 13, 15, 31, 32, 35, 45.

CHAPTER 5 Integration

5.1 Calculus and Area

Objectives

- Approximate the area under the graph of a nonnegative continuous function by using rectangle approximation methods.
- Find the sum of a series written in sigma notation.

Key Ideas

Regions bounded by curves

Area under a graph of a nonnegative continuous function

The rectangle approximation method (RAM)

Sigma notation and algebra rules for finite sums

Computing area

Teaching Notes

The problem of calculating the area of a region under the graph of a nonnegative continuous function is introduced in this section. The first step is to approximate the area by a RAM method. In this method, the interval is divided into n equal subintervals. For each subinterval, a rectangle is then drawn whose base is the subinterval and whose height is the function value taken at either the left endpoint, right endpoint or midpoint. The sum of the areas of the n rectangles approximates the area of the region. This sum is denoted $LRAM_n$ when the left endpoints are used, $RRAM_n$–when the right endpoints are used, and $MRAM_n$ when the midpoints are used.

It is important that students graph the curve over the desired interval in order to visualize the area being sought. When this is done on the graphing calculator make sure that the viewing window is square. The built in shade feature of many calculators can be helpful here.

For small values of n, students should be able to calculate these sums by hand. For large values of n, students should use a RAM program entered on their graphing utility. As n increases, students will see the approximating sums converge to a limit, which after all, is the whole idea of integral calculus. If students understand the RAM method, later on they will develop a much greater appreciation of the Fundamental Theorem.

When the function is increasing, LRAM gives the sum of the areas of inscribed rectangles and RRAM gives the sum of the areas of circumscribed rectangles. When the function is decreasing the reverse is true. In the general case it is easier to generate a

RAM program that picks a particular point in each interval as a right or left endpoint or midpoint rather than to require inscribed or circumscribed rectangles.

Once the RAM method is established, sigma notation needs to be introduced to allow for a simpler and more effective way to express the sums. The use of this notation will be utilized in defining the definite integral. The three formulas for sums, (1)–(3) on page 364, are given without an induction proof. These are used to compute other sums by using the rules of algebra. The connection to the numerical computation of the area to one that depends on algebra relies on the rules and properties of finite sums.

Common Errors

The average of the LRAM and the RRAM is not the MRAM. In fact, the average is the trapezoidal rule.

Notes on Examples

- Examples 2 and 3. Example 2 is easy to do without the RAM program, whereas Example 3 is much more difficult and should use the program. Students should realize when the program is appropriate and when it is not . Graphing the curves in both examples will help students to visualize the problem.

Notes on Exercises

- Exercises 1–6. The emphasis in these exercises is on computing the sums by writing them out.
- Exercises 7–14. Due to the large values of n, the program should be used.
- Exercises 19–53. These exercises familiarize students with sigma notation.
- Exercises 54–69. These exercises begin showing students how exact areas are computed.
- Exercise 69. The algebra rules for finite sums are used to do this exercise.
- **Cooperative Learning:** Exs. 69, 74–76.

Assignment Guide

Day 1: Exs. 1, 5, 7, 11, 15, 19, 25, 31, 35, 37, 43, 45, 47.
Day 2: Exs. 53, 55, 57, 59, 61, 63, 69.

5.2 Definite Integrals

Objectives

- Express the definite integral as a limit of Riemann sums.
- Express the area under a curve as a definite integral.
- Compute the area under a curve using a numerical integration procedure.

Key Ideas

Riemann sums

Terminology of integration

The definite integral and area

Constant functions

Evaluating definite integrals numerically with technology— the NINT procedure

Discontinuous integrable functions

Teaching Notes

The formal definition of the definite integral as a limiting value of Riemann sums is presented in this section.

To understand how the definition works it is easiest to first assume the function is nonnegative. In that case the value of the definite integral is the exact area under the curve, and a Riemann sum is a rectangular approximation of that area. Students should understand that in the Riemann sum, $f(c_k)$ and Δx_k represent the height and width of the kth rectangle, so the Riemann sum represents the sum of the areas of n rectangles. As the norm of the partition approaches 0, these approximating Riemann sums approach the exact value of the area. Emphasize Exploration 1 which observes that $LRAM_n f$, $RRAM_n f$, and $MRAM_n f$ are special Riemann sums which select the subintervals and the points c_k in specific ways.

Students should then be led in a discussion of the case when the function takes on negative values at all or some of the points in the interval of integration. The main idea to establish here is that the definite integral represents the *signed* or net area of the region between the graph of the function and the x-axis.

Many machine graphers have a built in numerical integrator. Make sure that the student can translate the definite integral to the notation utilized by the calculator which can be entered into the calculator. As students begin to explore and compute a variety of areas, they should continue to examine the graphs of these regions and estimate the area to ensure that the computation is reasonable.

Common Errors

In finding the area of a region between a curve and the x-axis, functions that are both positively valued and negatively valued warrant special consideration. The region must be divided so that intervals for which the curve is above the x-axis and below the x-axis are considered separately. For any region below the x-axis, the value of the integral will be negative and is negated to represent the area. If the interval of integration is not divided in this manner, the definite integral will yield the *net* area, which is a signed number.

Notes on Examples

- Example 6a. Students should graph the curve to establish that it is indeed nonnegative. Students can then estimate the area based upon the graph. The area of two triangles is a good approximation for $f(x) = x \sin x$.
- Example 6b. The idea that not all functions bound areas that can be computed by analytical means is established by this example.

Notes on Exercises

- Exercises 7–14. These exercises connect the definite integral to the summation notation. They help reinforce the idea of the limit of Riemann sums as the definite integral.
- Exercises 15–20. The sign of the function must be considered in establishing the area of the given region.
- Exercises 21–24, 26, 28–30. These exercises cannot be done by analytical means. Over the course of Chapters 5–8, students should learn to recognize when they need to use NINT to calculate a definite integral.
- **Cooperative Learning:** Exs. 45, 49, 52.

Assignment Guide

Day 1: Exs. 1, 7, 13, 15–29 odd.
Day 2: Exs. 31–53 odd.

5.3 Definite Integrals and Antiderivatives

Objectives

- Apply the rules for definite integrals.
- Find the average value of a function over a closed interval.
- Compute the area under a curve using antiderivatives.

Key Ideas

The average value of a function

Connecting differential and integral calculus

Teaching Notes

At the end of Chapter 4 the process for finding antiderivatives and solving initial value problems was established. Students are expected to know those basic rules and formulas as they begin this section. The connection between solving the initial value problems and finding the area under the graph of a nonnegative function is the main focus of the section.

The algebra rules of the definite integral are given without detailed proofs except for Rule 3. Others could be verified by a similar argument.

The mean value theorem for integrals states that there exists some c in $[a, b]$ such that $f(c)(b-a) = \int_a^b f(x)\,dx$, whereas the average value definition finds $f(c)$. Exploration 1 graphically shows that the value of $f(c)$ represents the height of the rectangle with base length $b-a$ whose area is the same as the area under the curve. This idea is used in Section 5.4 to establish the fundamental theorem.

The powerful idea that the area under a curve can be found by solving a differential equation with a given initial condition establishes the method typically used to compute definite integrals and foreshadows the fundamental theorems established in the next section.

Notes on Examples

- Example 1. This example allows students to investigate the definite integral rules without the use of particular functions. This type of problem reinforces the idea that the capabilities of machines are not always necessary or sufficient in finding answers.

Notes on Exercises

- Exercise 1–18. Practice for finding areas using definite integrals is provided by these exercises. NINT can be used to verify the results.
- Exercises 19–22. The properties of the definite integral are illustrated. Point out that NINT is of no use in solving these problems.
- Exercises 23–38. These are average value problems.
- **Cooperative Learning:** Exs. 30, 35, 36.

Assignment Guide

Day 1: Exs. 1–21 odd.
Day 2: Exs. 23–37 odd.

5.4 The Fundamental Theorem of Calculus

Objectives

- Use the Fundamental Theorem of Calculus to establish the link between differential and integral calculus.
- Compute the definite integral by using the Fundamental Theorem of Calculus.
- Apply definite integrals in business applications.

Key Ideas

The Fundamental Theorem, Part 1

Graphing the function $\int_a^x f(t)\,dt$ numerically

The Fundamental Theorem, Part 2

(Integral Evaluation Theorem)

Evaluating definite integrals

Viewing graphs never seen before

The area connection

Business applications

Average daily inventory

Teaching Notes

This section relies heavily on the capabilities of a machine grapher to graph an anti-derivative using $y = \text{NINT}(f(t), a, x)$. The notation $\text{NINT}(f(t), a, x)$ represents finding the area under $f(t)$ from a to x for each value of x in the interval xMin to xMax. When graphing, NINT f will indicate using either the machine capabilities or the program to graph an antiderivative numerically. NINT f may also mean finding the value of the definite integral. The two uses are much different and will depend upon the context of the problem.

If the grapher has the capability of graphing NINT $(f(t), a, x)$ directly, this process can be speeded up considerably by graphing $x(t) = t$ and $y(t) = \text{NINT}(f(t), a, t)$ in parametric mode, with an appropriate t-step.

Defining a function in the form $F(x) = \int_a^x f(t)\, dt$ plays a critical role in the fundamental theorems. When $f(x)$ is a positive function, $F(x)$ can be interpreted as the area under the graph of f over the interval $[a, x]$. Observe in this case that $F(x) > 0$ when $x > a$, $F(x) < 0$ when $x < a$ and $F(a) = 0$. Changing the value of "a" will create a new function which differs from $F(x)$ by a constant. In fact, if $G(x) = \int_{a'}^x f(t)\, dt$ then $G(x) = F(x) - F(a')$. By varying "a" we obtain the entire class of antiderivatives of $f(x)$, whose graphs are all parallel to the graph of $F(x)$.

By graphing $\text{NDER}(\text{NINT}(f(t), a, x), x)$, part 1 of the theorem can be verified visually. Since the graphing of this function is quite slow in function plotting mode, this should be done in parametric mode letting $x = t$ and $y = \text{NDER}(\text{NINT}(f(t), a, t), t)$. All such graphs will be the same no matter what "a" value is chosen.

Common Errors

In calculating a definite integral by the Fundamental theorem, a very common mistake is to evaluate the expression $[F(x)]_a^b = F(b) - F(a)$ incorrectly. Emphasize the use of parentheses as in Example 5 to overcome this kind of mistake.

Notes on Examples

- Example 8. An antiderivative of a function that does not have a closed form antiderivative is graphed. It is suggested that a slopefield be drawn for this curve. The toolbox program SLOPEFLD is needed to accomplish this. This program will draw a family of parallel curves that represent the antiderivatives for different "a" values. Superimposing the graph of antiderivatives with different "a" values using NINT f will show how these curves fit to one of the family of curves drawn by SLOPEFLD.

Notes on Exercises

- Exercises 1–14. These exercises provide practice in using the second part of the fundamental theorem. They should be done analytically and verified with NINT.
- Exercises 19–24. The need for continuous curves is emphasized.
- Exercises 25–28. Students need to examine the shaded region to establish a way to find the area. Exercises 25 and 26 will need two integrals and 27 and 28 will require subtracting an area to find the shaded region. The values can be found analytically.
- Exercises 29–42 and 61–68. The use of a grapher is required to complete these exercises.
- **Cooperative Learning:** Exs. 56, 62, 67–68.

Assignment Guide

Day 1: Exs. 1–27 odd.
Day 2: Exs. 29–39 odd, 43, 45.
Day 3 Exs. 51, 53, 56, 57, 59, 61.

5.5 Indefinite Integrals

Objectives

- Apply the formulas and rules for indefinite integrals.
- Apply indefinite integrals to solving initial value problems.

Key Ideas

The indefinite integral of a function

Formulas and rules for indefinite integrals

Supporting indefinite integral evaluation graphically

The integrals of $\sin^2 x$, $\cos^2 x$, $(\sin x)/x$

Solving initial value problems with indefinite integrals

Teaching Notes

In this section the text introduces the notation $\int f(x)\,dx = F(x) + C$ for the indefinite integral of f. Emphasize that $F(x)$ is a *particular* antiderivative of f, and C is the arbitrary constant which must be part of the expression since $\int f(x)\,dx$ represents the set of *all* antiderivatives. Recall Corollary 3 of the Mean Value Theorem for derivatives (Page 337), which states that any two antiderivatives of f must differ by a constant. Explain how the notation for the indefinite integral derives from the Fundamental Theorem, which states that $F(x) = \int_a^x f(t)\,dt$ is one particular antiderivative of f.

Students should learn to apply the general rules in Tables 5.4 and 5.5 to find indefinite integrals whose formulas can be found by reading known differentiation formulas "backwards". Students should develop the habit of always checking their results by differentiating the answer $F(x) + C$ and confirming that the derivative F' and the integrand f are equivalent. Results can be confirmed graphically by comparing the graphs of NDER F and f, or the graphs of F and NINT f. NDER F and f should be identical, whereas the graphs of F and NINT f should be parallel.

For a continuous function f with no closed form antiderivative or whose antiderivative is found by techniques yet to be developed, by graphing $\text{NINT}(f(t), a, x)$ for an appropriate "a", the student can see the graph of an antiderivative without knowing its formula. Example 9 is an illustration.

Common Errors

At first, some students will be reluctant to include the constant of integration. Its importance should be emphasized. Examples such as number 3 illustrate the need for this constant since there exists an infinite number of antiderivatives for any indefinite integral. The constant takes on specific values when initial conditions are given.

Rewriting the constant of integration in indefinite integrals, as in Example 5, is often confusing to students since the symbol C is actually being redefined. In some cases, to verify an antiderivative is equivalent to a known formula, an algebraic transformation *and* a redefining of the constant are required.

Errors in algebra commonly occur in the simplest of all integration formulas,

$$\int x^n dx = \frac{x^{n+1}}{n+1} + C, \ (n \neq -1),$$

especially when n is a fraction or is negative. These errors can be avoided if students routinely check their results by differentiating.

Notes on Examples

- Example 3 illustrates that NINT f can be used to verify an antiderivative. The graph of NINT f and $x \sin x + \cos x$ differ only by a constant since the two graphs are parallel. The graphical derivatives of each found by using NDER will be the same. A challenge is to determine the value of "a" in NINT f that will produce the graph $x \sin x + \cos x$. The value will be the solution to the equation $a \sin a + \cos a = 0$ since the constant of integration should be 0.

Notes on Exercises

- Exercises 1–30. Practice for finding antiderivatives is provided.
- Exercises 39–46. Practice in solving initial value problems is provided. This will help students see the need for the constant of integration. Answers can be verified with NINT, SLOPEFLD or by NDER.
- Exercises 43–49. These exercises require solving differential equations involving second and third derivatives. Students will need to see examples of these before assigning.
- Exercises 33–38. The verification of formulas by differentiating is required. These formulas are obtained by the method of substitution in section 5.6.
- **Cooperative Learning:** Exs. 49, 51, 52.

Assignment Guide

Day 1: Exs. 1–29 odd.
Day 2: Exs. 31–47 odd, 50.

5.6 Integration by Substitution—Running the Chain Rule Backward

Objectives

- Apply the power rule to compute indefinite and definite integrals.
- Find indefinite and definite integrals of trigonometric integrands.
- Use the substitution method of integration.

Key Ideas

The generalized power rule in integral form

Trigonometric integrands

The substitution method of integration

Substitution in definite integrals

Teaching Notes

The method of substitution is the most important of all algebraic methods for finding antiderivatives and evaluating definite integrals. It takes a certain amount of skill and experience to recognize the correct substitution to be used and indeed, to recognize those forms in which a substitution will work. Discuss Examples 1 through 6 carefully, stressing the three basic steps for finding an antiderivative by substitution, which are found on page 417. When the antiderivative is differentiated to verify its correctness, point out that the Chain Rule is being used, and that u-substitution is a method for the much more difficult task of reversing that calculation.

The formula for substitution in definite integrals, formula (9), is of fundamental importance. The instructor may want to include additional examples using this formula besides Example 7. Pay particular attention to Exploration 4 which discusses the two basic strategies for calculating a definite integral.

Common Errors

Student errors in the substitution method are legion. One of the most common is to insert the wrong constant multiplier. To prevent this type of mistake, emphasize the mechanical nature of the process, once the correct substitution is identified. For example if $u = 2x$, then $du = 2dx$ so $dx = \frac{1}{2}du$ (Solve for dx!). Thus $\int \cos 2x \, dx$ becomes $\int \cos u \cdot \frac{1}{2}du$.

Many different types of mistakes occur when substituting into definite integrals. Before starting a calculation, students should decide which of the two methods discussed in Exploration 4 is to be used and should use that method throughout.

Notes on Examples

- Example 4. Students are asked to find the antiderivative and support the answer graphically. In using NINT f, students should change the lower bound, which is 0 in the example, to see the effect on the graph.

Notes on Exercises

- The exercises of this section allow the student to practice the methods outlined in this section. In using NINT f for the problems that are indefinite integrals, students must understand how the lower bound effects the graph. Students may also confirm their results by graphing the NDER of their antiderivative.

- **Cooperative Learning:** Exs. 55–56, 57.

Assignment Guide

Day 1: Exs. 1–25 odd.
Day 2: Exs. 29–47 odd.
Day 3: Exs. 49–57 odd.

5.7 Numerical Integration: The Trapezoidal Rule and Simpson's Method

Objectives

- Approximate the definite integral by using the Trapezoidal rule.
- Approximate the definite integral by using Simpson's rule.
- Estimate the error in using the trapezoidal and Simpson's rules.

Key Ideas

Trapezoidal rule

Simpson's rule

Error analysis

Controlling the error in an integral approximation

Working with numerical data

Computer programs

Teaching Notes

Many definite integrals cannot be computed algebraically by any means. The two numerical techniques of finding the definite integral, the trapezoidal rule and Simpson's rule, are powerful tools for finding those integrals.

In the trapezoidal rule, the region between the graph of f and the x-axis is partitioned into n equal subintervals as the RAM method, but trapezoids are used in place of rectangles. The top of each trapezoid is the line segment connecting two consecutive partition points on the curve. The approximation of the integral is the sum of the areas of the n trapezoids. Since the chord joining two consecutive points will in general fit a curve better than a horizontal line, the trapezoidal rule gives generally better results than a RAM method.

In Simpson's rule, the interval of integration is divided into an even number, $2n$, of equal lengthened subintervals. Over each consecutive *pair* of subintervals, the curve is approximated by the *parabola* determined by the three consecutive partition points. The approximation of the integral is the sum of the integrals of the n parabolic arcs. This rule gives very accurate results for relatively small values of n.

Programs exist that allow students to compute the value of the integral by use of these two methods. The values of these should be compared to the values given by the RAM methods. Students should note how many more subintervals are required for the RAM to get answers that are as accurate as those given by the trapezoidal rule and by Simpson's rule.

By using the error formulas, the amount of error will quickly decrease as the number of partitions increase. Computing the error of each will help establish the accuracy of the two methods.

Common Errors

Students may confuse the trapezoidal rule with the midpoint rule. The difference in the two should be illustrated. The two methods given in this section do not use Riemann sums. Riemann sums are rectangular approximations to the area under the curve.

Notes on Examples

- Example 6. This is a real world problem that cannot be done by a definite integral. By use of Simpson's rule the required area is simple to compute. This illustrates the need for numerical techniques of computing definite integrals. NINT f is useless for this problem.

Notes on Exercises

- Exercises 1–6. The approximations are compared to the exact area which are computed analytically.
- Exercises 7–12. The approximations are to be compared to values obtained by NINT f.
- Exercises 29–32. By completing these exercises the relationship of the trapezoidal rule and Simpson's rule to the RAM approximations is established.
- Exercises 31 and 32. The formulas that are used by programs to find the trapezoidal and Simpson approximations are stated.
- Exercises 33–36. Students work with real world situations that require numerical approximations.
- **Cooperative Learning:** Exs. 33–36.

Assignment Guide

Day 1: Exs. 1–11 odd; 15, 19, 21, 23.
Day 2: Exs. 25, 29, 31; 33–36.

Chapter 6 Applications of Definite Integrals

6.1 Areas between Curves

Objective

- Find the area between two curves.

Key Ideas

The basic formula: Area $= \int_a^b (f_1(x) - f_2(x))dx$, where $f_1 \geq f_2$

Finding the limits of integration

Boundaries with changing formulas

Integrating with respect to y

Combining integrals with formulas from geometry

Teaching Notes

The first step in finding the area of a region between two curves is to graph the region. By graphing the two curves in sequential mode students will be able to see which formula gives the upper curve. The SHADE function can also help in this regard. For example, on our grapher SHADE(f_2, f_1) will shade only the region having $y = f_2(x)$ as the lower boundary.

Determining the limits of integration may involve finding the points where $y = f_1(x)$ and $y = f_2(x)$ intersect. This will mean solving $f_1(x) = f_2(x)$ to find the x-coordinates of the intersection points. Students sometimes have trouble with the algebra here. Being able to visually estimate these points on the grapher can be a big help.

As in all of the applications in this chapter, the formula for the area is established by first approximating with a Riemann sum, (Eq. (1) page 442), then letting the partition norm approach 0 to obtain the exact area. Using the Riemann sum approximation, in fact, is a good way to remember the correct integration formula. Draw a thin vertical strip of thickness Δx between the two curves. The area of the strip is approximately $\Delta A = [f_1(x) - f_2(x)]\Delta x$, where x is a value selected in the base interval of width Δx. Thus, the exact area of the region is $\int_a^b [f_1(x) - f_2(x)]dx$.

Use the four step summary on page 443 as a reference for the basic techniques developed in this section. An important variation occurs in finding the area of a region whose right and left boundaries are the curves $x = f_1(y)$ and $x = f_2(y)$. This merely requires integrating with respect to y rather than x. Finding the correct formula for $f_1(y)$ or $f_2(y)$ may involve calculating the inverse of a function $y = g(x)$.

Common Errors

Algebraic mistakes sometimes occur when students simplify the expression $f_1(x) - f_2(x)$ in the integrand. Another common error students make is to not recognize when a boundary curve changes formulas and thus requires separate integrations.

Notes on Examples

- Examples 3 and 4. The formula for the lower curve changes, so the area is found by summing two separate integrals. In Example 4 the same area is found by a single integration by integrating with respect to y.

Notes on Exercises

- Exercises 3, 4 and 25. In these exercises integration with respect to y is easier.
- Exercises 17 and 18. These exercises can be solved only with a grapher and NINT.
- **Cooperative Learning:** Exs. 29–33.

Assignment Guide

Day 1: Exs. 1–15 odd, 23, 25.
Day 2: Exs. 17, 19, 21, 27, 29.

6.2 Volumes of Solids of Revolution—Disks and Washers

Objectives

- Find the volume of a solid of revolution by using the disk method.
- Find the volume of a solid of revolution by using the washer method.

Key Ideas

Solids of revolution

The disk method

The washer method

Teaching Notes

Visualizing the result of rotating a plane region about an axis is difficult. It is much easier to visualize what happens if a single rectangle with sides drawn perpendicular to that axis is rotated about the axis. For the disk method, if a rectangle of height $f(x)$ and width Δx, with base lying on the x-axis, is rotated about the x-axis, the result will be a *disk* of volume $\Delta V = \pi f(x)^2 \Delta x$. The volume of a solid of revolution about the x-axis is approximated by summing the volumes of such disks (Eq. (1), page 452). Interpreting Eq. (1) as a Riemann sum leads to Eq. (2) which is the formula for the exact volume.

The same idea is used for the washer method. In this case, if we rotate a single rectangle whose base lies *above* the x-axis about the x-axis, the result is a *washer* whose volume is $\Delta V = \pi[R(x)^2 - r(x)^2]\Delta x$, where $R(x)$ is the outer radius and $r(x)$ is the inner radius. This leads to Eq. (4) on page 456.

The washer method can of course be applied to calculating the volume of a solid of revolution about the y-axis or some other axis.

A grapher can display a cross section of a solid of rotation in the xy-plane by graphing the bordering curves and their reflections in the axis of rotation.

Common Errors

In the washer method the volume element is sometimes mistakenly written as $\pi[R(x) - r(x)]^2 dx$ instead of $\pi[R(x)^2 - r(x)^2]dx$.

Errors are often made by incorrectly determining the plane region being rotated. Stress the 4-step summary for the washer method on page 457.

Notes on Examples

- Example 3. In this example the solid is obtained by rotating a region about the line $y = 1$. A discussion of the example will help reinforce the concepts involved in this section.

- Example 5. To obtain a graph of the cross section of this solid in the xy plane, store $y_1 = -x + 3$, $y_2 = x^2 + 1$, $y_3 = -x^2 - 1$, and $y_4 = x - 3$, graph these in the window $[-2, 1]$ by $[-5, 5]$, and shade the two regions.

Notes on Exercises

- Exercises 1–30. The method required is stated clearly. Students should realize why the method is being used, since they will be expected to choose the correct method later.

- Exercises 31–34. Discuss one or two of these exercises in class to demonstrate how the correct integral is set up.

- Exercises 35–37. The emphasis in these exercises is on establishing the integral. Different axes of rotation are used, requiring different outer and inner radii. Use Example 3 as a model. Once the integrals are found, their values can be found algebraically or with NINT.

- **Cooperative Learning:** Exs. 40, 43, 44.

Assignment Guide

Day 1: Exs. 1, 5, 9, 13, 15, 19, 23, 25, 27.
Day 2: Exs. 31, 33, 35, 37, 39.

6.3 Cylindrical Shells—An Alternative to Washers

Objective

- Find the volume of a solid of revolution by using the shell method.

Key Ideas

The basic shell formula

Rotation about the x-axis

Shifts

Shells versus washers

Teaching Notes

Consider again a thin rectangular region whose sides of length h are parallel to the y-axis and whose base of width Δx lies along the x-axis. If we rotate this region about the y-axis the result will be a thin cylindrical shell of volume $\Delta V = 2\pi rh\Delta x$, where r is the distance from the y-axis to the *midpoint* of the base. The shell method uses this idea to find the volume of a solid generated by revolving a region of the form $\{(x,y) \mid a \leq x \leq b, 0 \leq y \leq f(x)\}$ about the y-axis, where $0 \leq a \leq b$. The volume is approximated by summing the volumes of shells obtained in the above manner. Interpreting this sum as a Riemann sum leads to the integral formula for the exact volume, Eq. (1) on page 465. The method extends to finding volumes of solids obtained by rotating regions of the form $\{(x,y) \mid a \leq x \leq b, f_2(x) \leq y \leq f_1(x)\}$ about the y-axis.

The shell method can be adapted to rotation about any axis. For certain regions this allows the possibility for using either the shell method or the washer method to calculate the volume of the solid of rotation. Stress the importance of carefully determining the generating region and the formulas for the upper and lower boundary curves of the region (or the right hand and left hand boundary curves). There is a four step summary for the shell method and a schematic for remembering the integrand for the formula on page 466.

Common Errors

Having two different methods, the shell method and washer method to calculate a volume, will cause some confusion. Students will confuse the formulas for the two methods and may have difficulties deciding which one to use. Do examples in class where only one of the two methods is feasible or where one of the methods is demonstrably easier to employ than the other.

Notes on Examples

- Example 1. Note that this example can also be done with washers. A cross section of the solid can be viewed by graphing $y_1 = \sqrt{abs(x)}$ on the interval $[-4, 4]$ and shading the region under the curve.

- Example 2. The volume of the solid in Example 1 of 6.2 is recalculated using the shell method. Point out to the students that the two methods really do produce the same results.

Notes on Exercises

- Exercises 1–15. Students are to use only the shell method in computing the volumes. Have them decide if another method is more appropriate or equally easy to use. Exercise 15 is a good example of a volume that would be difficult to find without shells. Notice in this problem that a rectangle drawn perpendicular to the x-axis would need the same curve to find the outer and inner radii.

- Exercises 17–26. Students should use a variety of methods. Graph the generating region and key in on the form in which the equations are given to help establish the method to be utilized.

- **Cooperative Learning:** Exs. 27–30.

Assignment Guide

Day 1: Exs. 1, 5, 9, 11, 13, 15.
Day 2: Exs. 19, 21, 23, 25.

6.4 Lengths of Curves in the Plane

Objective

- Compute the length of a curve.

Key Ideas

The basic formula

Dealing with discontinuities in dy/dx

The short differential formula

Teaching Notes

The formula for arc length is one of the fundamental applications of integration. If you have the time, a careful discussion of the derivation of this formula will be very rewarding. The length of a curve is approximated by the length of a polygonal path which closely fits the the curve. Using the Mean Value Theorem, the length of the polygonal path can be interpreted as a Riemann sum and this leads to the definition of arc length as a definite integral.

Applying the formula requires some amount of algebraic manipulation since dy/dx must be calculated, then the expression $\sqrt{1 + (dy/dx)^2}$ has to be formed and simplified before integrating. Point out to the students that this integral often has to be evaluated numerically. In Examples 1 and 3 and in many of the exercises, the functions are chosen carefully so that the integral can be evaluated algebraically.

The formula requires dy/dx to exist and be continuous on the interval for which the arc length is sought. If this condition fails at a point, it may be possible to find arc length by expressing the function defining the curve as a function of y and integrating the expression $\sqrt{1 + (dx/dy)^2}$ over the appropriate range of y values.

Common Errors

Algebraic errors will inevitably occur when simplifying the expression $1 + (dy/dx)^2$. Solutions can be checked numerically setting $y_1 = \text{NDER}(f(x), x)$ and finding $L = \text{NINT}(\sqrt{1 + y_1{}^2}, a, b)$. The curve could also be graphed in a square window and its length visually approximated.

Notes on Examples

- Example 2. Numerical methods are required in this example. The value of the integral can be found accurate to three decimal places using Simpson's Rule with $n = 40$.
- Example 3. At $x = 0$, dy/dx does not exist. By rewriting the formula for the curve as $x = 2y^{3/2}$, the arc length can be found by regarding y as the independent variable. Note that the limits of integration are now the y *values* of the end points of the curve.

Notes on Exercises

- Exercises 5–10. In Exercises 5–8 the radicand is a perfect square, so the integral can be found algebraically. The same is true for Exs. 9 and 10 except that the differentiation formulas for e^x and $\ln x$ have yet to be presented. At this point these problems would have to be done using NDER and NINT.
- Exercises 21–28. Point out that most applications of finding an arc length do not work easily by analytical means. Technology allows students to see the uses of this formula in real world applications.
- **Cooperative Learning:** Exs. 23–26.

Assignment Guide

Day 1: Exs. 1–11 odd.
Day 2: Exs. 15, 17, 21, 25, 27.

6.5 Areas of Surfaces of Revolution

Objectives

- Find the surface area of revolution about the x-axis.
- Find the surface area of revolution about the y-axis.

Key Ideas

The basic formula: revolution about the x-axis

Revolution about the y-axis

The short differential formula

Teaching Notes

The formula for the area of a surface of revolution is the most complex formula students will encounter in this chapter. The text can only partially justify the formula since a rigorous derivation requires concepts from advanced calculus. The basic idea behind the derivation is similar to the derivation of the arc length formula. The generating curve is approximated by a polygonal path. If we rotate the polygonal path about the x-axis it generates a surface area whose formula, Eq. (3) on page 483, looks like a Riemann sum but isn't. Nonetheless, the theory tells us that as the partition norm approaches 0, that is, as the polygonal path better and better approximates the curve, the values of the sums in Eq. (3) will approach the value of the definite integral defined by Eq. (4).

The short differential formula is easy to remember and it conveys the idea behind the derivation. If a small piece of arc of length ds is rotated about an axis, the surface area generated will be approximately $\int 2\pi\rho\, ds$, where ρ is the distance from the axis to the arc. Thus the surface area is $S = \int 2\pi\rho\, ds$. The limits are omitted in the integral since the formula applies equally well to rotation about either axis.

Notes on Examples

Example 3. The use of the short formula is illustrated in this example. Since rotation is about the x-axis, $\rho = y$ and the differential of arc $ds = \sqrt{1 + (dy/dx)^2}\, dx$. The integration limits are the x values of the endpoints of the generating curve. Calculation of the integral is left for Exercise 15.

Notes on Exercises

- Exercises 1–18. Except for Ex. 12, the integrals can all be done algebraically. At this point Ex. 12 will have to be done numerically since the derivative formula for e^x is not introduced until Chapter 7.

- Exercises 1–2. A cone is generated in these two exercises. The formula for the lateral surface area of a cone is $S = \pi r L$, where L is the slant height.

- Exercises 3–4. These exercises generate frustums of cones. The surface area is given by Eq. (1).

- Exercises 8 and 16. These exercises generate spheres. Confirm the results with $S = 4\pi r^2$.

- **Cooperative Learning:** Exs. 19–22.

Assignment Guide

Day 1: Exs. 1–11 odd.
Day 2: Exs. 13, 17, 19, 21.

6.6 Work

Objective

- Compute the work done in a variety of real world applications.

Key Ideas

The constant-force formula for work

The variable-force integral formula for work

Hooke's law for springs, $F = kx$

Pumping liquids from containers—do-it-yourself integrals

Teaching Notes

An argument using Riemann sums shows that the work done by a continuously varying force acting along a straight line path can be defined as the integral of the force over the length of the path (Eq. (2), page 489). This section considers three different types of applications in which work is calculated: lifting an object whose weight varies with height, stretching or compressing a spring, and pumping a liquid from a container. Problems involving these applications can be challenging. In the first two kinds of problems students have to establish an axis and set up the formula for the variable force $F(x)$ acting along that axis. In the liquid pumping problems, the formula for the work done has to be derived by setting up the appropriate Riemann sum.

Two systems of units are used in this section. In the British engineering system, work is measured in foot-pounds. In the International System of units, one unit of work is the newton-meter or joule.

Common Errors

In the problems of this section, errors will occur in improperly modeling the problem or in setting up the wrong integral. The actual integrals usually will be simple to evaluate.

Notes on Examples

- Example 1. There are three force components in this example: the weight of the water in the leaking bucket, the constant weight of the bucket, and the weight of the paid-out rope. It may help students to point out that in Diagram 6.40 establishing the point $x = 0$ on the axis is purely arbitrary. What matters in this problem is the length of the interval over which the forces are acting, and the net force acting at each point along the interval.

- Example 2. This is an application of Hooke's Law. Exploration 1 provides a follow-up. The spring constant k can be determined by attaching a weight and measuring the distance the weight stretches the spring.

- Example 3. For this pumping problem the Riemann sum has to be constructed and the integral formula inferred from that sum. A careful discussion of the solution is necessary if you are going to assign problems of this kind. The SUPPORT comment in the margin of page 490 regarding this example is important because it confirms the reasonableness of the answer.

Variations on the situation in Example 3 can be posed. For example, how does the formula change if water is pumped to a point 5 ft above the top of the tank? Or what if the tank is initially only half full?

Notes on Exercises

- Exercises 1–6. These exercises involve lifting or raising problems.
- Exercises 7–10. Applications of Hooke's law are studied.
- Exercises 11–22. Pumping problems are involved in these exercises.
- **Cooperative Learning:** Exs. 6, 10, 20–22.

Assignment Guide

Day 1: Exs. 1–10.
Day 2: Exs. 11–21 odd.

6.7 Fluid Pressures and Fluid Forces

Objective

Compute the force exerted on a submerged surface by a fluid.

Key Ideas

The constant-depth formula for fluid force

The variable-depth integral formula for force

Teaching Notes

In a container of fluid with a flat horizontal base, like a fish tank, the total force exerted by the fluid on the base is $F = whA$, where h is the depth of the surface, A is the area of the surface, and w is the weight per cubic unit of the fluid. The magnitude of the force per unit area, $p = wh$, is called the *pressure*. Calculating the total force exerted on a *side* of the container is more complicated than calculating the total force on the base because the pressure changes with depth.

For a submerged vertical plate, let y be a given depth and consider the horizontal strip of all points on the plate whose depth is between y and $y + \Delta y$. If $L(y)$ is the strip length at depth y, then the total force of the fluid on one side of the strip is approximately $\Delta F = wyL(y)\Delta y$. The total force on one side of the plate is approximated by dividing the plate into narrow strips like these and summing the approximate forces on each strip (Eq. (3), page 498). Interpreting Eq. (3) as a Riemann sum and letting the partition norm approach 0 we obtain the integral formula for fluid force, Eq. (4). The latter assumes a coordinate system in which y represents the depth below the surface. If another coordinate system is used, for example one in which the origin is at the bottom of the plate, then Eq. (4) has to be modified. The more general formula would be $\int_c^d wD(y)L(y)\,dy$ where $D(y)$ is the depth at y and $L(y)$ is the width of the plate at y. A two step summary for modeling these problems is found on page 500.

...non Errors

Here again, most errors will be made in setting up the correct integral, in this case in determining $D(y)$, $L(y)$ and the limits of integration. Encourage students to use test values of y to check their formulation of $D(y)$ and $L(y)$.

Notes on Examples

Example 2. This example should be thoroughly discussed, especially with regard to forming the coordinate system, sketching a graph of the triangular plate, determining the integration limits, and determining the function $L(y)$. In this instance y represents the depth below the surface of the fluid, so Eq. (4) gives the correct integration formula.

In Exploration 1 another coordinate system is used for the same problem. The fluid force on one side of the plate is now given by $F = \int_0^3 (62.5)(5 - y)2y\,dy$. Note that the u-substitution, $u = 5 - y$, transforms this back to the original integration formula in Example 2.

Notes on Exercises

- Exercises 3, 4, 12–14. In these exercises it is easiest to establish the origin at the bottom of the plate, as the diagrams suggest. You may want to show how one of these problems is formulated.
- **Cooperative Learning:** Exs. 12–14.

Assignment Guide

Exs. 1, 3, 5, 6, 7, 12, 13.

6.8 Centers of Mass

Objective

- Compute moments about the origin and centers of mass in one and two dimensional systems.

Key Ideas

Masses along a line

Wires and thin rods: moments, mass and center of mass

Masses distributed over a plane region

Thin, flat plates

Center of gravity and centroid

Teaching Notes

For a system of discrete masses placed along the x-axis, the concepts of moment about the origin and center of mass are familiar ones which students may have encountered in algebra or elementary statistics. Using integral calculus, these concepts readily extend to the notions of moment, mass, and center of mass of a thin rod or strip whose density at a point x is a continuous function of x. The center of mass is, of course, the point where the rod would balance if it were placed on a fulcrum. If the rod has constant density the center of mass is the midpoint of the rod.

For a finite system of discrete masses in 2-space, moments about the axes are defined in a similar manner. The moment about the y-axis is $M_y = \sum m_k x_k$ and the moment about the x-axis is $M_x = \sum m_k y_k$. The center of mass is the point $(\bar{x}, \bar{y}) = (M_y/M, M_x/M)$ where M is the total mass of the system. If we have a thin plate covering a region in 2-space whose density at any point (x, y) is a continuous function of (x, y), integration can be used again to calculate the moments about the two axes, the mass, and the center of mass of the plate.

To calculate M_y, M_x, and M, choose either axis and divide the region into thin rectangular strips that are perpendicular to that axis. Calculate the mass Δm and the center of mass $(\tilde{x}, \tilde{y})$ of each strip and approximate $My \approx \sum \tilde{x} \Delta m$, $My \approx \sum \tilde{y} \Delta m$, and $M \approx \sum \Delta m$. In approximating the moments it is assumed that the mass of each strip is concentrated at its center of mass. As the width of all the strips approach 0, these sums approach the integral formulas for M_y, M_x, and M.

There is a 5-step summary on page 510 for doing these calculations. Since either axis can be used, there are two ways to calculate moments and mass. This provides a way to confirm results.

In the simple but important case when the density δ is *constant* at each point of the region,
$(\bar{x}, \bar{y})$ = midpoint of the strip,
$dm = \delta \, dA = \delta \cdot$ (length of the strip) $\cdot$ (width of the strip), and
$M = \delta A$, where A is the area of the region.

Since the constant δ cancels out in the formulas $\bar{x} = M_y/M$ and $\bar{y} = M_x/M$, the center of mass is purely a function of the geometric shape of the region. The center of mass is called the *centroid* of the region in this case.

Common Errors

It is easy for students to confuse the notation M_y and M_x since M_y is calculated using the x-coordinates of the point masses and M_x is calculated using the y-coordinates.

Notes on Examples

Example 3. Discuss both methods for finding M_y of the triangular plate. When using horizontal strips, the integration is with respect to y, and $\bar{x}$ and dm are both expressed as functions of y. Since δ is constant, the center of mass is the centroid of the triangular region, which happens to be the point where the three medians intersect.

Notes on Exercises

- Exercises 7–18. In each of these exercises δ is constant, so to calculate the center of mass we can assume $\delta = 1$. Thus, in setting up the formulas, $dm = dA$ for each strip and $M = A$ = the area of the region.

- Exercises 25–34. These are applications of the theorems of Pappus which are stated in the exercises. In Exercise 31 the centroid of the region is deduced from the first theorem by knowing the volume of the solid of rotation.

- **Cooperative Learning:** Exs. 25–27, 31.

Assignment Guide

Exs. 1–15 odd.

6.9 The Basic Idea; Other Modeling Applications

Objectives

- Find the volume of a solid with a known cross-section.
- Compute the total distance traveled by a particle along a coordinate line.
- Compute the position shift of a particle along a line.

Key Ideas

Volumes of solids by slicing

Position shift and distance traveled

Delesse's rule

Invalid modeling

Teaching Notes

The section begins by reviewing applications of the preceding sections and comparing how the definite integral arises in the modeling process for each. (See Table 6.2.) Additional integration formulas are derived which reinforce the common thread of these preceding applications.

The first new application is the method of calculating the volume of a solid by integrating the cross-sectional area $A(x)$. As the text points out, this generalizes the washer method of Section 6.2.

The second application involves rectilinear motion. For a body moving along a straight line, the integral of the speed equals the distance traveled over the given time interval. The integral of the velocity gives the displacement or shift in the body's position over the given time interval. These are certainly fundamental results. The derivation of the integration formula for distance traveled by arguing from Riemann sums is classic and should be discussed in class. Students can readily see that $|v(t_k)|\Delta t_k$ approximates the distance traveled during the kth time interval, and that the Riemann sum $\sum |v(t_k)|\Delta t_k$ does approximate the trip distance.

In these problems remind students that when integrating $|v(t)|$ by algebraic means, the interval of integration must be divided into subintervals on which $v(t)$ has constant sign in order to write the integrand without absolute value signs.

Common Errors

Errors will occur when integrating $|v(t)|$ by analytic means. Graphing the function $v = v(t)$ will help students determine the intervals where $v(t)$ is positive and where it is negative. Answers can be confirmed using NINT.

Notes on Examples

- Examples 1–3. These examples illustrate the method of calculating volumes by slicing. The principle involved, Eq. (1) on page 515, plays an important role in multiple integration.
- Example 4. The difference between displacement and distance traveled is clearly shown in this example. The total distance traveled can be interpreted as the total area between the graph of $v = v(t)$ and the t-axis, whereas the position shift is the *net* area.

Notes on Exercises

- Exercise 1–12. These exercises involve finding the volume of a solid with a known cross-section. These can be done with NINT, algebraically, or both.
- Exercises 13–20. In these exercises, students are required to find the total distance and the position shift.
- Exercise 21. It would be instructive to graph the distance traveled and the displacement as functions of time for the given velocities.
- **Cooperative Learning:** Exs. 21–24.

Assignment Guide

Exs. 1–19 odd.

Chapter 7 The Calculus of Transcendental Functions

7.1 The Natural Logarithm Function

Objectives

- Learn the definition and properties of the natural logarithm function.
- Calculate derivatives involving the natural logarithm.
- Perform logarithmic differentiation.
- Use integration techniques involving the natural logarithm.

Key Ideas

The natural logarithm function

Logarithmic differentiation

$\int \frac{1}{u} \, dw = \ln|u| + C$

Teaching Notes

The definition of the natural logarithm as an integral is a difficult concept for students to understand because it is abstract and seemingly has nothing to do with logarithms. Here it's best to follow the approach of the book. If we set out to construct an antiderivative of $f(x) = 1/x$ on the interval $(0, \infty)$, the Fundamental Theorem tells us that $\ln x = \int_1^x 1/t \, dt$ is a theoretical formula for one such antiderivative. Establish right away that $\ln 1 = 0$, and that the domain of $\ln x$ is $(0, \infty)$ (We cannot integrate $1/t$ past 0). Have the students graph $y_1 = \text{NINT}(1/t, 1, x)$ and $y_2 = \ln x$ in the same window to convince them that this definition is consistent with the way our calculator computes $\ln x$. Interpret values of $\ln x$ as areas under the curve $y = 1/t$. Explain why $\ln x$ is negative when $0 < x < 1$.

By the Fundamental Theorem, $d/dx \ln x = 1/x$. From this we can show that $\ln x$ satisfies the three basic rules of logarithms on page 531. Given the way $\ln x$ was defined this is surprising. Spend some time with the arguments to establish these rules.

By examining the first and second derivatives of $\ln x$, the main features of its graph can be confirmed analytically. The limits $\lim_{x \to \infty} \ln x = \infty$ and $\lim_{x \to 0^+} \ln x = -\infty$ can be informally verified. (Since $\ln 2 > 0$ and $\ln 2^n = n(\ln 2)$, values of $\ln x$ do get arbitrarily large.) From these limits and the continuity of $\ln x$ you can infer that the range of $\ln x$ must be the entire real line $(-\infty, \infty)$.

Explore a number of differentiation problems involving $\ln x$. When differentiating $y = \ln f(x)$ encourage students to simplify $\ln f(x)$, if possible, before differentiating. Logarithmic differentiation should be covered since it greatly simplifies calculating certain derivatives.

The more general differentiation formula $d/dx \ln |x| = 1/x$ can be established by the Chain Rule: for $x < 0$, $d/dx \ln x = d/dx \ln(-x) = 1/(-x) \cdot (-1) = 1/x$. This establishes the important integration formula $\int 1/u \, du = \ln u + C$. With the substitution $u = f(x)$, we can now integrate $f'(x)/f(x) \, dx$. The integral formulas for $\tan x$ and $\cot x$ are obtained in this way.

Finally, the formula $d/dx \ln |y| = 1/y \, dy/dx$ allows us to apply logarithmic differentiation to negative functions. In fact, if $y = f(x)$, differentiating both sides of $\ln |y| = \ln |f(x)|$ yields a formula for dy/dx which is valid for $y > 0$ or $y < 0$.

Common Errors

A variety of errors occur when students attempt to simplify expressions involving logarithms. The most common is rewriting $\ln(a + b)$ as $\ln a + \ln b$. Another is rewriting $(\ln x)^n$ as $n(\ln x)$.

A common error in integration is for students to evaluate $\int 1/f(x) \, dx$ as $\ln f(x) + C$, no matter what $f(x)$ is.

In logarithmic differentiation, once y is substituted into the formula for dy/dx it is generally best to leave the answer in that form. Recommend to students not to simplify beyond that point.

Notes on Examples

- Example 3. This example illustrates the technique of logarithmic differentiation. Differentiating $\ln |y|$ will show that the formula for dy/dx computed in Example 3 is also valid for $-3 < x < 1$.

- Example 6. Notice in this example that the absolute value signs are needed in the antiderivative. The antiderivative $\int 1/u \, du$ should routinely be written as $\ln |u| + C$. The absolute value signs are dropped only when you are satisfied that $u > 0$.

Notes on Exercises

- Exercises 31–48. A number of these integrals transform to $\int_a^b 1/u \, du$, where a and b are negative, so the absolute value signs are needed in the antiderivative. See Example 6.

- **Cooperative Learning** : Exs. 61, 62, 70, 71.

Assignment Guide

Exs. 1, 2, 6, 7, 9, 10, 16, 19, 20, 27, 31, 32, 34, 35, 38, 41, 46, 49, 53, 59, 66.

7.2 The Exponential Function

Objectives

- Learn the definition and properties of the exponential function.
- Solve logarithmic and exponential equations.
- Differentiate and integrate expressions involving the exponential function.
- Solve applied problems involving exponential change.

Key Ideas

The exponential function $y = \exp(x)$

The inverse pair $\ln x$ and e^x

Rules for exponents

The derivative rule for inverses

The derivative of $y = e^x$

The law of exponential change $y = y_0\, e^{kt}$

Teaching Notes

The exponential function $y = \exp(x)$ is defined to be the inverse function of $y = \ln x$. You can establish properties of $\exp(x)$ from this definition. From our knowledge of $\ln x$, the domain of $\exp(x)$ must be the real line $(-\infty, \infty)$ and the range $(0, \infty)$. Its graph can be obtained by reflecting the graph of $y = \ln x$ through the line $y = x$. This is done on the grapher by graphing the curve $x_1 = \ln t$, $y_1 = t$ in parametric mode.

Next, e is defined to be the unique number satisfying $\ln e = 1$. In keeping with the spirit of this development, have students estimate e by finding the intersection of $y = 1$ and $y = \ln x$ on their graphers. For every rational number r, since $\ln e^r = r(\ln e) = r$, we must have $e^r = \exp(r)$. Now comes the key definition: For every *real* number x, *define* $e^x = \exp(x)$.

Three things should be mentioned about this definition.

1. For the first time *irrational* powers of some number are being defined.

2. The definition is consistent with the previous definition of rational powers, which says if $r = m/n$ where m, n are integers and $n \geq 1$ then
$e^r = e^{m/n} = (e^{1/n})^m$.

3. The fact that $\exp(x)$ is continuous means that if r is a close rational approximation of x, then e^r will be a close approximation of e^x.

The notation e^x is better than $\exp(x)$ so e^x is used from now on. It is important to emphasize that e^x means e *raised to the power x*, that $e^2 = e \cdot e$, $e^{-1} = 1/e$, $e^{1/2} = \sqrt{e}$, and so forth. Equations (1) show the inverse relationship between e^x and $\ln x$. Three of the rules of exponents (page 542) can be derived from these equations and the logarithm rules. Observe that from equations (1) we now know that $\ln x = \log_e x$; thus $\ln x$ really is a logarithm.

Theorem 1 plays a useful role in this section and in Section 7.8. It says that the inverse of a differentiable function $f(x)$ is itself differentiable provided $f'(x)$ is never 0. By Theorem 1, we know that $y = e^x$ is differentiable. Once assured of that, it is an easy matter to find the derivative formula for e^x using implicit differentiation.

A number of computational examples using the new rules $d/dx\, e^u = e^u\, du/dx$ and $\int e^u\, du = e^u + C$ should be done in class along with one or two of the applications involving exponential change.

Common Errors

When using Eq. (3) of Theorem 1 to calculate a derivative of $g = f^{-1}$, a common error is to calculate $g'(x)$ as $1/f'(x)$. The book mentions this in the Exploration Bit on page 544. The correct formula to find $g'(x)$ is $g'(x) = 1/f'(f^{-1}(x))$. Equation (3) is always a source of confusion to beginning students in calculus.

An error that occurs frequently is to evaluate $\int e^{ax}\, dx$ as $a \cdot e^{ax} + C$, rather than as $a^{-1} \cdot e^{ax} + C$.

Notes on Examples

- Examples 1–4. These examples are meant to reinforce the arithmetic rules of logarithms and exponents, and the inverse relationship between $\ln x$ and e^x.
- Example 5. Use a simple example like this one to illustrate Eq. (3) of Theorem 1. Generate a table of values like the one in Exploration 2.
- Example 10. Since this type of integral occurs so often you may want to establish the formula $\int e^{ax}\, dx = a^{-1}\, e^{ax} + C$, where a is a nonzero constant.
- Example 11. It would be instructive to evaluate this definite integral by making the substitution $u = \sin x$ and showing how the limits of integration are changed.

Notes on Exercises

- Exercises 7–18. Students should find the exact solutions for Exs. 7–17. Ex. 18 requires a numerical approximation.
- Exercises 55–58. The intention of these exercises is for students to verify directly Eq. (3) of Theorem 1 at a particular value $x = a$; that is to show $g'(f(a)) = 1/f'(a)$ for a given f and a given value $x = a$, where $g = f^{-1}$. Examples 5 and 6 can be used as models.
- **Cooperative Learning:** Exs. 84, 93, 95, 97.

Assignment Guide

Day 1: Exs. 1, 2, 5, 7, 8, 10, 11, 15, 16, 18, 19, 21, 22, 24, 26–28, 30, 31, 34.
Day 2: Exs. 35, 37, 39, 42, 45, 50, 55, 58, 62, 68, 71, 72, 79, 88, 92.

7.3 Other Exponential and Logarithmic Functions

Objectives

- Learn the definition and properties of exponential and logarithmic functions to any base.
- Differentiate and integrate exponential and logarithmic functions to any base.

Key Ideas

The function a^x

The power rule for differentiation—final form

The derivatives of a^x and a^u

Integrals involving a^x

Base a logarithms and their graphs

Extending the power and exponential functions

Teaching Notes

For $a > 0$, the exponential function a^x is defined using $\exp(x)$. The definition is motivated by the observation that for a rational exponent r, $a^r = \exp(\ln a^r) = e^{r(\ln a)}$. So $a^x = e^{x(\ln a)}$ is defined for all real numbers x and $a > 0$. From this definition it can be shown that all the rules of exponents are valid for *real* exponents (page 558) and that the rule $\ln x^n = n(\ln x)$ is valid for any real number n. As a bonus, the validity of the power rule $d/dx\ x^n = nx^{n-1}$ can be established for all real constants n and $x > 0$.

The derivative and integral formulas for a^x are easily established from the definition of a^x. Graphs of $y = a^x$ for $a > 1$ and $0 < a < 1$ are confirmed analytically by examining the first and second derivatives. The limits of $y = a^x$ at ∞ and $-\infty$ should be discussed. Stress the difference between the derivative formulas for power functions $y = x^a$ (variable base, constant exponent) and exponential functions $y = a^x$ (constant base, variable exponent).

The function $y = \log_a x$ is defined by inverting $y = a^x$. It might help at this point to review the definition of logarithm from Section 1. The change of base formula $\log_a x = \ln x/\ln a$ is especially useful as it allows students to calculate logarithms to any base and relates the graph of $y = \log_a x$ to the graph of $y = \ln x$. In any differentiation or integration problem involving $\log_a x$, $\log_a x$ can be replaced by $\ln x/\ln a$, so no new formulas need to be learned.

Power and exponential functions can be extended to functions of the form $y = f(x)^{g(x)}$ where both the base and the exponent vary with x. Derivatives of these functions are calculated using logarithmic differentiation.

Notes on Examples

- Examples 5 and 6. Both of these examples can be done by first converting the base a logarithm to a natural logarithm.
- Example 9. The first derivative of $y = x^x$ is found using logarithmic differentiation. Note that higher order derivatives can be found using the formula for y' and the Product Rule.

Notes on Exercises

- Exercises 9–14. For these exercises students should use logarithmic differentiation as in Example 9.
- Exercise 15–23. Students should simplify and convert to natural logarithms before differentiating.
- Exercises 35–40, 43–44. Suggest to students that they first convert the logarithm in the integrand to a natural logarithm, as in Example 6.
- Exercise 41. This exercise is the same problem as Example 4.
- **Cooperative Learning:** Exs. 71, 75.

Assignment Guide

Day 1: Exs. 1, 3, 6, 7, 9–11, 13, 15, 17, 20, 21, 24–27, 30, 32.
Day 2: Exs. 35, 38, 41, 42, 45, 48, 52, 53, 55, 56, 61, 64.

7.4 The Law of Exponential Change Revisited

Objective

- Apply the law of exponential change to problem situations.

Key Ideas

Radioactive decay

Resistance to a moving object

Heat transfer—Newton's law of cooling

Teaching Notes

Section 7.4 continues the discussion of applications involving exponential change that was begun in Section 7.2. The problems in this section primarily model exponential decay, and thus the quantity being measured is decreasing with time. Make sure that students are familiar with the graph of $y = y_0 e^{-kt}$, where k and y_0 are *positive* constants.

In one of the radioactive decay applications be sure to show a graphical interpretation of *half-life*. Note that the book denotes the decay constant as $-k$ where $k > 0$.

A special feature occurs in the problems involving resistance to a moving object. The equation $v = v_0 e^{-(k/m)t}$ can be integrated to find the distance traveled $s(t)$ from time 0 to t. The total distance traveled from $t = 0$ until the time the object stops is the limit of $s(t)$ as $t \to \infty$. In all of these applications ensure that students use the correct units of measure.

Common Errors

Errors can occur using the wrong units of measure or in converting to the correct units. Always establish the correct units of measure from the given data at the beginning of the problem.

Note on Examples

- Example 2. Notice that in this example the original amount of the sample is irrelevant. The value y_0 cancels in the equation to determine t.
- Example 3. Exploration 3 discusses a linear animation model for the problem in this example.

Notes on Exercises

- Exercises 5–6. These exercises involve radioactive decay.
- Exercises 7–8. Resistance to motion is the central idea of these two exercises.
- Exercises 9–12. Students apply Newton's Law of Cooling.
- Exercises 15–17. These exercises involve Carbon-14 dating.
- **Cooperative Learning:** Exs. 10, 16, 21.

Assignment Guide

Exs. 2, 4, 7, 8, 11, 13, 14.

7.5 Indeterminate Forms and l'Hôpital's Rule

Objective

- Find limits of indeterminate forms using l'Hôpital's rule.

Key Ideas

The indeterminate form 0/0

The indeterminate forms ∞/∞, $\infty \cdot 0$, and $\infty - \infty$

The indeterminate forms 1^{∞}, 0^0, and ∞^0

Teaching Notes

You may want to review those parts of Chapter 2 where limits of the form 0/0 or ∞/∞ were solved by simplifying or rewriting the fraction $f(x)/g(x)$. L'Hôpital's Rule now provides a more general method for calculating limits of these forms.

Once students are comfortable with first form of the rule (Theorem 2), introduce the more general version (Theorem 3), which allows repeated applications, applies to the form ∞/∞, and extends to limits at ∞. Emphasize that in applying Theorem 3, the fraction f/g must *always* be verified to have one of the indeterminate forms 0/0 or ∞/∞.

The forms $0 \cdot \infty$ and $\infty - \infty$ can usually be rewritten algebraically as 0/0 or ∞/∞. The forms 0^0, 1^{∞} and ∞^0 are usually converted to 0/0 or ∞/∞ using logarithms. The limits are then found by applying l'Hôpital's Rule and the result of Eq. (1).

Graphical support can be helpful in these problems because the graph of $y = f(x)/g(x)$ will often suggest the correct limit at $x = a$ or ∞. However, in cases where f and g approach 0 or ∞ too quickly, the grapher may lack sufficient precision to give an accurate graph near the limit point. Exploration 2 discusses one such example.

Common Errors

The text mentions two *traps* when applying l'Hôpital's Rule. The first is to misapply the rule by replacing $\lim f/g$ with $\lim (f/g)'$ rather than with $\lim f'/g'$. This is mentioned in Exploration 1. The other trap is to apply l'Hôpital's Rule to a form which is not indeterminate. See the example in the Exploration Bit on page 580.

A common error students make is to not recognize a form 1^∞ or ∞^0 as being indeterminate and to evaluate it, perhaps incorrectly, as 1.

Notes on Examples

- Example 3. Note the use of l'Hôpital's Rule to compute infinite limits.
- Example 5. Writing the expression as a single fraction converts the form $\infty - \infty$ to the form $0/0$.
- Example 6. This example illustrates the method for handling the form 1^∞. Further properties of $f(x) = (1 + 1/x)^x$ are explored in Ex. 35.

Notes on Exercises

- Exercises 1–8. L'Hôpital's Rule is to be used, but notice that each of these limits can be calculated using the techniques and results of Chapters 2 and 3.
- Exercise 14. Students should rewrite this limit in the form $0/0$.
- Exercises 19–20. These limits should be converted to the form $0/0$ as in Example 5.
- Exercises 27–30. The key in these exercises is to determine if y has a finite limit as $x \to 0^+$.
- Cooperative Learning: Exs. 35, 41, 42, 45.

Assignment Guide

Exs. 1, 2, 4, 7–9, 12, 15, 18, 20, 21, 23, 27, 34, 44.

7.6 The Rates at Which Functions Grow

Objective

- Determine, investigate, and compare rates of growth.

Key Ideas

Relative rates of growth

Order of magnitude as $x \to \infty$

Teaching Notes

The definitions of relative rates of growth as $x \to \infty$, given on page 585, are the key ideas of this section. For particular functions f and g these relations are often established using l'Hôpital's Rule.

The idea of f and g growing at the same rate is central to the Limit Comparison Test in Section 8.6 for the convergence of an improper integral. Later on the same test reappears in Section 9.3 for the convergence of an infinite series. "Growing at the same rate" is an equivalence relation on the class of positive valued functions with domain $(0, \infty)$. A special instance of f and g growing at the same rate is when g is an end behavior model of f.

Related to these ideas are the definitions of $f = o(g)$ and $f = O(g)$, which are a standard part of the literature in real analysis.

Graphical support for the examples and exercises can be accomplished by graphing $y = f(x)/g(x)$. In some instances it may be a challenge to find the appropriate viewing window for doing this. When f and g have too rapid a growth rate it may be impossible to graphically support $f/g \to L$ in a direct manner because of the range limitations on the calculator. One way around this would be to graphically support the equivalent limit statement $\ln f - \ln g \to \ln L$.

Notes on Examples

- Exploration 2. For part 1b, one argument could be:
  $\ln(e^x/x^n) = x - n(\ln x) \to \infty$ so $e^x/x^n \to \infty$. It would be instructive to graph $y = x^n/e^x$ for $n = 2, 3, 4$ to graphically support $x^n/e^x \to 0$. Use a $[0, 12] \times [0, 5]$ window.

- Example 4. The transitivity of the relation "f and g grow at the same rate" is used to show y_1 and y_2 grow at the same rate. It is easier to establish the two limits using algebraic means rather than l'Hôpital's Rule. Note that a direct application of l'Hôpital's Rule to the first limit doesn't work.

Notes on Exercises

- Exercises 1–10. These exercises concern relative rates of growth. A number of them can be answered without resorting to l'Hôpital's Rule. Aside from Ex. 2d, the end behavior of the quotient can be seen on the grapher.

- Exercises 11–12. These exercises concern big O and little o.

- **Cooperative Learning**: Exs. 37, 38, 40.

Assignment Guide

Exs. 1 (a, b, c, d, g), 2 (b, e, f, h), 3 (a, c, e, j), 4 (b, c, h, j), 6, 8, 9, 17, 21, 24, 26, 29.

7.7 The Inverse Trigonometric Functions

Objectives

- Learn the definitions and properties of the inverse trigonometric functions.
- Evaluate expressions involving inverse trigonometric functions.

Key Ideas

The Arc Sine, Arc Cosine, Arc Tangent

The inverses of sec x, csc x, cot x

Right-triangle Interpretations

Teaching Notes

Inverse trigonometric functions were first introduced in Section 1.7. The rest of these functions are defined in this section and a number of useful identities are explored. Pay particular attention to the ranges and graphs of these functions.

For positive arguments, the values of all the inverse trigonometric functions fall in the interval $[0, \pi/2]$. An output angle θ can be constructed using a reference triangle.

For negative arguments, values of $f = \sin^{-1}$, $\tan^{-1}$, or $\csc^{-1}$ fall in the interval $[-\pi/2, 0]$. These are *odd* functions, so if $x > 0$ and $f(x) = \theta$, then $f(-x) = -\theta$.

For negative arguments, values of $g = \cos^{-1}$, $\cot^{-1}$, or $\sec^{-1}$ fall in the interval $[\pi/2, \pi]$. If $x > 0$ and $g(x) = \theta$, then $g(-x) = \pi - \theta$.

Scientific calculators typically have keys for $\sin^{-1}$, $\cos^{-1}$ and $\tan^{-1}$. To calculate values of the other functions use the identities $\csc^{-1}(x) = \sin^{-1}(1/x)$, $\sec^{-1}(x) = \cos^{-1}(1/x)$, and $\cot^{-1}(x) = \pi/2 - \tan^{-1}(x)$. You may want to point out why the last of these formulas differs from the first two.

Common Errors

A common error students make is to evaluate $\cos^{-1}$, $\cot^{-1}$, and $\sec^{-1}$ at a negative argument with an angle outside the defined range. Answers can always be confirmed with a calculator.

Notes on Examples

- Examples 1–3. The use of the reference triangle is illustrated in these examples.
- Example 5. This type of calculation will be used in Section 8.4 when making trigonometric substitutions in integrals. The expression is first simplified by using a reference triangle assuming the variable $x > 0$. This result is then checked to ensure its validity when $x < 0$.

Notes on Exercises

- Exercises 1–28. These exercises should be done using reference triangles, obtaining exact answers.
- Exercises 29–40. See the note in Example 5.
- **Cooperative Learning:** Exs. 49–53.

Assignment Guide

Exs. 1, 3, 4, 6, 7, 10, 12, 13, 15, 18, 19, 23, 27, 29, 34, 35, 40, 41, 44, 47.

7.8 Derivatives of Inverse Trigonometric Functions; Related Integrals

Objectives

- Differentiate the inverse trigonometric functions.
- Compute integrals leading to inverse trigonometric functions.

Key Ideas

Derivatives of inverse trigonometric functions

Integrals leading to inverse trigonometric functions

Teaching Notes

Since the inverse trigonometric functions are obtained by inverting differentiable functions, Theorem 1 of Section 7.1 tells us that these functions are all differentiable on the interior of their domains. Using implicit differentiation we can determine formulas for their derivatives. The most important of these are the derivative formulas for $\sin^{-1} x$, $\tan^{-1} x$, and $\sec^{-1} x$. The derivatives of $\sin^{-1} x$ and $\sec^{-1} x$ are presented in the text. The derivative of $\tan^{-1} x$ is left as an exercise. The derivatives of the other three inverse trigonometric functions are just the negatives of the derivatives of their respective cofunctions, so they lead to no new antiderivative formula.

Common Errors

In computing definite integrals that lead to inverse trigonometric functions, students will sometimes overlook those cases when the answer can be simplified by considering a 30-60-90 or 45-45-90 reference triangle. Exact answers should be given whenever possible.

Notes on Examples

- Example 1. The new differentiation formulas provide a good test of students' understanding of the Chain Rule.
- Example 3. Finding the correct u-substitution is a matter of skill and experience. In Exploration 4 it may be easier to write the substitution $x = 3u$, obtaining
$$\int 1/\sqrt{9 - x^2}\, dx = \int 1/\sqrt{9 - 9u^2} \cdot 3\, du = \int 1/\sqrt{1 - u^2}\, du.$$

Notes on Exercises

- Exercises 1–18. The answers to these exercises should be simplified whenever possible.
- Exercise 22. Note that the absolute value signs are needed in the antiderivative.
- Exercises 24–38. Finding the correct u-substitution is the key to computing these integrals. Discuss a few of these exercises. For example, in Exs. 26 and 27 we want $u^2 = 4x^2$ so take $u = 2x$. In Ex. 33 we want $x^2 = 17u^2$ so take $x = \sqrt{17} \cdot u$.
- **Cooperative Learning:** Exs. 53, 62, 64, 72.

Assignment Guide

Exs. 1, 3, 4, 6, 10, 12, 14, 19, 21, 22, 24, 25, 27, 30, 31, 34, 35, 37, 40, 42, 55, 58, 64.

7.9 Hyperbolic Functions

Objectives

- Learn the definitions and properties of the hyperbolic functions and their inverses.
- Differentiate and integrate the hyperbolic functions.
- Differentiate inverse hyperbolic functions and evaluate integrals leading to inverse hyperbolic functions.

Key Ideas

The hyperbolic functions

The inverse hyperbolic functions

Teaching Notes

This section is sometimes omitted, but it is worthwhile to cover if time is available. Because of their occurence in engineering and physics, the hyperbolic functions are useful in certain integration techniques, and their inverses arise in antidifferentiation formulas for a number of algebraic functions.

The most important functions to emphasize are $\cosh x$ and $\sinh x$ because all of the other hyperbolic functions are defined in terms of these two. These functions are defined in terms of e^x and e^{-x}, and thus all of the identities and the differentiation and integration formulas can be derived in routine fashion.

You could derive the identity $\cosh^2 x - \sinh^2 x = 1$ and from this make the observation that $x = \cosh t$, $y = \sinh t$ are parametric equations for the right branch of the hyperbola $x^2 - y^2 = 1$. (See page 616.)

Unlike the inverse trigonometric functions, formulas for the inverse hyperbolic functions can be calculated directly from the defining equations for the hyperbolic functions. These formulas are listed in Table 7.7 in the exercises.

Scientific calculators usually have keys for sinh, cosh, tanh and their inverses. To evaluate the other inverse hyperbolic functions use the reciprocal identities in Table 7.5.

Notes on Examples

- Example 3. This integral must be done numerically.
- Example 4. The differentiation formulas for the inverse hyperbolic functions can be derived by using implicit differentiation or by directly differentiating their logarithmic formulas in Table 7.7.

Notes on Exercises

- Exercises 27–38. Simplify the answers to these exercises whenever possible.
- Exercises 61–67. The integrals all lead to inverse hyperbolic functions.
- **Cooperative Learning:** Exs. 73, 81, 85, 86, 89.

Assignment Guide

Exs. 1, 7, 9, 10, 15, 17, 19, 28, 29, 31, 33, 39, 42, 43, 61, 64, 65, 67, 77, 80.

CHAPTER 8 Techniques of Integration

8.1 Formulas for Elementary Integrals

Objectives

- Evaluate indefinite integrals by using substitution.
- Evaluate indefinite integrals by completing the square.
- Evaluate definite integrals and support results numerically.

Key Ideas

Standard elementary forms

Integration procedures

Teaching Notes

This section provides an excellent opportunity to review the techniques of integration learned in previous chapters. It is always more challenging to work a set of exercises requiring a variety of techniques. Stress Table 8.1. Note that the integrals for sec u and csc u are now presented and complete the list of trigonometric forms.

Definite and indefinite integral evaluation should be supported by numerical integration. Note the word of caution in Exploration 1 concerning limits of integration and viewing windows.

Common Errors

Students sometimes evaluate definite integrals improperly when the substitution process is used. Remind students either to write the antiderivative in terms of the original variable or to change the limits of integration.

Notes on Examples

- Example 2. This example demonstrates the important technique of completing the square to obtain an elementary form.
- Example 4. This example illustrates the important technique of separating a fraction. This technique is often overlooked by students.
- Example 5. Be sure to discuss this example. The integrals for sec u and csc u were not presented in earlier chapters.

Notes on Exercises

- Exercises 23–28. Completing the square is required in these exercises.
- Exercises 33–36. These exercises require separating the fraction.
- Exercises 37–40. Several applications of integration are reviewed in these exercises.
- **Cooperative Learning:** Exs. 59–60.

Assignment Guide

Day 1: Exs. 1, 3, 6, 7, 9, 13, 15, 17, 19, 21, 47, 53.
Day 2: Exs. 23, 25, 27, 29, 31, 33, 35, 36, 37, 40, 41, 42, 59.

8.2 Integration by Parts

Objectives

- Use integration by parts to evaluate indefinite and definite integrals.
- Use tabular integration for integrals that require repeated use of integration by parts.

Key Ideas

The formula $\int u \, dv = uv - \int v \, du$

Solving for the unknown integral

Tabular integration

Teaching Notes

Integration by parts is a very powerful technique. Derive the formula by using the Product Rule for derivatives.

Students will need coaching on the correct choice for u. Some teachers use the acronym LIPET as an aid to choosing u. Choose u to be the type of function occuring first in the list: logarithmic, inverse trigonometric, polynomial, exponential, trigonometric. The method isn't foolproof, but often helpful.

After establishing the basic technique, demonstrate that the process can be repeated if the new integrand is still not an elementary form. If the original integrand reappears, apply the algebraic method of Example 4.

Tabular integration is an efficient shortcut. Students appreciate the simplicity of the technique.

Be sure to mention that integration by parts is sometimes used when the integrand is not a product, such as $\int \cos^{-1} x \, dx$.

Common Errors

It is important to keep track of signs. Errors commonly occur when the expression for du or $\int v \, du$ involves a minus sign. Similarly, minus signs must be used for the appropriate terms in tabular integration. Another common mistake is to antidifferentiate incorrectly to find v, or to antidifferentiate incorrectly in the tabular integration format.

Notes on Examples

- Example 4. This is a classic example of the algebraic technique and is worthwhile to demonstrate.
- Example 6. The power of tabular integration is illustrated by this example.

Notes on Exercises

- Exercises 7 and 8. These exercises show how to integrate inverse trig functions.
- Exercises 21–24. The algebraic technique is required for these exercises.
- Exercises 25–29. Applications of integrals are reviewed.
- **Cooperative Learning:** Exs. 31–33.

Assignment Guide

Exs. 1, 4, 5, 7, 9, 11, 17, 20, 21, 23, 25, 27, 33.

8.3 Integrals involving Trigonometric Functions

Objectives

- Evaluate integrals involving powers and products of trigonometric functions.
- Compute definite integrals involving even or odd functions.

Key Ideas

Products of sines and cosines

Powers of tangents and secants

Definite integrals of even and odd functions

Teaching Notes

Review important trigonometric identities. The Pythagorean identities will be used, as well as the half angle formulas such as $2 \cos^2 x = 1 + \cos 2x$. It's important to establish the correct replacement to make. Flowchart 8.1 is a nice summary for sines and cosines.

Plot the graphs of several even and odd functions. The definite integrals can be interpreted as sums of signed areas, thus the doubling or canceling effects are reinforced.

Common Errors

Care must be taken to replace the arguments of functions correctly. We know $\cos^2 x = (1 + \cos 2x)/2$, which implies $\cos^2 2x = (1 + \cos 4x)/2$. Sometimes the coefficients are replaced incorrectly.

Notes on Examples

- Example 3. This is the most complicated sine and cosine example. Both powers are even. There is a great deal of algebraic manipulation in this example.
- Example 6. This example illustrates a valuable time saving technique.

Notes on Exercises

- Exercises 1–38. A variety of trigonometric integrals are provided.
- Exercises 39–42 and 45–52. These exercises investigate even and odd functions.
- **Cooperative Learning:** Exs. 43, 45–46.

Assignment Guide

Day 1: Exs. 1, 3, 7, 9, 13, 15, 17, 23, 25, 29, 33, 37.
Day 2: Exs. 39, 41, 45, 47–50.

8.4 Trigonometric Substitutions

Objectives

- Evaluate integrals involving $a^2 - x^2$, $a^2 + x^2$, and $x^2 - a^2$ by trigonometric substitution.
- Evaluate integrals involving quadratic expressions by completing the square and trigonometric substitution.

Key Ideas

Trigonometric substitution

Integrals involving $ax^2 + bx + c$

Teaching Notes

The key to the substitution process is to choose the correct replacement. Emphasize the three different replacements and their connections to the Pythagorean identities. Encourage the use of right triangles when replacing trigonometric functions in antiderivatives. Point out that the useful formulas (2) and (3) are just special cases of the general method that will be used often.

Integrals involving $ax^2 + bx + c$ require completing the square, then making a trig substitution. These integrals require much manipulation. Graphical or numerical support is a must.

Common Errors

Students often forget to complete their calculation of indefinite integrals. The variables in the antiderivative must be replaced so that the result is in terms of the original variable. For definite integrals, use the original variable or change the limits of integration.

Notes on Examples

- Example 2. Emphasize that three replacements are made.
- Example 5. A good illustration of two techniques combined.

Notes on Exercises

- Exercises 13–16 and 25–28. These exercises require completing the square.
- Exercises 29, 30, 33, and 34. Important applications are reviewed by these exercises.
- **Cooperative Learning:** Exs. 30, 35, 36.

Assignment Guide

Day 1: Exs. 1, 3, 5–7, 9, 11, 17, 19, 21–23.
Day 2: Exs. 14, 15, 25, 27–30, 33–35.

8.5 Rational Functions and Partial Fractions

Objectives

- Use the method of undetermined coefficients to obtain partial fraction decompositions.
- Use partial fractions to evaluate integrals of rational functions.
- Use the special substitution $z = \tan(x/2)$ to evaluate integrals involving rational functions of sine and cosine.

Key Ideas

Partial fractions

The substitution $z = \tan(x/2)$

Teaching Notes

First develop the method of undetermined coefficients with one or two examples that are not integrals. Stress the special rules when irreducible quadratic factors or repeated factors occur. Then use the process to evaluate several integrals. Be sure to remind students to use division if the numerator is of equal or greater degree. Observe that ln occurs often in the antiderivatives. Emphasize equations (4), (5), and (6) for rational functions of sin and cosine.

Common Errors

Students often forget to use division when the numerator is of equal or greater degree.

Notes on Examples

- Example 7. The use of three different variables and several important techniques are illustrated by this example.

Notes on Exercises

- Exercises 1–8. The basic method of undetermined coefficients is established.
- Exercises 33–36. These are applications of integrals
- Exercises 37–44. The special z substitution is required.
- **Cooperative Learning:** Exs. 35, 36, 43.

Assignment Guide

Day 1: Exs. 2, 3, 5, 10, 11, 13, 15, 21, 23, 25, 29, 31.
Day 2: Exs. 33–37, 39, 40, 43.

8.6 Improper Integrals

Objectives

- Use limits to evaluate improper integrals.
- Apply tests to determine convergence of integrals.

Key Ideas

Convergence and divergence

Domination Test

Limit Comparison Test

Teaching Notes

Reinforce the idea that the integral converges when the limit exists. Demonstrate an example of convergence as well as divergence. Emphasize the fact that an unbounded region may have a finite area. Students should be familiar with the results for $\int_0^1 1/x^P \, dx$ and $\int_1^\infty 1/x^P \, dx$.

The Domination Test, and the Limit Comparison Tests are very useful techniques for determining convergence. They do not evaluate integrals.

Support results numerically or graphically.

Common Errors

Students often overlook infinite discontinuities which occur at *interior points* of the interval of integration. They should use proper limit symbolism when improper integrals are evaluated.

Notes on Examples

- Example 1. This example has two different solutions involving integrals which are improper for different reasons.
- Example 5. An infinitely large object with a finite volume is described.
- Example 9. This example concerns the area under the standard normal curve.

Notes on Exercises

- Exercises 1–10. Evaluation of improper integrals is practices.
- Exercises 11–44. These exercises test for convergence, but do not require a numerical result.
- Exercises 53–58. Applications involving improper integrals are involved.
- **Cooperative Learning:** Exs. 48, 58, 63, 64.

Assignment Guide

Day 1: Exs. 1–3, 5, 8, 9, 12, 14, 17, 20, 22, 23, 26, 30, 41.
Day 2: Exs. 47–49, 50, 51, 53, 55–57, 59, 64.

8.7 Differential Equations

Objectives

- Verify solutions to differentiable equations.
- Solve separable differential equations.
- Evaluate the constant for differential equations with initial conditions.
- Use numerical methods to approximate solutions to differential equations with initial values.

Key Ideas

Separable first-order equations

Differential equations and integration

Numerical methods

Teaching Notes

Separable first-order differential equations are the most common type for a first year calculus course. Stress the technique of *separate and integrate.*

Make the connection between the differential equation and rate of change proportional to amount, which is commonly used in population growth, decay, and compound interest. Refer back to examples from previous chapters. Extend this familiar idea to the logistic growth model.

The numerical techniques are powerful. They require a programmable calculator or computer.

Common Errors

Students may not recognize alternate versions of a solution, particularly if the solution has been rewritten to isolate y.

It is important to write the constant of integration at the time an integration is made. Further transformations of the solution must take the constant of integration into account.

Notes on Examples

- Example 3. This is a good illustration of the traditional type of equation.
- Example 4. This is an excellent realistic application.

Notes on Exercises

- Exercises 11–20. The traditional separate and integrate technique is emphasized.
- Exercises 9, 10, 42, 43. These are common types of applications.
- **Cooperative Learning:** Exs. 44–47.

Assignment Guide

Day 1: Exs. 3–5, 7, 11, 13, 15, 17, 19, 21, 23, 24.
Day 2: Exs. 9, 10, 25, 27, 28, 31, 33, 35, 42, 43, 46.

8.8 Computer Algebra Systems (CAS)

Objectives

- Evaluate integrals using computer algebra systems or tables of integrals.
- Sketch the graph of a function defined by an integral.
- Compute x in an equation of the form $\int_a^x F(t)\,dt = y$ for a given y value.

Key Ideas

Computer algebra systems

Tables of integrals

Functions defined by integrals

Graphical solutions

Teaching Notes

The most effective procedures would be to work on a CAS in a laboratory setting, or to obtain a class set of hand held computers with symbolic algebra, or to demonstrate a CAS on a computer with overhead projection.

All students should be able to plot functions defined by integrals on their calculators. This process is particularly useful for nonelementary integrals. The plot can be used to find x-coordinates as described in objective 3.

Notes on Examples

- Example 3. This example describes how a solution to a nonelementary integral can be found.

Notes on Exercises

- Exercises 1–16. These exercises introduce CAS, but can be done with tables.
- Exercises 17–28. Graphical techniques are used in these exercises.
- **Cooperative Learning:** Exs. 29, 30, 36.

Assignment Guide

Exs. 1–3, 5, 7, 11, 13, 16, 17, 21, 23, 25–27, 29.

Chapter 9 Infinite Series

9.1 Limits of Sequences of Numbers

Objectives

- Write the terms of a sequence given by a formula or defined recursively.
- Determine whether a given sequence is convergent or divergent.
- Find the limit of a convergent sequence.

Key Ideas

Definitions and notation

Convergence and divergence

Theorems

Teaching Notes

Emphasize the definition of a sequence as a function whose domain is the set of all integers $n \geq n_1$, for some integer n_1. The sequence whose nth term is given by $a_n = a(n)$ can be graphed in parametric mode using dot format, with $x_1 = t$, $y_1 = a(t)$, $t\text{Min} = n_1$ and t-step $= 1$, as in Exploration 1. To support the limit statement $a_n \to L$, graph $x_2 = t$, $y_2 = L$ in the same window.

The grapher can be used to illustrate the definition of the sequence $\{a_n\}$ converging to L. For a given $\varepsilon > 0$, graph

$$x_1 = t, \; y_1 = a(t)$$
$$x_2 = t, \; y_2 = L - \varepsilon$$
$$x_3 = t, \; y_3 = L + \varepsilon$$

in the same window. TRACE along the sequence to find an N for which all the points (n, a_n) for $n \geq N$ appear to lie inside the horizontal band $L - \varepsilon < y < L + \varepsilon$. See Exploration 3. Generating a table of values is also a good way to demonstrate the existence of N. Theorems 1–4 are all fundamental results for finding limits of convergent sequences. The limit formulas in Table 9.1 are very useful and should be discussed.

Common Errors

Alternating sequences with subsequences converging to two different limits are often interpreted as convergent by students.

Another common error is not to recognize an indeterminate form 1^∞ or ∞^0. For example, a student may carelessly and mistakenly conclude that $\left(\dfrac{n}{n+1}\right)^n \to 1$.

Notes on Examples

- Example 6. This example is an important illustration of the Sandwich theorem.
- Example 7. The use of Theorem 3 is demonstrated in this example.
- Examples 9 and 10. These examples connect with earlier work on limits using l'Hôpital's Rule.

Notes on Exercises

- Exercises 11–26. Students find the limit of each convergent sequence analytically and support graphically.
- Exercises 35–58. For these exercises students find the limit of each convergent sequence graphically and confirm analytically. They should first simplify the formula for a_n if possible. When graphing the sequence it may help to use connected mode to see the end behavior. Note that the grapher will have range limitations evaluating factorials and exponential functions.
- Exercise 58. The term a_n begins to decrease at $n = 36$. Since $a_{36} \approx 2.86E14$, use a viewing window of $[0, 70]$ by $[0, 3E14]$ to graph $\{a_n\}$.
- Exercises 59–62. These exercises illustrate the definition of $a_n \to L$. For a given $\varepsilon > 0$, graphically determine the smallest N which satisfies $|a_n - L| < \varepsilon$ for all $n > N$.
- **Cooperative Learning:** Exs. 67–70.

Assignment Guide

Day 1: Exs. 1–3, 5–8, 11, 18–20, 23.
Day 2: Exs. 27, 30, 33, 35, 39, 41, 53, 59, 61, 63, 67–70.

9.2 Infinite Series

Objectives

- Learn the definition of an infinite series converging to a sum.
- Compute sums of geometric and telescoping series.
- Determine the divergence of certain series.

Key Ideas

The sequence of partial sums

Geometric series

Telescoping series

Convergent and divergent series

Teaching Notes

The key idea of this section is the definition of an infinite series converging to a sum L. A convergent infinite series is one whose sequence of partial sums converges. The sum of an infinite series is the limit of its sequence of partial sums. Geometric series and telescoping series are good examples to illustrate this definition because their partial sums have simple formulas.

Since the partial sums of most series will not have simple closed form formulas, the use of a program like PARTSUMT to generate a table of values of partial sums can be a valuable instructional aid. For a convergent series it can be used it to estimate the sum. Make note of the terminology introduced on page 706, of partial sums s_n *stabilizing* on a calculator.

The nth-Term Test for divergence and Theorem 5 are the first of a number of results which will be used use to determine the convergence or divergence of a given series.

Common Errors

A common error students make is to confuse the nth-Term Test with its converse and falsely infer that a series converges if $a_n \to 0$. Another error students make is to overlook the nth-Term Test as an easy way to prove divergence.

Notes on Examples

- Examples 1 and 2. In discussing these geometric series be sure to demonstrate the PARTSUMG and PARTSUMT programs.
- Example 4. This is a telescoping series. Confirm the formula derived for s_k with PARTSUMT.
- Example 7. This example illustrates the use of Theorem 5.

Notes on Exercises

- Exercises 1–6. These exercises reinforce the definition of the sum of a series as the limit of the sequence of its partial sums.
- Exercises 15–18. These are telescoping series and require the use of partial fractions as shown in Example 4.
- **Cooperative Learning:** Exs. 53, 54, 56, 58.

Assignment Guide

Day 1: Exs. 1, 3, 5, 7, 10, 11, 13, 15, 18, 19, 21, 23, 25.
Day 2: Exs. 26, 29, 30, 33, 35, 37–39, 45, 48, 49, 51.

9.3 Series without Negative Terms: Comparison and Integral Tests

Objective

- Apply the Integral Test, Comparison Test, or Limit Comparison Test to determine whether a series converges or diverges.

Key Ideas

Nondecreasing sequences

Tests for convergence

Teaching Notes

Begin with a discussion of Theorem 6 since that result forms the basis of all the convergence tests presented in Sections 9.3 and 9.4. If a series has no negative terms the sequence of its partial sums is *nondecreasing*. By Theorem 6 only one of two things can happen: (1) Either this sequence is bounded above and converges to its least upper bound, or (2) the sequence diverges to ∞. Thus, the convergence or divergence of the series is simply a matter of whether or not its sequence of partial sums is bounded above.

Point out the analogy between the Comparison Test for convergent series and Theorem 1 of Section 8.6. Conceptually, the Comparison Test is the easiest test to understand. However, students have difficulty using this text since it requires selecting the right series for comparison and then establishing the correct inequality.

When employing the Integral Test make sure that students verify all the conditions that $f(x)$ must satisfy on some $[n, \infty)$. Remind them that the easiest way to show that f is decreasing is to show $f'(x) < 0$. Once the Integral Test is introduced, establish right away the convergence of the p-series when $p > 1$ and divergence when $p \leq 1$.

When discussing the Limit Comparison Test, review the related ideas in Sections 7.6 and 8.6. In many instances this test is easier to use than the Comparison Test. It is necessary only to find an appropriate end behavior model for the nth term a_n and calculate a limit. The Limit Comparison Test is usually the test used when a_n is a rational function of n.

Continue to use graphical and numerical support. In those examples where convergence is fairly rapid, use PARTSUMT to estimate the sum of a series which the theory indicates is convergent.

Notes on Examples

- Example 2. This is a direct application of Theorem 6. The argument establishing convergence motivates the proof of the Comparison Test. Convergence of the series with $a_n = 1/n!$ is very fast so this is a good opportunity to demonstrate PARTSUMT and PARTSUMG.

- Example 3. You may prefer to show the divergence of the harmonic series using the Integral Test, but the argument used here has great appeal. Demonstrate the truth of the inequality $s_n \geq k/2$ where $n = 2^k$ with PARTSUMT.

- Example 5. The argument for convergence motivates the proof of the Integral Test.

Notes on Exercises

- Exercises 1–24. Use the tests to determine convergence, then estimate the sum of those series which are convergent. For some of the convergent series, namely those in Exs. 9, 18 and 19, convergence is very slow. You may want to provide some additional guidelines for these problems.
- **Cooperative Learning:** Exs. 26, 29, 30, 32.

Assignment Guide

Exs. 1–25 odd.

9.4 Series with Nonnegative Terms: Ratio and Root Tests

Objective

- Apply the Ratio Test or n-th Root Test to determine whether a series converges or diverges.

Key Ideas

The Ratio Test

The nth-Root Test

Teaching Notes

The Ratio Test and nth-Root Test are important because they are *intrinsic* tests. They are often used when exponential functions or factorials occur as factors in the numerator or denominator of the nth term a_n. They are much too crude to determine convergence when a_n is a rational function of n. A notable application of their use is in finding the radius of convergence of a power series.

When employing these two tests the limits in Table 9.1 are frequently encountered, so you may want to review those results.

Students should be familiar with all five tests for series with nonnegative terms that are found in Sections 9.3 and 9.4. A major task for students will be learning how to select the appropriate test for a given series.

Common Errors

When using the Ratio Test, errors are often made by students when simplifying the fraction a_{n+1}/a_n, especially when factorials are involved. Numerical support is useful for detecting errors.

When employing the Ratio Test or the nth-Root Test, students may not know how to evaluate the limit. A review of some of the techniques in Section 9.1 may be helpful.

For students who are tempted to use the nth-Root Test when a_n has a factorial as a factor, they should know that $(n!)^{1/n} \to \infty$.

Notes on Examples

- Example 1. Notice the nth term can be defined nonrecursively by
  $a_n = 2^{n-1}(n-1)!^2/(2n-1)!$.
- Example 2. This example illustrates the Ratio Test. In part (a) since $\rho = 1/4$, convergence should be fast. This is a good example to demonstrate PARTSUMT and PARTSUMG. In part (b), even though $\rho = 1$ we can still conclude the series diverges since $a_{n+1}/a_n > 1$ and therefore a_n is increasing.

Notes on Exercises

- Exercises 1–26. Test for convergence. Estimate the sum of those series which are convergent.
- Exercises 27–32 and 35. In these exercises the terms of the series are defined recursively.
- **Cooperative Learning**: Exs. 26, 35, 36.

Assignment Guide

Exs. 3–31 odd.

9.5 Alternating Series and Absolute Convergence

Objectives

- Test alternating series for convergence.
- Estimate sums and the error for convergent alternating series.
- Test for absolute and conditional convergence.

Key Ideas

Alternating series

Absolute convergence

Teaching Notes

This section discusses two results for determining the convergence of series whose terms have mixed signs. The Alternating Series Theorem provides sufficient conditions for the convergence of an alternating series. Just as important, its sequel, Theorem 8, provides a bound on the error when estimating the sum of an alternating series with its nth partial sum s_n.

For a converging alternating series, the oscillating convergence of its sequence of partial sums should be compared with the monotone convergence obtained when all terms of a series are positive. PARTSUMG and PARTSUMT can be used to illustrate these two fundamental convergence patterns.

The importance of the Absolute Convergence Theorem lies in its generality. Now a tool exists to show convergence of any series provided its absolute convergence can be shown. Of course, the five tests in Sections 9.3 and 9.4 are available to show absolute convergence. The alternating p-series with $p \leq 1$ are about the easiest examples of series which converge conditionally.

Flowchart 9.1 is a very useful summary of the last three sections.

Notes on Examples

- Example 4. Note the value of Theorem 8 in estimating the sum of the alternating series. This calculation could be contrasted with that of estimating the sum of the corresponding series of absolute values, which was discussed in Section 9.3, Exploration 2.
- Example 5. This is a good example to illustrate Theorem 9 since the Alternating Series Theorem does not apply.
- Example 7. In the course of applying Theorem 8, the grapher is used to find the first n such that $a_{n+1} < .001$. For graphers with a seq routine, this could also be done by generating a list of values of a_n.

Notes on Exercises

- Exercises 1–10. Students should decide which alternating series converge and then use Theorem 8 to approximate the sum of the ones that converge. For the estimation, the technique used in Example 7 is useful.
- Exercises 11–36. Students determine whether each series converges absolutely, converges conditionally or diverges.
- **Cooperative Learning**: Exs. 43, 46–48.

Assignment Guide

Day 1: Exs. 1, 3, 5, 7, 9, 11, 12, 17, 19, 21.
Day 2: Exs. 26–28, 35, 37, 39, 41, 42, 44, 45.

9.6 Power Series

Objectives

- Determine the radius of convergence and interval of convergence of a power series.
- Graph the partial sums of a power series using GRAPHSUM.
- Estimate the maximum error over a specified interval when a power series is represented by one of its partial sums.
- Find a range of values over which a partial sum of a power series approximates the infinite sum within a given error.
- Differentiate and integrate a power series.

Key Ideas

Power series and convergence

Differentiation and integration of power series

Teaching Notes

The key idea of this section is that a power series defines a function f whose domain is the interval of convergence of the series and whose value at any x is the sum of the series at x. If the series is a power series in $x - a$, the interval of convergence is symmetric about a. The radius of convergence is found by the Ratio Test or nth-Root Test. If the radius is finite, separate calculations are needed to determine if convergence occurs at either endpoint. By Theorem 11, a function f defined in this manner is differentiable on the interior of its domain. Power series representations of its derivative and antiderivative are found by differentiating or integrating the series term-by-term.

The partial sum $s_{n+1}(x)$ of the series is a polynomial of degree $\leq n$ and is denoted $P_n(x)$. By definition, $P_n(x) \to f(x)$ at each x in the interval of convergence, which suggests that for n sufficiently large, $P_n(x)$ will closely approximate $f(x)$ over an *entire subinterval* of the domain of f.

Graphs of the polynomials $P_n(x)$ can be generated on the grapher either using a built-in feature of the grapher or using the program GRAPHSUM. If a formula for $f(x)$ is known, as is the case in Examples 1 and 2 where $f(x) = 1/(1 - x)$, then graphing $y_1 = P_n(x)$ and $y_2 = f(x)$ in the same window can demonstrate how well the approximation works. The maximum error of the approximation over an interval can be estimated graphically by generating the graph of $y_1 - y_2$ and using TRACE.

Common Errors

Students often neglect to check the endpoints when determining the interval of convergence.

Notes on Examples

- Example 2. How these calculations are done will depend on the capabilities of the grapher. Note that range limits could also be found analytically. For $x < 0$ the series is alternating so Theorem 8 can be applied to find a lower limit. Bounding the remainder $R_{10}(x) = x^{11}/(1 - x)$ could be used to find both limits.

- Example 4. This example demonstrates the techniques for determining the interval of convergence.

- Example 7. New representations can be obtained by differentiating and integrating known power series representations.

Notes on Exercises

- Exercises 1–14. The interval of convergence is found.
- Exercises 15–18, 27–32. In each of these exercises students are to estimate the range of values of x for which $|P_n(x) - f(x)| < .01$ for a given n. Refer students to the graphing technique used in Example 2. In Exs. 15–18 the range limits can be found analytically since $R_n(x)$ has a simple formula.
- Exercises 20, 52–54. All of these exercises involve $\tan^{-1}$.
- Exercises 25, 26 and 33. These exercises should be assigned together.
- **Cooperative Learning:** Exs. 43, 45, 48, 53.

Assignment Guide

Day 1: Exs. 1, 5, 7, 13, 15, 17, 19, 21, 22, 24, 33.
Day 2: Exs. 20, 25–27, 30, 31, 35, 39–41, 52–54.

9.7 Taylor Series and Maclaurin Series

Objectives

- Find the Maclaurin series or a Taylor series for a given function.
- Estimate the truncation error.
- Differentiate, integrate and multiply series.

Key Ideas

Taylor polynomials and series

Taylor's theorem with remainder

Estimating the remainder

Combining Taylor series

Teaching Notes

The definition of the Taylor polynomials can be motivated as in Exploration 1. It is plausible that if we were constructing an nth degree polynomial which best approximates a function f on a small interval about $x = a$, we would want the polynomial to have the same function value and the same first n derivatives at $x = a$ that f does. These $n + 1$ conditions uniquely determine the $n + 1$ coefficients of the nth order Taylor polynomial $P_n(x)$. $P_1(x)$ is the standard linear approximation of f at $x = a$, which was encountered in Section 3.8. Graphing $y_1 = P_n(x)$ and $y_2 = f(x)$ for small values of n in the same window using functions like e^x, $\sin x$, $\ln(1+x)$ should convince students that these polynomials do a remarkable job of estimating $f(x)$ when x is sufficiently close to a. Furthermore, the approximation gets better as n increases.

If f has derivatives of all orders at $x = a$, the above observations suggest that the Taylor *series* of f at $x = a$ is an exact representation of f on an interval about a. Taylor's Theorem confirms this, under suitable conditions. For a given x, to show that the Taylor series represents f at x it is necessary to show that the remainder $R_n(x) = f(x) - P_n(x) \to 0$, as $n \to \infty$. The formula for $R_n(x)$ given by Taylor's Theorem serves this purpose for a number of important cases.

The formula for $R_n(x)$ involves some unknown value c that is between a and x. However, if we can bound the values of $f^{(n+1)}$ on the interval between a and x, then it is possible to find a bound for the absolute error $|R_n(x)|$ when approximating $f(x)$ with $P_n(x)$. In Section 9.6 graphical methods were used to estimate this error. Students should appreciate that Taylor's Theorem now provides an analytical method for doing this.

Other power series representations can be derived by algebraically manipulating, differentiating and integrating known Taylor series representations. The new representations obtained are themselves Taylor series since the Taylor series is the unique power series in $x - a$ that can represent a function on an interval about a. This is a nice shortcut to establishing Taylor series representations. See Example 6 and the discussion on page 765.

Common Errors

Algebraic errors may occur when calculating Taylor polynomial coefficients. Graphing support can be used to detect errors.

Notes on Examples

- Examples 4 and 5. These examples are fundamental as they demonstrate how Taylor's Theorem establishes that e^x and $\sin x$ are represented by their Maclaurin series.

- Example 6. By substituting $2x$ for x in Eq. (9) a power series representation for $\cos 2x$ is obtained. By uniqueness, this has to be the *Maclaurin* series for $\cos 2x$.

- Examples 7 and 8. These examples show how Theorem 15 is used to find an upper bound on the truncation error.

Notes on Exercises

- Exercises 1–8. To construct a Taylor polynomial have students organize their calculations in a table with columns: $k, f^{(k)}(x), f^{(k)}(a), f^{(k)}(x)/k!$.

- Exercises 9–18. These exercises can all be derived from the Maclaurin series for e^x, $\sin x$ and $\cos x$.

- Exercises 19–24. Apply Taylor's Theorem with $n = 2$.

- Exercises 27–34. These exercises concern estimations and error. See Examples 7 and 8.

- Exercises 37–38. The purpose of these exercises is to demonstrate Theorems 11 and 12.

- **Cooperative Learning**: Exs. 41, 44–47.

Assignment Guide

Day 1: Exs. 1, 3, 5–7, 9, 13, 14, 21, 24.
Day 2: Exs. 27, 29, 31–33, 35–38, 43.

9.8 Further Calculations with Taylor Series

Objectives

- Construct a binomial series expansion and analyze the truncation error when approximating the sum with $P_n(x)$.
- Choose a series with an appropriate center to estimate a particular function value.
- Use series to approximate definite integrals.
- Find power series expansions of functions defined by integrals.

Key Ideas

The binomial series

Choosing centers for Taylor's series

Evaluating nonelementary integrals

Teaching Notes

This section discusses three more topics involving Taylor series. The first is the binomial series. Review the Binomial Theorem and introduce the generalized binomial coefficient defined in (3). When m is a nonnegative integer show that the series expansion for $(1 + x)^m$ is just the expansion given by the Binomial Theorem. The text illustrates the case when $m = -1$. An example when m is a fractional exponent would be appropriate.

The second idea concerns the selection of a Taylor series to approximate a particular function value. There are two considerations. The choice of the center a should be near the given number, and the function value and all its derivatives should be easily computed at a.

Finally, Maclaurin series can be used to evaluate nonelementary integrals. These are powerful techniques, in some cases producing much faster and more accurate results than numerical integration. The results here can be supported using NINT.

Page 775 has a useful summary of commonly used series.

Notes on Examples

- Example 2. For $\theta = 35° = 35\pi/180$, $a = \pi/6$ is the nearest point where the exact value of sin and all its derivatives are known.
- Example 3. The indefinite integral of sin x^2 has no closed form formula, but its Maclaurin series is derived easily.
- Example 4. The expansion in Example 3 is used to approximate the definite integral. Theorem 8 is used to bound the error. The approximation is amazingly accurate.

Notes on Exercises

- Exercises 1–6. Select the appropriate Taylor series to evaluate the function near a given x.
- Exercises 9–14. For these exercises, use the binomial series expansion to construct the Taylor polynomials.
- Exercises 19–22. Use power series expansions to approximate the definite integral. Support with NINT
- **Cooperative Learning:** Exs. 15, 18, 23, 24.

Assignment Guide

Exs. 1–4, 6, 9, 10, 13, 17, 19–22.

Chapter 10 Plane Curves, Parametrizations, and Polar Coordinates

10.1 Conic Sections and Quadratic Equations

Objectives
- Find the equation of a conic section in standard position.
- Identify the equation of a conic section in standard position and graph the conic section.

Key Ideas

Conic sections

Distance formula

Circles

Parabolas

Ellipses

Hyperbolas

End behavior and asymptotes of a hyperbola

Eccentricity

Focus-directrix equation

Teaching Notes

The main purpose of this section is to define parabolas, ellipses, and hyperbolas and to derive their standard equations. Students should be able to identify the curves from these equations and sketch their graphs. The concept of *eccentricity* is important because all three curves can be unified in the single family of curves generated by the focus-directrix equation $PF = e \cdot PD$.

Physical modeling is an integral part of the instructional process. In this section physical models of the conic sections can be constructed with inexpensive materials. The "double cone" mentioned in the caption, and shown in diagram 10.1, can be modeled with wooden figures or with a tag board. Wooden cones, some of which actually "break apart" to reveal different conic sections when cut by an imaginary plane, can be purchased commercially, but they are expensive.

Pay particular attention to the physical construction of the parabola as modeled by Kepler and given on page 782 in the margin. This model will help students to understand how the parabola is traced because the string connecting the focus to the directrix will always remain constant. The degenerate conics also can be shown easily by using physical models. Have students work in small groups and provide each group with enough materials so that students can have hands-on experience constructing the various conics. Make the connections among the physical model, the definition of the conic being modeled, and the algebraic representation in the xy-plane.

Use square viewing windows when graphing conics so that the curves will not be distorted. The Exploration Bit on page 791 suggests that if your grapher has "list" capabilities, then use it. Students should define the list L_1 as {0.25, 0.5, 1, 2, 4, 8} and then use L_1 in place of b in the equation stored in Y_1:

$$Y_1 = L_1\sqrt{x^2-1}$$
$$Y_2 = -Y_1$$

Common Errors

Students sometimes confuse the eccentricity e with the base e of the natural logarithm.

Notes on Examples

- Examples 1 and 2. You may want to have students give the equations for parabolas that open to the left or to the right. Table 10.1 will assist them in writing these equations. Example 2 shows students how to find the focus and directrix of a parabola.

- Example 3. This example is very important in helping students to organize their thinking into how the different attributes of the ellipse can be ordered. Follow up Example 3 by having students do the Exploration Bits in the margin on page 785. You should do Exploration 1 in class.

- Example 4. This example categorizes the critical attributes of two types of hyperbolas.

- Example 5. Be sure to explore the concept of eccentricity in some detail so that students will be able to understand what conic results when $e > 1$, $e = 1$, or when $e < 1$.

Notes on Exercises

- Exercises 1–14. These are traditional exercises associated with the study of conics.

- Exercises 15–34. The sketch of the various ellipses or hyperbolas using a graphing utility will probably be new for most students. Use Explorations 1 and 2 as guides.

- Exercises 37–46. Applications of conics are presented.

- **Cooperative Learning:** Exs. 46, 49, 51.

Assignment Guide

Exs. 2, 5, 9, 13, 17, 20, 23, 26, 29, 32, 38, 40, 43, 46, 49, 51.

10.2 The Graphs of Quadratic Equations in x and y

Objectives

- Identify and graph a conic section whose equation is $Ax^2 + Bxy + Cy^2 + Dx + Ey + F = 0$.
- Find the equation of a conic section in standard position that is shifted and rotated about the origin to obtain the graph of a given quadratic equation.

Key Ideas

The general quadratic equation

Conics with standard orientation

Conics with oblique axes

Rotations

The discriminant

Teaching Notes

This section establishes the result that the graph of the general quadratic equation $Ax^2 + Bxy + Cy^2 + Dx + Ey + F = 0$ is a conic section (or a degenerate case). When $B = 0$, the graph can be identified by completing the square. It is a conic section that has been translated from the standard position. The various possibilities are described in a summary on page 796. These conic sections are said to have *standard orientation* since their axes are horizontal or vertical.

When $B \neq 0$, the text shows that the graph can be obtained by rotating a conic section with standard orientation about the origin. Thus, the graph in the case $B \neq 0$ is a conic section with oblique axes. The sign of the *discriminant* $B^2 - 4AC$ indicates which conic section the curve will be without enacting this transformation.

Exploration 1 describes the two-function method of graphing the general quadratic equation.

Notes on Examples

- Example 1. Some students may need a review of the technique for completing the square.
- Example 3. This is the key example of the section. It shows how to find the equation of the conic with standard orientation that was rotated to coincide with the graph of a given quadratic equation.
- Example 4. Students are asked to evaluate the discriminant to determine if the rotated conic is an ellipse, a parabola, or a hyperbola. The results of this example should be supported graphically using Eq. (12).

Notes on Exercises

- Exercises 1–20. Students are to use the discriminate to determine whether the equations represent parabolas, ellipses, or hyperbolas.
- Exercises 21–28. Use Example 3 as a guide to find the equation of the rotated conic. Note that the rotated conic in Ex. 26 is not in standard position.
- Exercises 31–34. Students are asked to apply the techniques illustrated by Example 2.
- **Cooperative Learning:** Exs. 35, 36.

Assignment Guide

Exs. 3, 7, 11, 16, 21, 25, 28, 30, 32, 34–36.

10.3 Parametric Equations for Plane Curves

Objectives

- Graph a curve defined by parametric equations.
- Describe the motion of a particle in the xy-plane whose position is given by parametric equations.
- Find a Cartesian equation describing a parametrically defined curve.
- Find parametric equations for conic sections in standard position.

Key Ideas

Parametric equations for a curve

Equations of motion for a particle in the plane

Parametric equations for conic sections in standard position

Cycloids

Teaching Notes

The explorations and examples of this section show how to graph curves in the xy-plane defined by parametric equations. An important application occurs when a particle moving in the xy-plane has a position at time t described by parametric equations of t. The graph of the equations show the path of the particle. If we use the TRACE key on the grapher, the motion of the illuminated pixel simulates the motion of the particle along its trajectory.

Parametric representation of conic sections is an important topic in this section. For conic sections in standard position, students should be able to convert between their rectangular equations and the equivalent parametric equations. A table summarizing these conversions is given on page 810.

A discussion of Exploration 1 in class will help to familiarize students with the basic terminology and techniques of this section.

Notes on Examples

- Example 3. This example shows how to parametrize an ellipse in standard position.
- Example 4. The path is the right branch of the hyperbola $x^2 - y^2 = 1$. Show how to obtain a parametric representation for the entire hyperbola. The extension of this idea to graphing $x^2/a^2 - y^2/b^2 = 1$ is discussed in Exploration 3.
- Example 5. The parametric equations of a cycloid are derived.

Notes on Exercises

- Exercises 1–24. You may want to discuss several of these exercises in class in order to review all aspects of graphing in parametric mode, in particular the selection of tMin, tMax and t-step and the use of the TRACE key to follow the motion of the particle. Note that in a number of these exercises the equivalent Cartesian equation must be suitably restricted in order to match the path of the particle. See Example 4 in this regard.
- Exercises 32 and 33. These are spirals and never return to their initial point $(0, 0)$.
- Exercises 49–56. These exercises involve the rotation of conics using parametric mode. See Exploration 3 and Example 2 of Section 10.2.
- **Cooperative Learning:** Exs. 35, 38.

Assignment Guide

Exs. 2, 5, 8, 11, 14, 17, 20, 23, 26, 29, 32, 35, 36, 38, 43, 46, 49, 51, 53.

10.4 The Calculus of Parametric Equations

Objectives

- Compute the slope and second derivative of a parametrically defined curve.
- Find the arc length of a parametrically defined curve.
- Find the area of a surface of revolution obtained by rotating a parametrically defined curve about the x- or y-axis.

Key Ideas

Differentiable parametrized curve

Slopes of parametrized curves

Tangent line to a parametrized curve

The parametric formula for d^2y/dx^2

Length of a parametric curve

Area of a surface of revolution

Teaching Notes

The formula for the slope of a parametrized curve is a nice application of the Chain Rule. It requires that x and y be differentiable functions of t and that $dx/dt \neq 0$. You should discuss what happens when $dx/dt = 0$.

To apply the slope formula at a particular point (x, y), you need to know the value of t which generates the point. This is sometimes a source of confusion to students.

The slope formula actually parametrizes $y' = dy/dx$ by the equations $x = x(t)$, $y' = y'(t)/x'(t)$. Applying the slope formula to these equations yields a formula for d^2y/dx^2. The three-step procedure in the margin on page 815 should help students with this calculation.

The formulas for arc length and surface area generalize the formulas developed in Sections 6.4 and 6.5. If $y = f(x)$, applying the present formulas to the parametrization $x = t$, $y = f(t)$ yields the formulas in Chapter 6.

Notes on Examples

- Example 1. The familiar problem of finding a tangent line is applied to a parametrically defined curve.
- Example 2. The three-step procedure for calculating d^2y/dx^2 is illustrated.
- Examples 3 and 5. Stress that the integrand should be simplified as much as possible before the integration process takes place.
- Example 4. The arc length can be calculated analytically. Challenge students to do this. $(L = 201.5946)$ In any case, a more accurate answer can be obtained numerically by first simplifying the radicand to $t^2 + 1$.

Notes on Exercises

- Exercises 13–22. The lengths of curves and surface areas of revolution are to be found by analytic methods and then confirmed using NINT. All of the integrands simplify nicely. The integration in Ex. 13 requires the technique described in Section 8.3, Exploration 1.
- **Cooperative Learning:** Exs. 26, 30, 32.

Assignment Guide

Exs. 3, 7, 12, 14, 17, 22, 26, 30, 32, 34, 37, 40, 45.

10.5 Polar Coordinates

Objectives

- Plot and identify points in the polar plane using their polar coordinates.
- Graph and identify elementary polar equations and regions in the polar plane.
- Convert between polar coordinates and rectangular coordinates of a point.
- Find a Cartesian equation equivalent to a given polar equation.
- Find a polar equation equivalent to a given Cartesian equation.

Key Ideas

Polar coordinates and the polar plane

Multiple representations of points

Elementary polar equations and inequalities

Converting between Cartesian and polar coordinates

Converting between the Cartesian equations and polar equations of a curve

Teaching Notes

An introduction to the polar plane is analogous to an introduction to the Cartesian plane. Show students how to plot a given polar point, identify a given point in the plane by its polar coordinates, graph simple polar equations, such as $r = a$ and $\theta = \theta_0$, and graph simple inequalities. Polar graph paper should be made available to the class to show what a polar grid looks like and to be used for sketching polar graphs. Mention that one of the distinctions between polar and Cartesian coordinates is that a point in the Cartesian plane is identified by a *unique* pair of Cartesian coordinates, whereas a point in the polar plane is represented by infinitely many polar coordinate pairs.

By superimposing a rectangular coordinate system onto a polar coordinate system, it is possible to pass from one system to the other whenever it is convenient for a given problem. Students should be able to convert between rectangular and polar coordinates, and convert between the polar and rectangular equations of a given curve. Converting a rectangular equation to its equivalent polar equation is perfectly straightforward. Going the other way is somewhat more involved.

Superimposing the two systems allows us to graph a polar equation $r = f(\theta)$ in a Cartesian viewing window by graphing $x = f(t) \cos t$ and $y = f(t) \sin t$ in parametric mode. ($\theta = t$.) Explorations 1, 2, and 3 illustrate the usefulness of this technique and will help students make the connection between polar and rectangular coordinates.

Some graphing utilities have a built-in polar graphing capability that will graph a polar equation on a polar grid. Students should take advantage of this capability if their grapher has it.

Notes on Examples

- Example 1. The infinitely many polar coordinates of the point $P(2, 30°)$ are calculated.

- Examples 2 and 3. The concept of multiple representations is pursued further by investigating the polar equations of a circle centered at the origin and a line through the origin.

- Example 4. Students are given the opportunity to graph regions defined by polar inequalities.

- Example 5. Graphing a polar curve using parametric mode is illustrated. This is a very useful technique.

- Example 6. Converting the polar equation to its equivalent Cartesian equation may involve a little luck, but with no effort at all the *graph* of the polar equation clearly suggests it is a straight line.

Notes on Exercises

- Exercises 4–22. These exercises directly pattern the examples of the section.
- Exercises 23–44. Analytical solutions supported by using a graphing utility are required. The techniques needed to solve these exercises are presented through the examples.
- **Cooperative Learning:** Ex. 45.

Assignment Guide

Exs. 4, 5, 11, 15, 19, 22, 23, 26, 29, 32, 35, 38, 41, 44.

10.6 Graphing in Polar Coordinates

Objectives

- Determine the complete graph of a polar equation.
- Find the points of intersection of two polar curves.

Key Ideas

Symmetry tests for polar graphs

Slope of a polar curve

Slope at the origin

Complete graph of a polar curve

Points of intersection of polar curves

Simultaneous solutions of two polar equations

Teaching Notes

This section discusses a number of analytical techniques for determining complete graphs of polar equations. Tests for symmetry about the x-axis, y-axis or the origin are stated in terms of polar coordinates. These tests are relevant since many of the curves being considered satisfy one or more of these symmetries. Recall that any two of these symmetries implies the third.

The slope dy/dx of a polar curve in the form $r = f(\theta)$ can be calculated from its parametric representation. The general formula is given by Eq. (1). Calculating the slope at the origin is a special case since the curve may pass through the origin more than once at different angles.

In graphing a curve of the form $r = f(\theta)$, the range of θ values used is an important matter. We always allow $0 \le \theta \le 2\pi$, so that every possible ray from the origin is considered. This interval may need to be larger depending on the period of f. For more general equations $F(r, \theta) = 0$, there may be restrictions on θ. Exploration 1 discusses these matters.

For graphs generated on the graphing utility, the TRACE key can be used to review how the curve was sequentially generated and can show if the curve retraces itself over the interval of t values (θ values) used. Remind students to use a square viewing window so that the curve is not distorted.

The last part of this section concerns the problem of finding the points where the graphs of two polar equations intersect. Intersections occur at points corresponding to the simultaneous solutions of the two equations, but because of multiple representations there may be other points of intersection. If the two curves are graphed together in *simultaneous* mode, the simultaneous solutions of the two equations occur at points where the two graphs "collide" while they are being drawn.

Notes on Examples

- Example 1. The basic analytical tools are demonstrated to determine the complete graph of a cardioid. You may want students to sketch the curve on polar graph paper before using their graphers.

- Example 2. Observe that the graph satisfies all three symmetries, and that the range of θ needs to be restricted. To generate the complete graph on the grapher, two parametrically defined curves need to be graphed.

- Example 3. Since $f(\theta) = 1 + \cos(\theta/2)$ has period 4π, let values of θ range from 0 to 4π. Observe that the graph is symmetric about the x-axis.

- Examples 5 and 6. These two examples concern the problem of finding the points of intersection of two polar graphs. By graphing the two curves together in simultaneous mode, you can determine which of the intersection points come from simultaneous solutions of the polar equations, either by observing the curves as they are being drawn or by using the TRACE key.

Notes on Exercises

- Exercises 1–10. The directions are to sketch the graph and confirm with a graphing utility. You may want students to provide an analysis which includes the symmetries the curve satisfies, the range of values of θ needed to generate a complete graph, and a table showing specific points (r, θ) on the curve.

- Exercises 13–16. Slopes of polar curves at given points are computed.

- Exercises 25 and 26. These exercises are similar to Example 4. The given pair does not satisfy the equation, but the point in question has another coordinate pair that does.

- Exercises 27–34. Points of intersection of two polar curves are found.

- **Cooperative Learning:** Exs. 46, 58.

Assignment Guide

Exs. 2, 5, 10, 14, 17, 21, 22, 25, 27, 30, 32, 36, 39, 42, 46, 53, 58.

10.7 Polar Equations of Conic Sections

Objectives

- Find polar equations for conic sections and lines.
- Identify and graph conic sections given by their polar equation.

Key Ideas

The standard polar equation for lines

Polar equations for circles

Polar equations for ellipses, hyperbolas, and parabolas

Rotations of conics in polar form

Teaching Notes

Polar equations for straight lines and circles are presented first in this section. The derivations are straightforward, and students should be able to convert between their polar equations and rectangular equations.

Next, the text starts with a parabola, ellipse, or hyperbola that has one focus at the origin and directrix $x = k$ to the right of the origin. Using the focus-directrix equation from Section 10.1, a single formula $r = ke/(1 + e \cdot \cos\theta)$ can be derived which describes all three curves. The simplicity of the derivation should be contrasted with the somewhat tedious computations that were needed to find the standard rectangular equations for these curves in Section 10.1, involving a different computation for each curve.

The above curve can be rotated about the origin to obtain the formula of *any* parabola, ellipse, or hyperbola that has a focus at the origin. To rotate a curve α radians counterclockwise about the origin, replace θ with $\theta - \alpha$ in the polar equation. Finally, as Example 7 illustrates, a conic section can now be graphed anywhere in the xy-plane.

Table 10.3 gives the polar equation for a parabola, ellipse, or hyperbola in each of the four orientations of the standard polar form. Notice that Eqs. 2–4 can be derived from Eq. 1 by a making a simple rotation.

Notes on Examples

- Example 2. This example shows how to convert the polar equation of a line to the equivalent rectangular equation. Exploration 1 discusses a method for converting the other way.
- Examples 4–6. These examples concern the interpretation of the basic equation, Eq. (6). The results can be supported graphically.

Notes on Exercises

- Exercises 1–4. These exercises concern the polar equations of a line and their conversion to equivalent rectangular equations.
- Exercises 5–8. Students find the polar equations of a given circle or identify a circle from its polar equations.

- Exercises 9–24. These exercises involve conic sections in standard polar form, so Table 10.3 is useful.
- Exercises 47–51. Students convert the rectangular equation of a line to its equivalent polar equation.
- **Cooperative Learning:** Ex. 42.

Assignment Guide

Exs. 4, 8, 11, 15, 17, 20, 24, 27, 29, 33, 38, 40, 42, 46, 49, 50.

10.8 Integration in Polar Coordinates

Objective

- Calculate areas of plane regions, lengths of curves, and areas of surfaces of revolution in polar coordinates.

Key Ideas

Area of a polar region

The length of a polar curve

The area of a surface of revolution

Teaching Notes

When calculating the area of a region in the polar plane, it is important to graph the region to determine the correct limits of integration and to observe any symmetries that may simplify the integration. This is particularly true when the region is bounded by two curves. The techniques developed in Section 10.6 for finding the intersections of two polar curves will be useful here.

The formulas for the arc length of a polar curve and the surface area generated by rotating a polar curve about the x- or y-axis are special cases of the corresponding formulas given in Section 10.4.

Common Errors

Equation (2) for finding the area of a region between two polar curves is sometimes mistakenly written $\int_{\alpha}^{\beta} \frac{1}{2}(r_2 - r_1)^2 \, d\theta$. The Exploration Bit on page 849 is motivated by this.

Notes on Examples

- Example 2. The key to this calculation is to graph the region correctly and determine the limits of integration.

Notes on Exercises

- Exercises 1–18. For these exercises, students graph the region and calculate the area.
- Exercises 19–24. Students graph the curve and calculate the arc length.
- Exercises 25–28. The surface area generated by rotating a polar curve about the x- or y-axis is found.
- **Cooperative Learning:** Exs. 35, 36.

Assignment Guide

Exs. 1, 4, 7, 10, 13, 16, 19, 22, 25, 27, 31.

Chapter 11 Vectors and Analytic Geometry in Space

11.1 Vectors in the Plane

Objectives

- Express a geometrically defined vector in its algebraic form $a\mathbf{i} + b\mathbf{j}$.
- Represent a given vector $a\mathbf{i} + b\mathbf{j}$ as a directed line segment.
- Perform addition, subraction and scalar multiplication of vectors.
- Find the length of a given vector.

Key Ideas

Vectors and scalars

Representation of a vector by a directed line segment

Algebraic representation of a vector

Addition, subtraction and scalar multiplication of vectors

Geometric interpretation of vector addition, subtraction and scalar multiplication

Length of a vector

Unit vectors

Direction of a vector

Slopes, tangents and normals

Teaching Notes

Discuss first how vectors can be represented as directed line segments, and how they can be added and rescaled geometrically. Then define the basic unit vectors $\mathbf{i}$ and $\mathbf{j}$ and show that any vector $\mathbf{v}$ can be uniquely written in the algebraic form $\mathbf{v} = a\mathbf{i} + b\mathbf{j}$. This is the representation used in calculations and reflects that a vector in the plane is an ordered pair of numbers. Using the algebraic representation, the key definitions of vector equality, addition, subtraction, magnitude and scalar multiplication are all very simple. Spend some time with the geometric interpretation of each of these. Especially important are the geometric interpretations of $\mathbf{u} + \mathbf{v}$, $\mathbf{u} - \mathbf{v}$, $c\mathbf{v}$ and $-\mathbf{v}$.

With these new concepts, students need to know what rules can be used when simplifying vector expressions or solving vector equations. A class discussion of Exploration 1 and the exploration bits on pages 861 and 862 would be helpful.

Common Errors

The fact that different directed line segments can represent the same vector is a source of confusion to students. For example, a student looking at Figure 11.4 might wonder, "How could two different line segments both be v_1?" The answer of course, is that both directed line segments *represent* v_1.

Notes on Examples

- Example 3. This example shows how to find the vector represented by the directed line segment.
- Example 5. This example shows that a vector can be written as the product of its length and direction.
- Example 7. This example recasts the familiar problem of finding a tangent line and normal line to a curve in terms of vectors. The concept of the *slope* of a vector is useful for this type of problem. All you need to do is find the slopes of the tangent and normal lines and then construct unit vectors having those slopes.

Notes on Exercises

- Exs. 1–44. All of these exercises deal with fundamental concepts. Two or three exercises should be assigned from each grouping.
- Cooperative Learning: Exs. 43, 44.

Assignment Guide

Exs. 1, 2, 4, 7, 10, 12, 13, 16, 17, 21, 24, 27, 30, 33, 35, 38, 41, 43, 44.

11.2 Cartesian (Rectangular) Coordinates and Vectors in Space

Objectives

- Sketch elementary curves, surfaces, and regions in 3-space.
- Describe elementary sets in 3-space with equations or inequalities.
- Perform operations with vectors in 3-space.

Key Ideas

3-dimensional Cartesian coordinate system

Vectors in 3-space

Sketching techniques

Spheres

Teaching Notes

Three-dimensional coordinate systems may be new to some students. Show how to locate points and how to identify and sketch elementary sets such as planes $x = c, y = c, z = c$ and straight lines parallel to an axis. The drawing lesson in this section presents some useful sketching techniques.

In contrast to Section 11.1, the introduction to vectors in space goes quickly. After defining the basic unit vectors $\mathbf{i}, \mathbf{j},$ and $\mathbf{k}$ the text proceeds immediately to describing vectors in their algebraic form $\mathbf{v} = a\mathbf{i} + b\mathbf{j} + c\mathbf{k}$. The definitions of vector operations proceed as in Section 11.1. The formula for vector length is derived on page 871 and is used later to develop the formula for distance between two points. By taking the $\mathbf{k}$ component to be zero, all of these formulas reduce to the formulas for vectors in the plane. Essentially, this section simply adds a third component to the formulas in Section 11.1. Continue to reinforce the geometric interpretation of the operations.

Notes on Examples

- Examples 1 and 2. Use these examples to present 3-dimensional coordinates.
- Examples 3–8. These are basic examples concerning the length and direction of vectors in 3-space.
- Example 9. Complete the square in the equation to find the center of a sphere.

Notes on Exercises

- Exercises 1–34, 69, 70. These exercises help students to learn about 3-space.
- Exercises 35–46. Students find the length and direction of vectors defined algrebraically.
- Exercises 47–52. The length and direction of vectors represented by directed line segments are found.
- Exercises 59–64. These exercises involve equations of spheres.
- **Cooperative Learning:** Exs. 65–68.

Assignment Guide

Exs. 2, 6, 11, 13, 16, 19, 22, 26, 28, 31, 35, 38, 41, 45, 48, 51, 54, 57, 59, 62, 65, 68, 70.

11.3 Dot Products

Objectives

- Find the dot product of two vectors.
- Find the angle between two vectors.
- Calculate the projection of one vector onto another.
- Express a vector as the sum of vectors parallel and perpendicular to a given vector.
- Find the distance from a point to a line in the xy-plane.
- Find the work done by a constant force acting over a straight line path.

Key Ideas

Definition of dot product

The formula to calculate dot product

The angle between two vectors

Orthogonal vectors

Vector projections and scalar components

Writing a vector as a sum of orthogonal vectors

Lines in the plane and distances from points to lines

Work

Teaching Notes

The dot product of two vectors is defined by the formula $\mathbf{A} \cdot \mathbf{B} = |\mathbf{A}||\mathbf{B}|\cos\theta$, where θ is the angle between $\mathbf{A}$ and $\mathbf{B}$. The formula normally used to calculate the dot product, Eq. (3), is derived from this definition using the law of cosines. The derivation is not difficult and could be shown in class. The fact that $\mathbf{A}$ and $\mathbf{B}$ are orthogonal if and only if $\mathbf{A} \cdot \mathbf{B} = 0$ is, of course, fundamental.

Of the different ways to write the formula for the projection of $\mathbf{B}$ onto $\mathbf{A}$, perhaps the best version is $\text{proj}_\mathbf{A}\mathbf{B} = (\mathbf{B} \cdot \mathbf{A}/|\mathbf{A}|) \cdot (\mathbf{A}/|\mathbf{A}|) = $ (scalar component of $\mathbf{B}$ in the direction of $\mathbf{A}$) $\cdot$ (direction of $\mathbf{A}$). In a number of problems where projections are used, what is needed is the *scalar component* of $\mathbf{B}$ in the direction $\mathbf{A}$, which is just $\mathbf{B} \cdot \mathbf{A}/|\mathbf{A}|$.

Calculating the distance from a point to a line in 2-space is a nice application of projections.

Common Errors

When computing a decomposition $\mathbf{B} = \mathbf{B}_1 + \mathbf{B}_2$ where $\mathbf{B}_1$ is parallel to $\mathbf{A}$ and $\mathbf{B}_2$ is orthogonal to $\mathbf{A}$ by using Eq. (13), the calculation can always be checked by verifying that $\mathbf{A} \cdot \mathbf{B}_2 = 0$. Computational errors are common in this type of problem.

Note on Examples

- Example 1. The angle between two vectors is calculated. Point out that $\mathbf{A} \cdot \mathbf{B} < 0$ means that the angle θ between $\mathbf{A}$ and $\mathbf{B}$ is obtuse.

- Example 3. Another way to do this example would be to find the scalar component first, then multiply it times $\mathbf{A}/|\mathbf{A}|$ to get the projection. Observe that since the scalar component is negative, the angle between the two vectors must be obtuse.

- Example 5. A very useful fact is that a normal vector to the line $Ax + By = C$ is $\mathbf{N} = A\mathbf{i} + B\mathbf{j}$.

- Example 6. The power of vector methods is demonstrated by this example. Compare this relatively simple calculation with the method used in Example 7 of Section 1.2.

Notes on Exercises

- Exercises 1–12. These exercises reinforce the basic definitions of the section.
- Exercises 13–16. The decompositon of a vector given by Eq. (13) is computed.
- Exercises 17–20. Example 5 can be used as a model.
- Exercises 21–24. The solution of Example 6 should be used as a model for these exercises.
- **Cooperative Learning:** Exs. 27, 28.

Assignment Guide

Exs. 2, 5, 8, 13, 16, 18, 19, 22, 23, 27, 28, 30, 31, 34, 35, 37, 40, 42.

11.4 Cross Products

Objectives

- Find the cross product of two vectors.
- Find the area of a triangle whose vertices are three given points in space.
- Find the volume of the parallelpiped determined by three vectors in space.

Key Ideas

The cross product of two vectors

Properties of the cross product

The determinant formula for $\mathbf{A} \times \mathbf{B}$

The triple scalar product

Torque

Teaching Notes

The definition of cross product given by Eq. (1) can be motivated by the concept of a torque vector. Some properties of cross product that follow immediately from the definition are the anticommutative rule, Eq. (2), the interpretation of $|\mathbf{A} \times \mathbf{B}|$ as the area of the parallelogram determined by $\mathbf{A}$ and $\mathbf{B}$, and the scalar distributive law, Eq. (4). From the definition we can also calculate the cross product of any two of $\mathbf{i}$, $\mathbf{j}$, and $\mathbf{k}$. These calculations are good for demonstrating the definition of cross product and the right-hand rule. The vector distributive laws, Eq. (5) and (6), are left unproved.

From these results $\mathbf{A} \times \mathbf{B}$ can be expanded to obtain the determinant formula, Eq. (7) or (8), which is the formula that is used to calculate the cross product. By definition, $\mathbf{A} \times \mathbf{B}$ is a vector which is orthogonal to both $\mathbf{A}$ and $\mathbf{B}$. This fact should always be used to verify that $\mathbf{A} \times \mathbf{B}$ has been calculated correctly.

From the definitions of cross product and dot product, we see that the magnitude of the triple scalar product $(\mathbf{A} \times \mathbf{B}) \cdot \mathbf{C}$ is the volume of the parallelpiped determined by $\mathbf{A}$, $\mathbf{B}$, and $\mathbf{C}$. The number $(\mathbf{A} \times \mathbf{B}) \cdot \mathbf{C}$ turns out to be the determinant of the 3×3 matrix whose rows are the components of $\mathbf{A}$, $\mathbf{B}$, and $\mathbf{C}$ respectively.

You may want to review the computation of 2×2 and 3×3 determinants. The formula for expanding a 3×3 determinant by row 1 is given in the margin of page 891. Most graphing calculators have the capability to evaluate determinants.

Notes on Examples

- Example 2. To check the calculation verify that $(-2i - 6j + 10k) \cdot A = 0$ and $(-2i - 6j + 10k) \cdot B = 0$.
- Example 4. To find the area of the triangle, find the area of the parallelogram determined by $\overrightarrow{PQ}$ and $\overrightarrow{PR}$ and divide by 2.

Notes on Exercises

- Exercises 1–8. For the given vectors find $A \times B$ and $B \times A$. Of course, once you find $A \times B$, then $B \times A = -(A \times B)$.
- Exercises 9–14. For A and B given, sketch A, B and $A \times B$ with initial points at the origin.
- Exercises 15–18. The area of the given triangle is found as in Example 4.
- Exercises 27–30. Calculate the triple scalar product to find the volume determined by the three given vectors.
- **Cooperative Learning:** Exs. 22–24.

Assignment Guide

Exs. 1, 4, 7, 10, 13, 16, 19, 21, 24, 26, 28, 30.

11.5 Lines and Planes in Space

Objectives

- Write equations for lines, line segments, and planes in space.
- Find the distance from a point to a line and from a point to a plane.
- Find the point in which a line meets a plane.
- Find the angle between a pair of planes and the parametric equations for the line where two planes intersect.

Key Ideas

Equations for lines and line segments

The distance from a point to a line

Equations for planes

The distance from a point to a plane

Angles between planes

Line of intersection of two planes

Teaching Notes

A straight line in space is determined by a direction and a point on the line or by two distinct points on the line. In either case it is a simple matter to write parametric equations for the line. Mention that Eqs. (2) have different equivalent forms, depending on the scalar multiple of the direction vector $\mathbf{v}$ and the point P_0 used. This method for parametric representation applies equally well to lines in the xy-plane. It should also be pointed out that lines and curves in 3-space have to be represented either parametrically or by a system of two Cartesian equations, since a single Cartesian equation generates a surface.

The equation of a plane is determined by a normal vector and a point. The plane $Ax + By + Cz = D$ has normal vector $\mathbf{N} = A\mathbf{i} + B\mathbf{j} + C\mathbf{k}$. This should be compared with the analogous result in 2-space given by Eq. (14) of Section 11.3.

The geometric problems involving lines and planes are an important part of this section because their solutions all involve basic principles and demonstrate the usefulness of vector methods.

Notes on Examples

- Example 2. To check solution (3), substitute $t = 0$ and $t = 1$ to verify that both points P and Q lie on the line defined by (3).
- Example 4. There is a vector method for doing this example: $d = |\overrightarrow{PS} \times \mathbf{v}|/|\mathbf{v}|$, where S is any point on the line and $\mathbf{v}$ is a direction vector for the line. The method given in the text is conceptually easier.
- Example 8. The method used in this example is very similar to that of Example 6 of 11.3.
- Examples 10 and 11. These examples illustrate the technique discussed in Exploration 1.

Notes on Exercises

- Exercises 1–52. These exercises are modeled on Examples 1–11. Several of them should be assigned from each grouping. In some, have students sketch the lines and planes involved by using the drawing techniques discussed in Section 11.2.
- Exercises 53–57. These exercises are simple variations of previous ones.
- **Cooperative Learning:** Exs. 55–58.

Assignment Guide

Exs. 1, 4, 7, 10, 13, 15, 18, 22, 24, 27, 30, 34, 37, 41, 44, 47, 50, 54, 56, 57.

11.6 Surfaces in Space

Objective

- Identify and sketch the graph of a quadric surface.

Key Ideas

Surfaces

Cylinders

Quadric surfaces

Sketching techniques

Teaching Notes

The graph of a second degree equation in x, y, and z is called a quadric surface. The equations of the most important quadric surfaces in standard position are presented in Examples 2–7. The technique used in sketching these graphs is to sketch traces, the curves formed by intersecting the surface with planes parallel to $x = 0$, $y = 0$, or $z = 0$. Each trace will be a conic section or a degenerate case. If the appropriate traces are drawn, the resulting mesh of curves will give a crude approximation of the graph. The two drawing lessons provided by this section are useful. Being able to visualize the surfaces defined by these equations will prove to be helpful to students.

Notes on Examples

- Example 1. Cylinders are about the easiest surfaces to graph.
- Examples 2–7. You may want to present and analyze specific examples. In some examples, change the orientation of the surface.

Notes on Exercises

- Exercises 1–50. Cylinders and the six quadric surfaces are sketched in various orientations.
- Exercises 51–64. Students identify the surface given by the equation and sketch the graph.
- **Cooperative Learning:** Exs. 16, 22, 32, 37, 47, 64.

Assignment Guide

Exs. 4, 7, 11, 16, 19, 22, 25, 28, 32, 35, 37, 41, 44, 47, 50, 53, 58, 62, 64, 66, 68, 69, 72.

11.7 Cylindrical and Spherical Coordinates

Objectives

- Convert between rectangular, cylindrical, and spherical coordinates.
- Translate equations from one coordinate system into equations of the other two systems.
- Graph elementary curves and surfaces in a cylindrical coordinate system.
- Graph elementary curves and surfaces in a spherical coordinate system.

Key Ideas

Cylindrical coordinates

Spherical coordinates

Equations relating Cartesian, cylindrical, and spherical coordinates

Teaching Notes

Cylindrical coordinates are easy for students to learn since in the rectangular coordinates (x, y, z) they replace (x, y) with an equivalent polar coordinate pair (r, θ). The z coordinate remanins the same. The conversions $x = r \cdot \cos\theta$, $y = r \cdot \sin\theta$ are the same as in polar coordinates; r and θ have the same meaning as in polar coordinates.

Spherical coordinates are completely new. It may help students to remember ϕ as "latitude" and θ as "longitude". Note that θ has the same meaning as in cylindrical coordinates. The coordinate ϕ is required to be between 0 and π, but there is no restriction on θ, so cylindrical and spherical coordinates are not unique. The equations to convert between rectangular, cylindrical, and spherical coordinates are given by Eqs. (2). These relations are evident from Figure 11.57.

Notes on Examples

- Examples 2–5. Use Eqs. (2) to translate an equation in one coordinate system to another.

Notes on Exercises

- Exercises 11–30. For the given equation in one system of coordinates, students find the equivalent equations in the other two systems and describe the graph.
- Exercises 31–46. Students graph surfaces and curves using cylindrical and spherical coordinates.
- **Cooperative Learning:** Exs. 41, 43, 46.

Assignment Guide

Exs. 1, 4, 7, 9, 12, 15, 18, 19, 22, 25, 29, 32, 35, 38, 41, 43, 46.

Chapter 12 Vector-Valued Functions, Parametrizations, and Motion in Space

12.1 Vector-Valued Functions and Curves in Space; Derivatives and Integrals

Objectives

- Differentiate and integrate vector-valued functions.
- Analyze the motion of a particle in space given its position, velocity or acceleration as a functions of time.

Key Ideas

Vector-valued functions

Limits and continuity

Derivatives and motion

Differentiation rules

Integrals of vector functions

Teaching Notes

A vector-valued function $\mathbf{r}(t) = f(t)\mathbf{i} + g(t)\mathbf{j} + h(t)\mathbf{k}$ can be regarded as the position vector at time t of a particle moving through space. It can also be used to define the curve in 3-space parametrized by its component functions.

Differentiation or integration of $\mathbf{r}(t)$ is defined by differentiating or integrating each component of $\mathbf{r}$. If $\mathbf{r}(t)$ is a position vector of a particle, then $\mathbf{r}'(t)$ and $\mathbf{r}''(t)$ are the velocity and acceleration vectors of the particle at time t, and $|\mathbf{r}'(t)|$ is the speed.

In discussing the differentiation rules for vector functions, pay particular attention to the Dot-Product Rule, Cross-Product Rule, and Chain Rule.

By taking $h(t) = 0$, all of the concepts and results of this section can be applied to vector functions $\mathbf{r}(t) = f(t)\mathbf{i} + g(t)\mathbf{j}$, and in particular, to particle motion in the xy-plane.

Notes on Examples

- Examples 2–4. Questions of limits and continuity of vector functions reduce to questions about limits and continuity of their components.
- Example 6. This example provides an interpretation of Eq. (2). If a particle moves so that it always has the same distance d from the origin, then its path must lie on the surface of the sphere of radius d about the origin, and its velocity vector must be tangent to that surface.
- Example 8. Just as is done in rectilinear motion problems, integrate velocity to find the position function, then use the initial condition to find the constant of integration.

Notes on Exercises

- Exercises 1–8. The purpose of these exercises is to reinforce the basic definitions involving particle motion. Students need to get used to thinking of position, velocity, and acceleration as vector quantities.
- Exercises 21–24, 31–32. In these exercises the particle motion is in the xy-plane (in Ex. 32, the yz-plane), so the particle motion can be simulated on the grapher.
- Exercises 25–30. These are initial value problems similar to Example 8.
- **Cooperative Learning:** Exs. 31, 32.

Assignment Guide

Exs. 2, 5, 8, 11, 14, 16, 19, 22, 24, 27, 30–32, 36.

12.2 Modeling Projectile Motion

Objectives

- Derive parametric equations that model ideal projectile motion.
- Find the maximum height, flight time, and range in problems involving ideal projectile motion.
- Derive parametric equations that model projectile motion with air resistance.

Key Ideas

Equations for ideal projectile motion

Height, flight time and range

Projectile motion with air resistance

Teaching Notes

In ideal projectile motion, the projectile moves in the vertical plane determined by the direction of its initial velocity vector. By identifying that plane as the xy-plane with the positive y-axis pointing directly upwards, the equation of motion will have the form $\mathbf{r}(t) = x(t)\mathbf{i} + y(t)\mathbf{j}$. The value of $\mathbf{r}(t)$ and is found by integrating the equation $\mathbf{r}''(t) = -g\mathbf{j}$

twice and then finding the constants of integration from the initial positon vector r_0 and initial velocity vector v_0. If $r_0 = 0$, the equation for r is given by Eqs. (5) or (6). More generally, if $r_0 = x_0 i + y_0 j$, r is given by Eqs. (11), which are obtained by simply adding x_0 and y_0 to the i and j components of (5). From these equations it is evident that the trajectory is a parabola in ideal projectile motion. The equations for the maximum height, flight time, and range can be easily derived from Eqs. (5) or (11). When $r_0 = 0$, these are given by Eqs. (8)–(10).

In the model with air resistance, it is assumed that the drag force at any time caused by air resistance is $-kv$, where k is a positive constant. The differential equation is now $r''(t) = -gj - kv$, which is solved by methods of Section 8.7. Note that the equations in Theorem 1 assume $r_0 = 0$.

Notes on Examples

- Example 1. We assume in this problem that there is no wind and no air resistance. The initial position is $r_0 = 3j$ and the initial velocity is given by the equation $v_0 = (152 \cdot \cos 20°)i + (152 \cdot \sin 20°)j$. By (11) the parametric equations for the motion of the baseball are $x(t) = (152 \cdot \cos 20°)t$ and $y(t) = 3 + (152 \cdot \sin 20°)t - 16t^2$. By graphing this curve in a square viewing window the flight of the baseball can be simulated. The questions in part (c) can be answered graphically or analytically. Exploration 1 continues with questions related to this model.

- Example 2. The maximum height, flight time, and range of a projectile launched from the origin are calculated using Eqs. (8)–(10). Simulate the motion of the projectile with the grapher as in Example 1, and use the TRACE key to support these results.

- Example 3. Air resistance is added to the problem in Example 1. The effect of air resistance can be seen by comparing the trajectories in the two different models.

Notes on Exercises

- Exercises 1–15. All of these exercises assume ideal projectile motion.
- Exercises 18, 19 and 21. These are projectile motion problems with air resistance.
- **Cooperative Learning:** Exs. 22, 24.

Assignment Guide

Exs. 2, 3, 6, 9, 11, 12, 18, 19, 21, 22, 24.

12.3 Directed Distance and the Unit Tangent Vector T

Objectives

- Find the length of a curve in space.
- Find the directed distance s along a space curve.
- Find the unit tangent vector T to a curve in space.

Key Ideas

Arc length of a curve in 3-space

Directed distance along a curve from t_0 to t

The unit tangent vector $\mathbf{T}$

Teaching Notes

The formula for the arc length of a space curve given by Eq. (1) generalizes the formula for the arc length of a parametrically defined curve in the plane given by Eq. (2) of Section 10.4. Students should appreciate the underlying assumptions of this definition, namely that $\mathbf{r}(t)$ is one-to-one and has continuously differentiable component functions.

For a fixed value t_0 and for all $t \geq t_0$, $s(t)$ is defined to be the arc length of the curve between the points $P(t_0)$ and $P(t)$ on the curve, as calculated by Eq. (1). The arc length $s(t)$ is called the *directed distance* along the curve from t_0 to t. By the Fundamental Theorem, $s(t)$ is differentiable and $ds/dt = |\mathbf{v}|$.

The additional assumption now made is that $|\mathbf{v}| > 0$ at all t. By Theorem 1 of Section 7.2, $s(t)$ has an inverse function which expresses t as a differentiable function of s. By the Chain Rule, $d\mathbf{r}/dt = d\mathbf{r}/ds \cdot ds/dt$ so $d\mathbf{r}/ds = \mathbf{v}/|\mathbf{v}| = \mathbf{T}$, which is the unit tangent to the curve at $P(t)$.

Notes on Examples

- Example 2. By Eq. (2) of Section 11.5, $\mathbf{r}(t) = \mathbf{r}_0 + t\mathbf{u}$ parametrizes a line parallel to $\mathbf{u}$. If $\mathbf{u}$ is a *unit* vector, this example demonstrates that $s = t$.
- Examples 4–6. The unit tangent vector is usually calculated by the formula $\mathbf{T} = \mathbf{u}/|\mathbf{u}|$.

Notes on Exercises

- Exercises 1–8. Students compute $\mathbf{T}$ as a function of t and compute the arc length of a section of a given curve.
- Exercises 9–12. For a given curve and t_0, students find s as a function of t.
- **Cooperative Learning:** Exs. 14, 15.

Assignment Guide

Exs. 2, 5, 8, 9, 12, 14, 15.

12.4 Curvature, Torsion, and the TNB Frame

Objectives

- Calculate $\mathbf{T}$, $\mathbf{N}$ and κ for a curve in the plane.
- Calculate $\mathbf{T}$, $\mathbf{N}$, $\mathbf{B}$, κ and τ for a curve in space.
- Express the acceleration vector of a moving body as the sum of its tangential and normal components.

Key Ideas

The curvature of a plane curve

The radius of curvature of a plane curve

The principal unit normal vector of a plane curve

The curvature of a curve in space

The principal unit normal vector of a curve in space

The binormal vector and torsion

Tangential and normal components of acceleration

Teaching Notes

The text first establishes some results for plane curves $\mathbf{r}(t) = x(t)\mathbf{i} + y(t)\mathbf{j}$, where $x(t)$ and $y(t)$ are twice differentiable. The *curvature* at a point is defined by $\kappa = |d\phi/ds|$, where ϕ is the angle between $\mathbf{T}$ and $\mathbf{i}$. One way to calculate κ is by Eq. (2), which says that $\kappa = |\mathbf{v} \times \mathbf{a}|/|\mathbf{v}|^3$. The text then shows that $|d\mathbf{T}/ds| = \kappa$, that $d\mathbf{T}/ds$ is orthogonal to $\mathbf{T}$ and, when it is nonzero, always points toward the concave side of the curve. The *principal unit normal vector* is then defined to be $\mathbf{N} = (d\mathbf{T}/ds)/|d\mathbf{T}/ds|$. Thus, $\mathbf{N}$ is a unit vector orthogonal to $\mathbf{T}$ which points in the direction that the curve is turning. The Chain Rule establishes that $\mathbf{N} = (d\mathbf{T}/ds)/|\mathbf{v}|$, which is the formula usually used to calculate $\mathbf{N}$.

These concepts are then extended to curves in space whose components are twice differentiable. Curvature is defined to be $\kappa = |d\mathbf{T}/ds|$ and the unit normal vector $\mathbf{N} = (d\mathbf{T}/ds)/|d\mathbf{T}/ds|$. $\mathbf{N}$ is a unit vector and is orthogonal to $\mathbf{T}$ since $|\mathbf{T}| = 1$ implies that $\mathbf{T} \cdot (d\mathbf{T}/ds) = 0$. Again, to compute $\mathbf{N}$ we usually use $\mathbf{N} = (d\mathbf{T}/dt)/|d\mathbf{T}/dt|$. To complete the definitions, the *binormal vector* is defined by $\mathbf{B} = \mathbf{T} \times \mathbf{N}$, and the torsion $\tau = |d\mathbf{B}/ds|$.

One of the nicest applications of the section is the method for expressing the acceleration of a moving body as the sum of its tangential and normal components. The formula for the decomposition is shown by Eq. (8). The main formulas for the entire section are summarized on page 951.

Notes on Examples

- Examples 1 and 2. These are basic results. The curvature of a circle motivates the definitions of the *circle of curvature* and *radius of curvature* at a point on a plane curve.

- Example 4. Eq. (4) is used to calculate the curvature of a helix. By varying the parameters a and b we can interpret what curvature means.

- Example 6. Eq. (6) is used to calculate the torsion of a helix. The interpretation of the **TNB** frame for simple curves like a helix may help students understand the relationship between these three vectors.

- Example 7. The scalar components a_T and a_N are found without calculating κ.

Notes on Exercises

- Exercises 1–8, 17–19. These exercises illustrate the basic definitions given in this section.

- Exercises 9–16. The acceleration a is expressed as the sum of its tangential and normal components. See Example 7.

- **Cooperative Learning:** Exs. 24, 25.

Assignment Guide

Exs. 1, 4, 6, 7, 9, 12, 14, 16, 18, 19, 22, 24, 25.

12.5 Planetary Motion and Satellites

Objective

- Apply Kepler's laws to planetery motion and motion of satellites.

Key Ideas

Vector equations for motion in polar and cylindrical coordinates

Coordinates for planetary motion; initial conditions

Kepler's three laws

Teaching Notes

The equations of motion in polar and cylindrical coordinates are derived first, since a cylindrical coordinate system is used to model the motion of a planet about the sun. By Newton's Law of Gravitation and Second Law of Motion, it is shown that the planet moves in a fixed plane which passes through the center of the sun. In setting up the coordinate system this plane is chosen to be the polar plane, positioned in such a way that the sun's center of mass is at the origin and the polar axis $\theta = 0$ passes through the perihelion position of the planet. Thinking ahead to Kepler's First Law, this will place the sun at one focus of the elliptical orbit of the planet. The z-axis is chosen so that r, dr/dt and k always form a right-handed system. Time is chosen so that $t = 0$ when the planet is at perihelion.

Starting from this model Kepler's laws can be derived from Newton's laws. The second law is derived in this section. For the derivation of the first and third laws see Thomas and Finney, *Calculus and Analytic Geometry*, 8th Edition.

Notes on Exercises

- Exercises 1–8. Kepler's three laws apply more generally to satellites orbiting a large mass. Some of these applications are illustrated.
- Exercises 9 and 12. These exercises concern the special case when a satellite has a circular orbit.
- **Cooperative Learning:** Ex. 12.

Assignment Guide

Exs. 1–3, 5, 8, 9, 12.

ANSWERS TO STUDENT EDITION EXERCISES

CHAPTER 1

PREREQUISITES FOR CALCULUS

1.1   COORDINATES AND GRAPHS IN THE PLANE

1. $(0,6)$, $(5,-5)$

2. $(1.5, 17.5)$, $(10, 100)$

3. One choice:
$[-17, 21]$ by $[-12, 76]$

4. One choice:
$[-42, 53]$ by $[-89, 31]$

5. One choice: $x\,\mathrm{Scl} = 5$, $y\,\mathrm{Scl} = 5$ gives many scale marks at convenient points which are still distinguishable.

6. One choice:
$x\,\mathrm{Scl} = 0.1$, $y\,\mathrm{Scl} = 0.05$

7. One choice
$x\,\mathrm{Scl} = 0.05$, $y\,\mathrm{Scl} = 10$

8. One choice: $x\,\mathrm{Scl} = 10$, $y\,\mathrm{Scl} = 0.5$

9. Intercepts: $x = -1$, $y = 1$.

10. Intercepts: $x = 1$, $y = 1$.

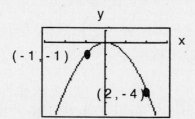

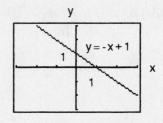

11. $y = -x^2$.
$(0,0)$ gives the only intercepts.

12. $y = 4 - x^2$.
x-intercepts: $x = \pm 2$
y-intercept: $y = 4$.

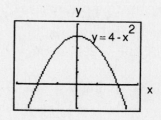

13. $x = -y^2$.

$(0, 0)$ gives the only intercepts.

14. $x = 1 - y^2$.

x-intercept: $x = 1$.

y-intercepts: $y = \pm 1$.

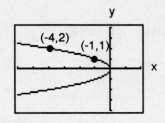

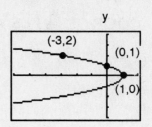

15. (e)   **16.** (b)   **17.** (e)   **18.** (c)   **19.** (e)   **20.** (d)

21. A complete graph of $y = 3x - 5$ may be viewed in the rectangle $[-2, 4]$ by $[-10, 5]$. x-intercept: $x = 5/3$. y-intercept: $y = -5$.

22. A complete graph of $y = 4 - 5x$ may be viewed in the rectangle $[-2, 3]$ by $[-10, 10]$. Intercepts: $x = 4/5$, $y = 4$.

23. A graph of $y = 10 + x - 2x^2$ may be viewed in the rectangle $[-6, 6]$ by $[-30, 15]$. Intercepts: $x = -2, 5/2$; $y = 10$.

24. The graph of $y = 2x^2 - 2x - 12$ may be viewed in the rectangle $[-10, 10]$ by $[-30, 70]$. Intercepts: $x = -2, 3$; $y = -12$.

25. A graph of $y = 2x^2 - 8x + 3$ may be viewed in the rectangle $[-7, 10]$ by $[-20, 70]$. x-intercepts: $x \approx 0.42, 3.58$. y-intercept: $y = 3$.

26. A graph of $y = -3x^2 - 6x - 1$ may be viewed in the rectangle $[-5, 3]$ by $[-30, 10]$. The x-intercepts, $(-3 \pm \sqrt{6})/3$, are approximately $-1.82, -0.18$. $y = -1$ is the y-intercept.

27. Using TRACE on the graph of $y = x^2 + 4x + 5 = (x + 2)^2 + 1$ in the rectangle $[-8, 4]$ by $[-2, 20]$, we see there are no x-intercepts, $y = 5$ is the y-intercept and $(-2, 1)$ is the low point.

28. Graphing $y = -3x^2 + 12x - 8$ in the rectangle $[-1, 5]$ by $[-20, 5]$, we get, using TRACE, x-intercepts: $0.85, 3.15$; y-intercept: $y = -8$ and high point $(2, 4)$.

29. We graph $y = 12x - 3x^3$ in the rectangle $[-4, 4]$ by $[-15, 15]$. $x = \pm 2, 0$ are the x-intercepts, $y = 0$ is the y-intercept. Using TRACE, $(-1.14, -9.24)$ and $(1.14, 9.24)$ are the approximate local low and high points, respectively.

30. A graph of $y = 2x^3 - 2x$ can be obtained in the viewing rectangle $[-2, 2]$ by $[-3, 3]$. The x-intercepts are $-1, 0, 1$ and the y-intercept is 0. Use of TRACE gives $(-0.57, 0.77)$ and $(0.57, -0.77)$ for an approximation of the local high and low point, respectively.

31. A complete graph of $y = -x^3 + 9x - 1$ can be obtained in the viewing rectangle $[-5, 5]$ by $[-35, 35]$. The y-intercept is -1. Use of TRACE yields the following approximations. x-intercepts: $-3.02, 0.08, 2.93$; low point: $(-1.75, -11.39)$; high point: $(1.75, 9.39)$.

32. Graph $y = x^3 - 4x + 3$ in $[-5, 5]$ by $[-5, 10]$. x-intercepts: $-2.30, 1, 1.30$; y-intercept: 3. High point: $(-1.15, 6.08)$, low point: $(1.15, -0.079)$.

33. An idea of a complete graph of $y = x^3 + 2x^2 + x + 5$ can be obtained by using the viewing rectangles $[-3, 2]$ by $[-2, 10]$ and $[-2, 1]$ by $[4, 6]$. The y-intercept is 5 and using TRACE in the first rectangle, we obtain -2.44 as the approximate x-intercept. In the second rectangle, we obtain $(-1, 5)$ and $(-0.33, 4.85)$ as the approximate local high and low points.

34. An idea of a complete graph of $y = 2x^3 - 5.5x^2 + 5x - 5$ can be obtained by using the viewing rectangles $[-2, 4]$ by $[-10, 2]$ and $[0.73, 1.06]$ by $[-3.51, -3.48]$. The y-intercept is -5 and using TRACE in the first rectangle, we obtain 2.13 as the approximate x-intercept. In the second rectangle we obtain $(0.832, -3.495)$ and $(1.00, -3.500)$ as the approximate local high and low points.

37. With $N = 127$, $M = 63$, $a = 116$, $b = 52$.

38. With $(N, M) = (127, 63)$, $a = 2.6$, $b = -3.8$.

39. With $(N, M) = (127, 63)$, $a = 53$, $b = 114$.

40. With $(N, M) = (127, 63)$, $a = 242$, $b = 610$.

41. Yes

42. Only b) and c) require a stop.

1.2 SLOPE, AND EQUATIONS FOR LINES

1. $\Delta x = -2$, $\Delta y = -3$　　　　　2. $\Delta x = 2$, $\Delta y = -4$

3. $\Delta x = -5$, $\Delta y = 0$　　　　　4. $\Delta x = 0$, $\Delta y = -6$

5. Slope is 3; slope of lines perpendicular is $-1/3$.

6. $m = -1/3$, $m_\perp = 3$

7. $m = 0$. The perpendicular lines are vertical and have no slope.

8. A and B determine the vertical line $x = 1$ which has no slope. The lines perpendicular to AB have slope 0.

9. $\sqrt{2}$　　10. 5　　11. 6　　12. 5/3　　13. $\sqrt{a^2 + b^2}$　　14. $\sqrt{x^2 + y^2}$

15. 3　　16. 5　　17. 5　　18. 4.1　　19. 6　　20. 2/7

21. a) $x = 2$　b) $y = 3$　　　　22. a) $x = -1$　b) $y = 4/3$

23. a) $x = 0$　b) $y = -\sqrt{2}$　　　24. a) $x = -\pi$　b) $y = 0$

25. $y = x$　　　26. $y = -x$　　　27. $y = x + 2$　　　28. $y = -x$

29. $y = 2x + b$　　30. $y = -2x + 2a$　　31. $y = \frac{3}{2}x$　　　32. $y = 1$

33. $x = 1$　　　34. $x = -2$　　　35. $3x + 4y + 2 = 0$　　36. $y = -x + 4$

37. $y = 3x - 2$　　38. $y = -x + 2$　　39. $y = x + \sqrt{2}$　　40. $y = -\frac{1}{2}x - 3$

41. $y = -5x + 2.5$　　　　42. $y = \frac{1}{3}x - 1$

43. x-intercept is 4, y-intercept is 3

44. x-intercept $= y$-intercept $= 2$

45. x-intercept: $x = 3$, y-intercept: $y = -4$

46. x-intercept: $x = 2$, y-intercept: $y = -4$.

47. x-intercept: $x = -2$ y-intercept: $y = 4$

48. x-intercept: $x = -4$, y-intercept: $y = -2$

49. $x = 3$, $y = 4$　　50. $x = -2$, $y = 3$　　51. $x = a$, $y = b$　　52. $x = 2a$, $y = 2b$

53. Perpendicular: $y = x$. $y = -x + 2$ and $y = x$ may be viewed in the rectangle $[-6, 6]$ by $[-4, 4]$. Distance $= \sqrt{2}$.

54. Perpendicular: $y = \sqrt{3}x$. $y = -\frac{1}{\sqrt{3}}x + \sqrt{3}$ and $y = \sqrt{3}x$ may be viewed in the rectangle $[-6, 6]$ by $[-4, 4]$. Distance $= \frac{3}{2}$.

55. Perpendicular: $y = 2x$. $y = -\frac{1}{2}x + \frac{3}{2}$ and $y = 2x$ may be viewed in the rectangle $[-6, 6]$ by $[-4, 4]$. Distance $= 2\sqrt{5}/5$.

56. Perpendicular: $y = \frac{1}{2}x + 3$. $y = -2x + 4$ and $y = \frac{1}{2}x + 3$ may be viewed in the rectangle $[-7, 8]$ by $[-3, 7]$. Distance $= \frac{6\sqrt{5}}{5}$.

57. Perpendicular: $y = x + 3$. $y = -x + 3$ and $y = x + 3$ may be viewed in the rectangle $[-7, 8]$ by $[-3, 7]$. Distance $= 3\sqrt{2}$.

58. Perpendicular: $y = 4$. Distance $= 7$.

59. $y = x - 1$. $y = x + 2$ and $y = x - 1$ may graphed in $[-10, 10]$ by $[-10, 10]$.

60. $y = 3x$ 　　　　　　**61.** $y = -2x + 2$ 　　　　　　**62.** $y = -x + 2$

63. a) $|x - 3|$　 b) $|x + 2|$ 　**64.** a) $|y + 1.3|$ 　 b) $|y - 5.5|$

65. The distance between 5 and x is 1.

66. The distance between x and -3 is 5.

67. a) $a = -2$ or any negative number 　 b) $a \geqq 0$ 　　　**68.** $x \leqq 1; x \geqq 1$

69. a) $-2.5°/\text{in}$ 　 b) $-16.1°/\text{in}$ 　 c) $-8\frac{1}{3}°/\text{in}$

70. Fiber glass is the best, gypsum wall board the poorest insulator.

71. 5.97 atmospheres 　　　　　　**72.** $y = x - 1$

73. a) $-40°C$ is equivalent to $-40°F$

b) Graphs of y_1 and y_3 are reflections of each other across the line $y_2 = x$, so they are inverse functions.

74. About 40.249ft $(m = 0.371)$

75. a) $d(t) = 45t$ 　　　　　　c) $m = 45$; slope is the car's speed

d) If $t = 0$ corresponds to a specific time, say 1:00 p.m., then negative values of t would correspond to times before 1:00 p.m.

e) The initial distance (from point P) is 30 miles.

76. a) $d(t) = 55t$

c) $m = 55$; slope is the car's speed

d) If $t = 0$ corresponds to a specific time, say 1:00 p.m., then negative values of t would correspond to times before 1:00 p.m.

e) The initial distance (from point P) is 40 miles.

77. The possibilities for the third vertex are $(-1, 4)$, $(-1, -2)$, $(5, 2)$

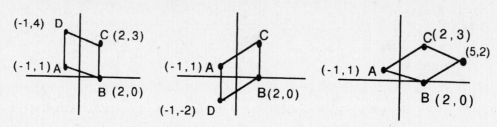

78. -2; 2 **79.** $x = 1$

1.3   RELATIONS, FUNCTIONS, AND THEIR GRAPHS

1. Not a function. There are x-values that correspond to two y-values.

2. This is the graph of a function. Each x in the domain corresponds to exactly one y.

3. This is a function. No value of x corresponds to two y-values.

4. Not a function. There are x-values that correspond to more than one y-value.

5. a) $(3, -1)$ b) $(-3, 1)$ c) $(-3, -1)$

6. a) $(-2, -2)$ b) $(2, 2)$ c) $(2, -2)$

7. a) $(-2, -1)$ b) $(2, 1)$ c) $(2, -1)$

8. a) $(-1, 1)$ b) $(1, -1)$ c) $(1, 1)$

9. a) $(1, \sqrt{2})$ b) $(-1, -\sqrt{2})$ c) $(-1, \sqrt{2})$

10. a) $(-\sqrt{3}, \sqrt{3})$ b) $(\sqrt{3}, -\sqrt{3})$ c) $(\sqrt{3}, \sqrt{3})$

11. a) $(0, -\pi)$ b) $(0, \pi)$ c) $(0, -\pi)$

12. a) $(2, 0)$ b) $(-2, 0)$ c) $(-2, 0)$

13. Domain: $[1, \infty)$, range: $[2, \infty)$ **14.** Domain: $[-4, \infty)$, range: $[-3, \infty)$

15. Domain: $(-\infty, 0]$, range: $(-\infty, 0]$ **16.** Domain: $(-\infty, 0]$, range: $[0, \infty)$

17. Domain: $(-\infty, 3]$, range: $[0, \infty)$ **18.** Domain: $(-\infty, 2]$, range: $(-\infty, 0]$

19. Domain: $(-\infty, 2) \cup (2, \infty)$, range: $(-\infty, 0) \cup (0, \infty)$

20. Domain: $(-\infty, -2) \cup (-2, \infty)$, range: $(-\infty, 0) \cup (0, \infty)$

21. Domain: $(-\infty, \infty)$, range: $[-9, \infty)$. Symmetric about the y-axis.

22. Domain: $(-\infty, \infty)$, range: $(-\infty, 4]$. Symmetric about the y-axis.

23. Domain $=$ range $= (-\infty, \infty)$. No symmetry.

24. Domain $=$ range $= (-\infty, \infty)$. No symmetry.

25. Domain $=$ range $= (-\infty, \infty)$. No symmetry.

26. Domain = range = $(-\infty, \infty)$. No symmetry.

27. Domain = range = $(-\infty, 0) \cup (0, \infty)$. Symmetric about the origin.

28. Domain = $(-\infty, 0) \cup (0, \infty)$, range: $(-\infty, 0)$. Symmetric about the y-axis.

29. Domain: $(-\infty, 0) \cup (0, \infty)$, range: $(-\infty, 1) \cup (1, \infty)$. No symmetry.

30. Domain: $(-\infty, 0) \cup (0, \infty)$, range: $(1, \infty)$. Symmetric about y-axis.

31. a) No   b) No   c) $(0, \infty)$

32. a) No   b) No   c) No   d) $(0, 1]$

33. Odd   **34.** Even   **35.** Neither   **36.** Neither   **37.** Even

38. Odd   **39.** Even   **40.** Neither   **41.** Odd   **42.** Even

43. Symmetric about the y-axis. Graph $y = -x^2$ in the viewing rectangle $[-10, 10]$ by $[-10, 10]$.

44. Symmetric about the x-axis. Graph $y = \sqrt{4-x}$ and $y = -\sqrt{4-x}$ simultaneously in the viewing rectangle $[-10, 4]$ by $[-5, 5]$.

45. Symmetric about the y-axis. Graph $y = 1/x^2$ in the viewing rectangle $[-5, 5]$ by $[0, 3]$.

46. Symmetric about the y-axis. Graph $y = 1/(x^2 + 1)$ in the viewing rectangle $[-5, 5]$ by $[0, 1]$.

47. Symmetric about the origin. Graph $y = 1/x$ in the viewing rectangle $[-4, 4]$ by $[-4, 4]$.

48. Symmetric about the x-axis. Graph $y = 1/\sqrt{x}$ and $-1/\sqrt{x}$ in the viewing rectangle $[0, 4]$ by $[-4, 4]$.

49. $x^2 y^2 = 1$ has graph symmetric about both axes and the origin. Graph $y = 1/|x|$ and $y = -1/|x|$ in the viewing rectangle $[-4, 4]$ by $[-4, 4]$.

50. Symmetric about both axes and the origin. Graph $y = \sqrt{1 - x^2}/2$ and $y = -\sqrt{1 - x^2}/2$ in the viewing rectangle $[-1, 1]$, by $[-1, 1]$.

51. Graph $y = |x + 3|$ in the viewing rectangle $[-7, 1]$ by $[0, 4]$.

52. Graph $y = |2 - x| = |x - 2|$ in the viewing rectangle $[-2, 6]$ by $[0, 4]$.

53. Graph $y = \frac{|x|}{x}$ in the viewing rectangle $[-2, 2]$ by $[-2, 2]$. There is no point on the graph when $x = 0$.

54. This is the last graph shifted to the right 1 unit.

55. $y = x$ when $x \leq 0$ and $y = 0$ when $x \geq 0$.

56. $y = 0$ when $x \leq 0$ and $y = x$ when $x \geq 0$.

57. a) Graph $y = 3 - x + 0\sqrt{1 - x}$ and $y = 2x + 0\sqrt{x - 1}$ in the viewing rectangle $[-10, 10]$ by $[0, 20]$.   b) $f(0) = 3$, $f(1) = 2$, $f(2.5) = 5$.

58. a) Graph $y = (1/x) + 0\sqrt{(-x)}$ and $y = x + 0\sqrt{x}$ in the viewing rectangle $[-4, 4]$ by $[-4, 4]$.   b) $f(-1) = -1$, $f(0) = 0$, $f(\pi) = \pi$.

59. a) Graph $y = 1 + 0\sqrt{5 - x}$ in the viewing rectangle $[-3, 10]$ by $[0, 2]$. It is understood that the x-axis for $x \geq 5$ is part of the graph and the point $(5, 1)$ is not.   b) $f(0) = 1$, $f(5) = 0$, $f(6) = 0$.

60. a) Graph $y = 1 + 0\sqrt{-x}$ and $y = \sqrt{x}$ in the viewing rectangle $[-4, 4]$ by $[0, 2]$. $(0, 1)$ is not a point of the graph.   b) $f(-1) = 1$, $f(0) = 0$, $f(5) = \sqrt{5}$.

61. a) Graph $y = 4 - x^2 + 0\sqrt{1 - x}$, $y = \frac{3}{2}x + \frac{3}{2} + 0\sqrt{x - 1} + 0\sqrt{3 - x}$ and $y = x + 3 + 0\sqrt{x - 3}$ in the viewing rectangle $[-3, 7]$ by $[-5, 10]$. b) $f(0.5) = 3.75$, $f(1) = 3$, $f(3) = 6$, $f(4) = 7$.

62. a) Graph $y = x^2 + 0\sqrt{-x}$, $y = x^3 + 0\sqrt{x} + 0\sqrt{1 - x}$ and $y = 2x - 1 + 0\sqrt{x - 1}$ in the viewing rectangle $[-3, 3]$ by $[0, 5]$.   b) $f(-1) = 1$, $f(0) = 0$, $f(1) = 1$, $f(2.5) = 4$.

63. Answers may vary. Possible answers:

a) $f(x) = 1 - |x - 1|$, $0 \leq x \leq 2$

b) $f(x) = \begin{cases} 2, & 0 \leq x < 1 \\ 0, & 1 \leq x < 2 \\ 2, & 2 \leq x < 3 \\ 0, & 3 \leq x \leq 4 \end{cases}$

64. Answers may vary. Possible answers: a) $y = 0$, $0 \leq x \leq \frac{T}{2}$, $y = \frac{2}{T}x - 1$, $\frac{T}{2} < x \leq T$ or $y = \frac{1}{T}[|\frac{T}{2} - x| - (\frac{T}{2} - x)]$, $0 \leq x \leq T$ b) $y = A$, $0 \leq x < \frac{T}{2}$, $y = -A$, $\frac{T}{2} \leq x < T$, $y = A$, $T \leq x < \frac{3T}{2}$, $y = -A$, $\frac{3T}{2} \leq x \leq 2T$

65. a) $0 \leq x < 1$ b) $-1 < x \leq 0$

66. $[x] = \lceil x \rceil$ if and only if x is an integer. If x is between n and $n+1$, $[x] = n$ and $\lceil x \rceil = n+1$.

67. a) Graph of $y = x - [x]$, $-3 \leq x \leq 3$

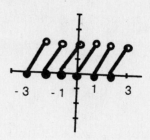

b) Graph of $y = [x] - \lceil x \rceil$, $-3 \leq x \leq 3$

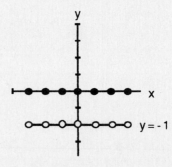

68. When x is negative or zero, $\lceil x \rceil$ is the integer part of the decimal representation of x.

69. Graph $y = abs(x+1) + 2abs(x-3)$ in the viewing rectangle $[-2, 5]$ by $[0, 12]$.

$$f(x) = \begin{cases} -3x + 5, & x \leq -1 \\ -x + 7, & -1 < x \leq 3 \\ 3x - 5, & x > 3 \end{cases}$$

70. Graph $y = |x + 2| + |x - 1|$ in the viewing rectangle $[-4, 3]$ by $[0, 6]$. $y = -2x - 1$, $x \leq -2$, $y = 3$, $-2 < x \leq 1$, $y = 2x + 1$, $x > 1$.

71. Graph $y = |x| + |x - 1| + |x - 3|$ in the viewing rectangle $[-1, 4]$ by $[0, 7]$. $y = -3x + 4$, $x \leq 0$, $y = -x + 4$, $0 < x \leq 1$, $y = x + 2$, $1 < x \leq 3$, $y = 3x - 4$, $x > 3$.

72. Graph $y = f(x) = |x + 2| + |x| + |x + 1|$ in the viewing rectangle $[-3, 1]$ by $[0, 7]$ and in $[-3, 1]$ by $[2, 7]$. $f(x) = -3x - 3$, $x \leq -2$, $f(x) = 1 - x$, $-2 < x \leq -1$, $f(x) = x + 3$, $-1 < x \leq 0$, $f(x) = 3x + 3$, $x > 0$

73. $f(x) = x$, domain: $(-\infty, \infty)$. $g(x) = \sqrt{x-1}$, domain: $[1, \infty)$. $f(x) + g(x) = x + \sqrt{x-1}$, domain $(f+g)$: $[1, \infty)$, complete graph in $[0, 5]$ by $[0, 10]$. $f(x) - g(x) = x - \sqrt{x-1}$, domain $(f-g)$: $[1, \infty)$, complete graph in $[0, 5]$ by $[0, 4]$. $f \cdot g(x) = x\sqrt{x-1}$, domain $f \cdot g$: $[1, \infty)$, complete graph in $[0, 5)$ by $[0, 10]$. $f(x)/g(x) = x/\sqrt{x-1}$, domain: $(1, \infty)$, complete graph in $[0, 10]$ by $[0, 5]$. $g(x)/f(x) = \sqrt{x-1}/x$, domain: $[1, \infty)$, complete graph in $[0, 10]$ by $[0, 0.5]$, graph starts at $(1, 0)$.

74. $f(x) = \sqrt{x+1}$, domain: $[-1, \infty)$. $g(x) = \sqrt{x-1}$, domain: $[1, \infty)$. $f(x) + g(x) = \sqrt{x+1} + \sqrt{x-1}$, domain: $[1, \infty)$, graph in $[0, 10]$ by $[0, 10]$. $f(x) - g(x) = \sqrt{x+1} - \sqrt{x-1}$, domain $(f-g)$: $[1, \infty)$, graph in $[0, 10]$ by $[0, 2]$. $f \cdot g(x) = \sqrt{x^2 - 1}$, domain $f \cdot g = [1, \infty)$, graph in $[0, 5]$ by $[0, 5]$. $f(x)/g(x) = \sqrt{x+1}/\sqrt{x-1}$, domain (f/g) : $(1, \infty)$, graph in $[0, 10]$ by $[0, 6]$. $g(x)/f(x) = \sqrt{x-1}/\sqrt{x+1}$, domain (g/f) : $[1, \infty)$, graph in $[0, 10]$ by $[0, 2]$.

75. a) 2 b) 22 c) $x^2 + 2$ d) $x^2 + 10x + 22$ e) 5 f) -2 g) $x + 10$ h) $x^4 - 6x^2 + 6$

76. a) 0 b) 0 c) 1 d) 1 e) x f) x

77. a) $\sqrt{x-7}$ b) $3(x+2)$ c) x^2 d) x e) $\frac{1}{x-1}$ f) $\frac{1}{x}$

78. a) $\frac{-x}{2(x+2)}$ b) $4t$

79. a) $C(10) = 72$ b) $C(30) - C(20)$ is the increase of cost if the production level is raised from 20 to 30 items daily.

80. Domain $\sqrt{x^2}$ = domain $|x|$ = $(-\infty, \infty)$, range $|x|$ = $[0, \infty)$. Domain $(\sqrt{x})^2 = [0, \infty)$ = range $(\sqrt{x})^2$.

81. The two functions are identical.

82. $f(x) = x^2$

83. $g(x) = \sqrt{x}$ is one possibility.

84. $f(x) = \sin^2 x$, $g(x) = \sqrt{x}$

85. Graph $y = abs(x+3) + abs(x-2) + abs(x-4)$ in the viewing rectangle $[-4, 5]$ by $[0, 15]$. We see that $d(x)$ is minimized when $x = 2$ so you would put the table next to Machine 2.

86. Next to Machine 2 or Machine 3 or anywhere between them.

87. $d(x)$ now has minimum value 17 when $x = 2$. The table should be placed next to Machine 3.

1.4 GEOMETRIC TRANSFORMATIONS: SHIFTS, REFLECTIONS, STRETCHES, AND SHRINKS

1. a) $y = (x + 4)^2$ b) $y = (x - 7)^2$

2. a) $y = x^2 + 3$ b) $y = x^2 - 5$

3. a) Position 4 b) Position 1 c) Position 2 d) Position 3

4. a) $y = (x + 2)^2$ b) $y - 1 = (x - 4)^2$ c) $y + 4 = (x + 1)^2$ d) $y + 3 = (x - 2)^2$

5. Shift the graph of $|x|$ to the left 4 units. Then shift the resulting graph down 3 units.

6. Shift the graph of $y = |x|$ three units to the right and then shift the resulting graph 2 units up.

7. Reflect the graph of $y = \sqrt{x}$ over the y-axis and then stretch the resulting graph vertically by a factor of 3.

8. Reflect the graph of $y = \sqrt{x}$ over the y-axis, shrink vertically by a factor of 0.2, and then reflect the resulting graph over the x-axis.

9. Stretch the graph of $y = \frac{1}{x}$ vertically by a factor of 2 and shift the resulting graph down 3 units.

10. Shrink the graph of $\frac{1}{x}$ by a factor of 0.5. Reflect the resulting graph over the x-axis and then shift the result up 1 unit.

11. Shift the graph of $y = x^3$ right 3 units. Shrink the resulting graph by a factor of 0.5. Reflect the last graph over the x-axis and shift the last graph up 1 unit.

12. Shift the graph of $y = \sqrt{x}$ 2 units to the left (obtaining the graph of $\sqrt{x + 2}$). Reflect the resulting graph over the y-axis (obtaining the graph of $\sqrt{-x + 2} = \sqrt{2 - x}$). Stretch the resulting graph vertically by a factor of 3, and then shift the last result down 5 units.

13. Shift the graph of $y = \frac{1}{x}$ to the right 2 units (obtaining the graph of $\frac{1}{x-2}$). Shift the resulting graph up 3 units.

14. Shift the graph of $\frac{1}{x}$ to the right 3 units. Stretch the resulting graph vertically by a factor of 2. Shift the resulting graph down 5 units.

15. Graph the function in the viewing rectangle: $[-8, 12]$ by $[-15, 5]$. Domain = range $= (-\infty, \infty)$.

16. Graph $y = 0.5|x + 3| - 4$ in the viewing rectangle $[-12, 6]$ by $[-4, 1]$. Domain $= (-\infty, \infty)$, range $= [-4, \infty)$.

17. Check your result by graphing y in $[-5, 5]$ by $[-10, 10]$. Domain = range $= (-\infty, \infty)$.

18. Sketch $y = -2\sqrt[4]{1 - x} + 3$ in the viewing rectangle $[-9, 2]$ by $[-1, 4]$; recognize that $(1, 3)$ is the point on the graph furthest to the right. Domain $= (-\infty, 1]$, range $= (-\infty, 3]$.

19. Check your result by graphing $y = -(x + 3)^{(-2)} + 2$ in the viewing rectangle $[-10, 5]$ by $[-3, 3]$. Domain $= (-\infty, -3) \cup (-3, \infty)$, range $= (-\infty, 2)$.

20. Shift the graph of $y = \frac{1}{x^2}$ to the right 2 units. Domain $= (-\infty, 2) \cup (2, \infty)$, range $= (0, \infty)$.

21. Check your result by graphing $y = -2((x - 1)^{(1/3)})^2 + 1$ in the viewing rectangle $[-1, 3]$ by $[-2, 1]$. Domain $= (-\infty, \infty)$, range $= (-\infty, 1]$.

22. Check your result by graphing $y = (x + 2)^{3/2} + 2$ in the viewing rectangle $[-2, 4]$ by $[0, 20]$. Domain $= [-2, \infty)$, range $= [2, \infty)$.

23. Check your result by graphing $y = 2[1 - x] = 2 \text{ Int}(1 - x)$ in the viewing window $[-3, 4]$ by $[-6, 8]$. (Graph this in Dot Mode if possible.) Domain $= (-\infty, \infty)$, range $= \{2n : n = 0, \pm 1, \pm 2, \ldots\}$.

24. Check your result by graphing $y = [x - 2] + 0.5$ in the viewing rectangle $[-3, 4]$ by $[-4, 2]$. (Use Dot Mode if possible.) Domain $= (-\infty, \infty)$, range $= \{0.5 + n : n = 0, \pm 1, \pm 2, \ldots\}$.

25. $y = 3x^2 + 4$

26. $y = 3(x^2 + 4)$

27. $y = 0.2(\frac{1}{x} - 2)$

28. $y = \frac{0.2}{x} - 2$

29. $y = 3|x + 2| + 5$

30. $y = 0.3|x - 3| - 1$

31. $y = -0.8(x - 1)^3 - 2$

32. $y = -2(x + 5)^3 - 6$

33. $y = 5\sqrt{-(x + 6)} + 5$

34. $y = 0.7\sqrt[4]{8 - x} - 7$

35. $y = \sqrt{\frac{3}{2}x} + 1$

36. $y = 8|x| - 3$

37. The resulting curve is the same in both cases. Let $c > 1$ be given. Applied to $y = x^n$, a vertical stretch by c has the same end result as a horizontal shrink by $\frac{1}{\sqrt[n]{c}}$.

38. Let $c > 1$ be given. Applied to $y = |x|$, a vertical stretch by c has the same end result as a horizontal shrink by $\frac{1}{c}$.

39. In #25 and #26 we obtain, respectively, $y = 3x^2 + 4$ and $y = 3(x^2 + 4) = 3x^2 + 12$. We obtain different geometric results by reversing the order of the transformations. The second graph is 8 units above the first graph.

40. In #27 and #28 we obtain, respectively, $y = 0.2(\frac{1}{x} - 2) = 0.2(\frac{1}{x}) - 0.4$ and $y = 0.2(\frac{1}{x}) - 2$. The second graph is 1.6 units below the first graph.

41. a) Reflect across the y-axis.   b) Reflect across the x-axis.   c) They are the same: $y = \sqrt[3]{-x} = -\sqrt[3]{x}$.

42. a) Reflect across the y-axis.   b) Reflect across the x-axis.   c) One is the reflection of the other through the origin.

43. $y = mx + b$

44. $y - y_0 = m(x - x_0)$

45. $(2, 3), (3, 2), (4, 3)$.

46. $(-2, -3), (-1, -4), (0, -3)$.

47. $(-1, -2), (0, 0), (1, -2)$.

48. $(-1, 4.3), (0, 4), (1, 4.3)$.

49.

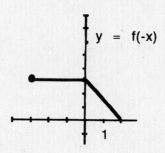

$y = f(-x)$

50.

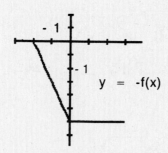

$y = -f(x)$

51.

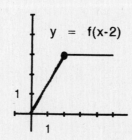

$y = f(x-2)$

52.

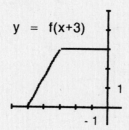

$y = f(x+3)$

53.

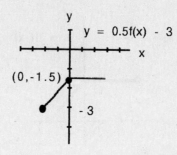

54.

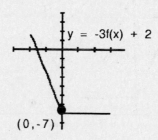

55.

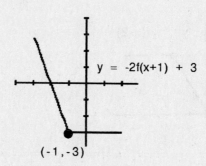

56.

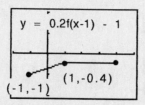

57.

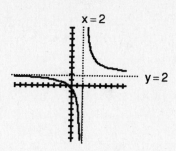

58.

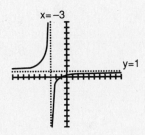

59. $y = -2(x-3)^2 + 7$, vertex $(3,7)$, axis of symmetry: $x = 3$. Check your result by graphing $y = -2x^2 + 12x - 11$ in the viewing rectangle $[-1,7]$ by $[-16,7]$.

60. Vertex: $(-2,-5)$, axis of symmetry: $x = -2$. Check your result by graphing the function in $[-5,1]$ by $[-5,10]$.

61. Vertex: $(-\frac{5}{2}, -6)$, axis of symmetry: $x = -\frac{5}{2}$. Check your result by graphing the function in $[-5,-0]$ by $[-6,10]$.

62. Vertex: $(\frac{3}{2}, 6)$, axis of symmetry: $x = \frac{3}{2}$. Check your sketch by comparing it with the graph of the function in $[-1,4]$ by $[-10,6]$.

63. $x = (y-3)^2 + 2$. Shift up 3, shift right 2. Check your sketch by graphing $y = 3 + \sqrt{x-2}$ and $y = 3 - \sqrt{x-2}$ in the viewing rectangle $[2,20]$ by $[-5,11]$. In parametric mode use $x = t^2 - 6t + 11$, $y = t$, $-5 \leqq t \leqq 11$.

64. $x = (y+2)^2 - 3$. Shift down 2, shift left 3. Check your sketch by graphing $y = -2 + \sqrt{x+3}$ and $y = -2 - \sqrt{x+3}$ in $[-5,24]$ by $[-4,8]$. In parametric mode $x = t^2 + 4t + 1$, $y = t$, $-4 \leqq t \leqq 8$.

65. $x = 2(y+1)^2 - 1$. Shift down 1, horizontal stretch by 2, shift left 1. Check your sketch by graphing $y = -1 + \sqrt{\frac{x+1}{2}}$ and $y = -1 - \sqrt{\frac{x+1}{2}}$ in $[-1,10]$ by $[-4,2]$. In parametric mode $x = 2t^2 + 4t + 1$, $y = t$, $-4 \leq t \leq 2$.

66. $x = -3(y-2)^2+5$. Shift up 2, horizontal stretch by 3, reflect across the y-axis, shift right 5. Check your sketch by graphing $y = 2+\sqrt{\frac{5-x}{3}}$ and $y = 2-\sqrt{\frac{5-x}{3}}$ in $[-9,5]$ by $[-1,5]$. In parametric mode $x = -3t^2+12t-7$, $y = t$, $-1 \leqq t \leqq 5$.

67. $x = -2(y-3)^2+5$. Shift up 3, horizontal stretch by 2, reflection across y-axis, shift right 5. Check your sketch by graphing $y = 3+\sqrt{\frac{5-x}{2}}$ and $y = 3-\sqrt{\frac{5-x}{2}}$ in $[-9,5]$ by $[0,7]$. In parametric mode $x = -2t^2+12t-13$, $y = t$, $0 \leq t \leq 7$.

68. $x = 4(y+2)^2-7$. Shift down 2, horizontal stretch by 4, shift left 7. $(y+2)^2 = \frac{x+7}{4}$, $y = -2 \pm \frac{\sqrt{x+7}}{2}$. Check your sketch by graphing $y = -2 + \frac{\sqrt{x+7}}{2}$ and $y = -2-\frac{\sqrt{x+7}}{2}$ in $[-7,30]$ by $[-5,1]$. In parametric mode $x = 4t^2+16t+9$, $y = t$, $-5 \leqq t \leqq 1$.

69. Two.

1.5 SOLVING EQUATIONS AND INEQUALITIES GRAPHICALLY

1. $\{-3/2, 2/3\}$

2. $\{2 - \sqrt{3}, 2 + \sqrt{3}\}$

3. $\{1 - \sqrt{5}/2, 2, 1 + \sqrt{5}/2\}$

4. $\{0\}$

5. $\{-4, \frac{1}{2}\}$

6. $\{-0.41, 1.08\}$ or $\{\frac{1\pm\sqrt{5}}{3}\}$

7. $\{-0.5, -0.41, 1.08\}$ or $\{-\frac{1}{2}, \frac{1\pm\sqrt{5}}{3}\}$

8. $\{0\}$

9. We give a sequence for the smallest solution only. $[-2, -1]$ by $[-1, 1]$, $x\,Scl = 0.1$; $[-2, -1.9]$ by $[-0.1, 0.1]$, $x\,Scl = 0.01$; $[-1.94, -1.93]$ by $[-0.01, 0.01]$, $x\,Scl = 0.001$; $[-1.931, -1.930]$ by $[-0.001, 0.001]$, $x\,Scl = 0.0001$.

10. $x^3 - 4x + 1 = 0$ has 3 solutions. We give a sequence of rectangles for the largest solution only. $[1, 2]$ by $[-1, 1]$, $x\,Scl = 0.1$. $[1.8, 1.9]$ by $[-0.5, 0.5]$, $x\,Scl = 0.01$. $[1.86, 1.87]$ by $[-0.01, 0.01]$, $x\,Scl = 0.001$. $[1.860, 1.861]$ by $[-0.001, 0.001]$, $x\,Scl = 0.0001$. We see that the root lies between 1.8608 and 1.8609.

11. No real solution

12. $\{-4, 3\}$

13. $\{3, \frac{1\pm\sqrt{7}}{2}\}$

14. $\{3.25\ldots\}$

15. $\{0.74, 7.56, 12.70\}$

16. $\{-11.67, -6.66, -0.67\}$

17. We assume that the number x satisfies $2 < x < 6$. The statement a) $0 < x < 4$ about x does not contain precise enough information about x to be able to determine whether the statement is true or false. The same goes for the statement g) which is equivalent to $-2 < x < 6$. Use of rules of inequalities shows that the remaining statements are all equivalent to $2 < x < 6$ whence they are true.

18. All statements are true.

19. $\{-2, 2\}$

20. $\{-4, 10\}$

21. $\{-9/2, -1/2\}$

22. $\{0, 2\}$

23. $\{-1/3, 17/3\}$

24. $\{0, 4\}$

25. $-1 \leqq y \leqq 3$

26. $-3 < y < -1$

27. $5/3 < y < 3$

28. $-30 \leqq y \leqq 30$

29. $0.9 < y < 1.1$

30. $5/3 < y < 3$

31. $|x - 6| < 3$

32. $|x - 3| < 6$

33. $|x + 1| < 4$

34. $|x + 4| < 3$

35. $3 < x < 7$

36. $-\frac{10}{3} < x < \frac{10}{3}$

37. $(-\infty, -1] \cup [3, \infty)$

38. $(-\infty, -\frac{5}{3}) \cup (\frac{1}{3}, \infty)$

39. $-8 \leqq x \leqq 2$

40. $[-\frac{5}{2}, \frac{5}{2}]$

41. $(-\infty, -5) \cup (-1, \infty)$

42. $(-\infty, -1] \cup [-\frac{1}{3}, \infty)$

43. $(-2/3, 2)$

44. $[8, 12]$

45. $[-5, 2]$

46. All real numbers

47. $(-\infty, 2 - \sqrt{7}] \cup [2, 2 + \sqrt{7}]$

48. $(-2.67, \infty)$

49. $(0, 1.9) \cup (2.1, \infty)$

50. $(-\infty, 4.99)$

51. $(15, 225)$

52. $(11, 100)$

53. b) If the y-range is too large, the graphing utility cannot distinguish between very close values of y.

54. $\{1.46\ldots\}$

55. We may multiply both sides of the equation by the least common multiple of the denominators of the coefficients. This produces an equivalent equation with integer coefficients. For the given example the l.c.m. is 6 and we obtain the equation $12x^3 + 3x^2 - 4x + 6 = 0$. The possible rational roots of this equation are $\pm\frac{p}{q}$ where $p = 1, 2, 3$ or 6 and $q = 1, 2, 3, 4, 6$ or 12.

56. Non-real roots always occur in conjugate pairs and therefore the real cubic will have 0 or 2 non-real roots. Since there are 3 roots, there will be at least one real root. To find all real roots, first find a complete graph, determine the number of x-intercepts, and zoom in on each of them. The set of x-intercepts is the solution set of the cubic.

57. a) $A(x) = x(50 - x)$ b) Check your sketch by graphing $y = x(50 - x)$ in $[-10, 60]$ by $[-100, 700]$ c) domain $= (-\infty, \infty)$, range $= (-\infty, 625]$ d) $0 < x < 50$ e) Using TRACE in b) leads to the approximation 13.8ft by 36.2ft. The exact dimensions are $25 - 5\sqrt{5}$ft by $25 + 5\sqrt{5}$ft   f) $\{0 < x < 25 - 5\sqrt{5}\} \cup \{25 + 5\sqrt{5} < x < 50\}$

58. a) $A(x) = x(100 - 2x) = 100x - 2x^2$.   b) Graph $A(x)$ in $[-20, 70]$ by $[-2000, 1300]$.   c) Domain $= (-\infty, \infty)$, range $= (-\infty, 1250]$. (The vertex occurs at $x = 25$ midway between the two x-intercepts 0 and 50.)   d) $0 < x < 50$. Graph $A(x)$ in $[0, 50]$ by $[0, 1250]$.   e) 5.64ft (perpendicular to the barn) by 88.72ft and 44.36ft (perpendicular to the barn) by 11.28ft. f) $(0, 5.64) \cup (44.36, 50)$.

59. a) $A(x) = (8.5 - 2x)(11 - 2x)$ b) Graph $y = A(x)$ in $[0, 10]$ by $[-2, 50]$ c) Domain $= (-\infty, \infty)$, range $= [-1.5625, \infty)$ d) $0 < x < 4.25$ only makes sense. This part of the graph is the graph of the problem situation.   e) 0.95in.

60. a) $A(x) = 4x^2 + 180x$ b) Graph $A(x)$ in $[-56, 8]$ by $[-2100, 1000]$.   c) Domain $= (-\infty, \infty)$, range $= [-2025, \infty)$ d) $x > 0$ for the problem situation. e) $(\sqrt{2525} - 45)/2 = 2.62\ldots$ft.

61. a) $V(x) = 0.1x + 0.25(50 - x)$ b) Graph $y = V(x)$ in $[-20, 100]$ by $[-2, 20]$ c) Domain $=$ range $= (-\infty, \infty)$ d) $0 \leq x \leq 50$, x an integer   e) 22 dimes, 28 quarters   f) There is no integral solution.

62. a) $I(x) = 0.065x + 0.08(10000 - x)$ b) Graph $I(x)$ in $[-1000, 11000]$ by $[-100, 1000]$.   c) Domain $=$ range $= (-\infty, \infty)$ d) $0 \leq x \leq 10000$. Use

$[0, 10000]$ for the domain in b). e) \$2250 is invested at 6.5% and \$7750 at 8%.

63. a) $V = x(20 - 2x)(25 - 2x)$ b) Graph $y = V$ in $[-2, 17]$ by $[-100, 900]$. c) Domain = range = $(-\infty, \infty)$ d) $0 < x < 10$. Graphing $y = V$ in $[0, 10]$ by $[0, 900]$ gives a graph of the problem situation. e) $x = 3.68$in., maximum volume is 820.53in^3.

64. a) $V = x(25 - 2x)(30 - 2x)$ b) Graph V in $[-1, 20]$ by $[-700, 1600]$ c) Domain = range = $(-\infty, \infty)$ d) $0 < x < 12.5$. Graph V in $[0, 12.5]$ by $[0, 1600]$. e) $x = 4.52686$in for $V_{max} = 1512.04$in^3.

65. a) $L = 5.5$ b) $V(x) = x(5.5 - x)(8.5 - 2x)$ c) Graph V in $[-1, 7]$ by $[-10, 50]$. The domain and range are both the set of all real numbers. d) $0 < x < 4.25$. Graph V in $[0, 4.25]$ by $[-10, 50]$. e) $x = 0.753$in or 2.592in. f) $x = 1.585$in. $V_{max} = V(1.585) = 33.074$in^3.

66. a) $V(x) = 2x(20 - 2x)(15 - 2x)$. b) Graph V in $[-1, 12]$ by $[-750, 864]$. The domain and range are both the set of all real numbers. c) $0 < x < 7.5$. Graph V in $[0, 7.5]$ by $[0, 760]$. d) $x = 0.574$in or 5.944in. e) $x = 2.829$in, $V_{max} = V(2.829) = 758.076$in^3.

1.6 RELATIONS, FUNCTIONS, AND THEIR INVERSES

1. Not one-to-one

2. It is one-to-one

3. One-to-one

4. Not one-to-one

5. Your graph should be the line through $(0, -3)$ and $(2, 0)$.

6. Graph $y = \sqrt{x - 1}$ and $y = -\sqrt{x - 1}$ in $[-4, 13]$ by $[-5, 5]$.

7.

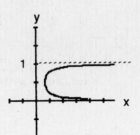

8.

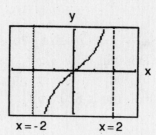

9. $x^2 + (y-2)^2 = 4$. Graph $y = 2 + \sqrt{4-x^2}$ and $y = 2 - \sqrt{4-x^2}$ in $[-3.4, 3.4]$ by $[0, 4]$.

10. $(x+2)^2 + y^2 = 9$. Graph $y_1 = \sqrt{9-(x+2)^2}$ and $y_2 = -y_1$ in $[-7.1, 3.1]$ by $[-3, 3]$.

11. $(x-3)^2 + (y+4)^2 = 25$. Graph $y = -4 + \sqrt{25-(x-3)^2}$ and $y = -4 - \sqrt{25-(x-3)^2}$ in $[-5.5, 11.5]$ by $[-9, 1]$.

12. $(x-1)^2 + (y-1)^2 = 2$. Graph $y_1 = 1 + \sqrt{2-(x-1)^2}$ and $y_2 = 1 - \sqrt{2-(x-1)^2}$ in $[-1.4, 3.4]$ by $[-0.42, 2.42]$.

13. $x^2 + y^2 = 4$

14. $(x-1)^2 + y^2 = 1$

15. $(x-3)^2 + (y-3)^2 = 9$

16. $(x+1)^2 + (y+1)^2 = 1$

17. $C = (3, -4)$, $r = 3$. Graph $x = 3 + 3\cos t$, $y = -4 + 3\sin t$, $0 \leq t \leq 2\pi$, in $[-2.1, 8.1]$ by $[-7, -1]$. Domain $= [0, 6]$, range $= [-7, -1]$.

18. $C = (-1, 2)$, $r = 4$. Graph $x = -1 + 4\cos t$, $y = 2 + 4\sin t$, $0 \leq t \leq 2\pi$, in $[-7.8, 5.8]$ by $[-2, 6]$. Domain $= [-5, 3]$, range $= [-2, 6]$.

19. $C = (-2, -3)$, $r = \sqrt{5}$. Domain $= [-2 - \sqrt{5}, -2 + \sqrt{5}]$, range $= [-3 - \sqrt{5}, -3 + \sqrt{5}]$. Graph $x = -2 + \sqrt{5}\cos t$, $y = -3 + \sqrt{5}\sin t$, $0 \leq t \leq 2\pi$, in $[-8.15, 4.15]$ by $[-5.7, 1.5]$.

20. $C = (1, 4)$, $r = \sqrt{7}$. Domain $= [1 - \sqrt{7}, 1 + \sqrt{7}]$, range $= [4 - \sqrt{7}, 4 + \sqrt{7}]$. Graph $x = 1 + \sqrt{7}\cos t$, $y = 4 + \sqrt{7}\sin t$, $0 \leq t \leq 2\pi$, in $[-5.5, 7.5]$ by $[-1, 6.7]$.

21. Graph $y = \frac{4}{3}\sqrt{x^2 - 9}$ and $y = -\frac{4}{3}\sqrt{x^2 - 9}$ in $[-10, 10]$ by $[-10, 10]$. The calculator screen shows incorrect gaps in the curve when the slopes of tangent lines become numerically very large.

22. Graph $y_1 = (2/3)\sqrt{9 - x^2}$ and $y_2 = -y_1$ in $[-3.4, 3.4]$ by $[-2, 2]$.

23. a) All points outside the boundary of the unit circle.   b) All points in the interior of the circular disk with center $(0, 0)$ and radius 2.   c) The ring between the two circles.

24. a) Outside and on the unit circle   b) Inside and on the circle with center $(0, 0)$ and radius 2.   c) The annular region between the two circles including the boundaries.

25. $(x + 2)^2 + (y + 1)^2 < 6$

26. $(x + 4)^2 + (y - 2)^2 > 16$

27. The graph of the inverse relation can be viewed by graphing $x_1 = 3/(t - 2) - 1$, $y_1 = t$, $-10 \le t \le 10$, Tstep $= .1$ in $[-10, 10]$ by $[-10, 10]$. It is a function.

28. The inverse relation can be graphed by using $x = t^2 + 5t$, $y = t$, $-7 \le t \le 2$ in $[-6.25, 14]$ by $[-8.5, 3.5]$. It is not a function.

29. Graph $x = t^3 - 4t + 6$, $y = t$, $-10 \le t \le 10$, tstep $= 0.1$, in $[-10, 20]$ by $[-15, 15]$. This is not a function.

30. Graph $x = t^3 + t$, $y = t$, $-2 \le t \le 2$ in $[-10, 10]$ by $[-5.9, 5.9]$. This is a function.

31. For the inverse graph $y = e^{x/2}$ and $y = -e^{x/2}$ in $[-2, 5]$ by $[-10, 10]$. This is not a function.

32. Inverse relation is a function. Graph $x = 2^{3-t}$, $y = t$, $-2 \le t \le 6$ in $[-2, 32]$ by $[-10, 10]$.

33. $f^{-1}(x) = (x - 3)/2$.

34. $f^{-1}(x) = \frac{5-x}{4}$

35. $f^{-1}(x) = \sqrt[3]{x + 1}$

36. $f^{-1}(x) = \sqrt[3]{2 - x}$. Graph $y_1 = 2 - x^3$ and $y_2 = (2 - x)^{1/3}$ in $[-10, 10]$ by $[-10, 10]$.

37. $f^{-1}(x) = \sqrt{x-1}$

38. $f^{-1}(x) = -\sqrt{x}$. Graph $y_1 = x^2 + 0\sqrt{-x}$ and $y_2 = -\sqrt{x}$ in $[-3.5, 5.1]$ by $[-3.9, 7.4]$.

39. $f^{-1}(x) = 2 - \sqrt{-x}$, $x \leq 0$

40. $f^{-1}(x) = -1 + \sqrt{x}$. Graph $y_1 = (x+1)^2 + 0\sqrt{x+1}$ and $y_1 = -1 + \sqrt{x}$ in $[-8, 11]$ by $[-3.8, 7.4]$.

41. $f^{-1}(x) = \frac{1}{\sqrt{x}}$

42. $f^{-1}(x) = \frac{1}{\sqrt[3]{x}}$. Graph $y_1 = x^{-3}$ and $y_2 = x^{(-3^{-1})}$ in $[-8.5, 8.5]$ by $[-5, 5]$.

43. $f^{-1}(x) = \frac{1-3x}{x-2}$, $x \neq 2$

44. $f^{-1}(x) = \frac{2x+3}{x-1}$. Graph f and f^{-1} in $[-10, 10]$ by $[-10, 10]$ in dot format.

45. Check your sketch by graphing $y = 2[\ell n(x-4)/\ell n(3)] - 1$ in $[3, 14]$ by $[-10, 4]$ noting that $x = 4$ is a vertical asymptote.

46. Graph $y = -3[\ell n(2-x)/\ell n\,5] + 1$ in $[-10, 2.7]$ by $[-4, 7]$. $x = 2$ is a vertical asymptote.

47. Check your sketch by graphing $y = -3[\ell n(x+2)/\ell n(0.5)] + 2$ in $[-2, 4]$ by $[-18, 10]$.

48. Graph $y = 2[\ell n(3-x)/\ell n(0.2)] + 1$ in $[-10, 3]$ by $[-2.2, 2.7]$.

49. Graph $y = 5(e^{3x}) + 2$ in $[-2, 1]$ by $[0, 20]$.

50. Graph $y = 3(e^{2-x}) - 1$ in $[-1, 9]$ by $[-2, 25]$.

51. Graph $y = -2(3^x) + 1$ in $[-4, 2]$ by $[-10, 2]$.

52. Graph $y = -5(2^{-x+1}) + 3$ in $[-1, 7]$ by $[-10, 5]$.

53. The graph of $\log x = \log_{10} x$ has the same shape as that in Figure 1.91. We start with the graph of $y = \log x$, reflect it through the x-axis and stretch vertically by a factor of 3. (We now have the graph of $y = -3\log x$.) We then shift left 2 and then up 1. The domain comes from $x + 2 > 0$ so it is $(-2, \infty)$ and the range is $(-\infty, \infty)$.

54. Domain $= (-\infty, 3)$, range $= (-\infty, \infty)$. Start with the graph of $y = \ln x$. Shift horizontally left 3 units $(y = \ln(x+3))$. Reflect through the y-axis $(y = \ln(-x+3) = \ln(3-x))$. Stretch vertically by a factor of 2. Finally, shift vertically downward 4 units.

55. Start with the graph of $y = 3^x$, shift left 1 $(y = 3^{x+1})$, reflect across the y-axis $(y = 3^{-x+1})$, stretch vertically by a factor of 2 and shift up 1.5 units. Domain $= (-\infty, \infty)$, range $= (1.5, \infty)$.

56. Domain $= (-\infty, \infty)$, range $= (-\infty, 3)$. Shift $y = 5^x$ horizontally 2 units right. Stretch vertically by a factor of 3. Reflect across the x-axis. Shift vertically up 3 units.

57. Shift the graph of $x^2 + y^2 = 9$ three units left and 5 units up. Domain $= [-6, 0]$, range $= [2, 8]$.

58. Domain $= [1, 11]$, range $= [-6, 4]$. Shift the graph of $x^2 + y^2 = 5^2$ horizontally 6 units right and vertically one unit down.

59. Graph $y_1 = 2^x$, $y_2 = \frac{\ln x}{\ln 2}$, $y_3 = x$ in $[-7.5, 14.6]$ by $[-5, 8]$.

60. Graph $y_1 = 0.5^x$, $y_2 = \log_{0.5} x = \frac{\ln x}{\ln 0.5}$, $y_3 = x$ in $[-7.5, 14.6]$ by $[-5, 8]$.

61. Graph $y_1 = \log_3 x = \frac{\ln x}{\ln 3}$, $y_2 = 3^x$, $y_3 = x$ in $[-7.5, 14.6]$ by $[-5, 8]$.

62. Graph $y_1 = \frac{\ln x}{\ln 0.3}$, $y_2 = (0.3)^x$, $y_3 = x$ in $[-2.1, 4.8]$ by $[-1.5, 2.6]$.

63. $\{\ln(\frac{3-\sqrt{5}}{2}), \ln(\frac{3+\sqrt{5}}{2})\}$

64. $-1 + \ln(5 \pm \sqrt{21})/\ln 2$

65. $\{2 - \sqrt{3}, 2 + \sqrt{3}\}$

66. $\frac{3\pm\sqrt{5}}{2}$

70. a) Domain $= (-\infty, \infty)$. If $a > 0$, range $= (d, \infty)$. If $a < 0$, range $= (-\infty, d)$.
b) Domain $= (c, \infty)$, range $= (-\infty, \infty)$

1.7   A REVIEW OF TRIGONOMETRIC FUNCTIONS

1. 8.901 rad

2. $\frac{2\pi}{3}$

3. -0.73

4. $-\frac{5\pi}{6}$ rad

5. $355.234°$

6. $-30°$

7. $-114.592°$

8. $135°$

9. $\frac{5\pi}{4}$

10. $\frac{25\pi}{6}$

11. 18

12. $\frac{72}{7\pi}$

13. $\frac{1}{2}$

14. $\frac{\pi}{4}$

15. a) $\sin\frac{\pi}{3} = \frac{\sqrt{3}}{2}$, $\cos\frac{\pi}{3} = \frac{1}{2}$, $\tan\frac{\pi}{3} = \sqrt{3}$, $\cot\frac{\pi}{3} = \frac{\sqrt{3}}{3}$, $\sec\frac{\pi}{3} = 2$, $\csc\frac{\pi}{3} = \frac{2\sqrt{3}}{3}$

b) $\sin(-\frac{\pi}{3}) = -\frac{\sqrt{3}}{2}$, $\cos(-\frac{\pi}{3}) = \frac{1}{2}$, $\tan(-\frac{\pi}{3}) = -\sqrt{3}$, $\cot(-\frac{\pi}{3}) = -\frac{\sqrt{3}}{3}$, $\sec(-\frac{\pi}{3}) = 2$, $\csc(-\frac{\pi}{3}) = -\frac{2\sqrt{3}}{3}$

16. a) $\sin(2.5) = 0.5985$, $\cos(2.5) = -0.8011$, $\tan(2.5) = -0.7470$, $\cot(2.5) = -1.3386$, $\sec(2.5) = -1.2482$, $\csc(2.5) = 1.6709$

b) $\sin(-2.5) = -0.5985$, $\cos(-2.5) = -0.8011$, $\tan(-2.5) = 0.7470$, $\cot(-2.5) = 1.3386$, $\sec(-2.5) = -1.2482$, $\csc(-2.5) = -1.6709$

17. a) $\sin(6.5) = 0.2151$, $\cos(6.5) = 0.9766$, $\tan(6.5) = 0.2203$, $\cot(6.5) = 4.5397$, $\sec(6.5) = 1.0240$, $\csc(6.5) = 4.6486$

b) $\sin(-6.5) = -0.2151$, $\cos(-6.5) = 0.9766$, $\tan(-6.5) = -0.2203$, $\cot(-6.5) = -4.5397$, $\sec(-6.5) = 1.0240$, $\csc(-6.5) = -4.6486$

18. a) $\sin(3.7) = -0.5298$, $\cos(3.7) = -0.8481$, $\tan 3.7 = 0.6247$, $\cot(3.7) = 1.6007$, $\sec(3.7) = -1.1791$, $\csc(3.7) = -1.8874$

b) $\sin(-3.7) = 0.5298$, $\cos(-3.7) = -0.8481$, $\tan(-3.7) = -0.6247$, $\cot(-3.7) = -1.6007$, $\sec(-3.7) = -1.1791$, $\csc(-3.7) = 1.8874$

19. a) $\sin\frac{\pi}{2} = 1$, $\cos\frac{\pi}{2} = 0$, $\tan\frac{\pi}{2}$ is undefined, $\cot(\frac{\pi}{2}) = 0$, $\sec\frac{\pi}{2}$ is undefined, $\csc\frac{\pi}{2} = 1$

b) $\sin\frac{3\pi}{2} = -1$, $\cos\frac{3\pi}{2} = 0$, $\tan\frac{3\pi}{2}$ is undefined, $\cot\frac{3\pi}{2} = 0$, $\sec\frac{3\pi}{2}$ is undefined, $\csc\frac{3\pi}{2} = -1$

20. a) $\sin 0 = 0$, $\cos 0 = 1$, $\tan 0 = 0$, $\cot 0$ is undefined, $\sec 0 = 1$, $\csc 0$ is undefined

b) $\sin \pi = 0$, $\cos \pi = -1$, $\tan \pi = 0$, $\cot \pi$ is undefined, $\sec \pi = -1$, $\csc \pi$ is undefined

21. $\frac{\pi}{6}$, 30°

22. $-\frac{\pi}{4}$, $-45°$

23. -1.3734, $-78.6901°$

24. 0.7954, $45.5730°$

25. In parametric mode graph $x_1(t) = \cos t$, $y_1(t) = \sin t$, t Min $= 0$, t Max $= 2\pi$, t Step $= 0.1$. Then use TRACE: For a given t value, the displayed $x = \cos t$ and $y = \sin t$.

26. In parametric mode and degree mode graph $x_1 = \cos t$, $y_1 = \sin t$, $0 \le t \le 360$, t Step $= 5$. Use TRACE. For a given t value, the displayed $x = \cos t$ and $y = \sin t$.

27. $[-\pi, 2\pi]$ by $[-1, 1]$, $[-\pi, 2\pi]$ by $[-1, 1]$, $[-1.5\pi, 1.5\pi]$ by $[-2, 2]$, respectively.

28. $[-1.5\pi, 1.5\pi]$ by $[-4, 4]$, $[-\pi, 2\pi]$ by $[-4, 4]$, $[-\pi, 2\pi]$ by $[-4, 4]$, respectively.

29. $[-270°, 450°]$ by $[-3, 3]$, $[-360°, 360°]$ by $[-3, 3]$, $[-180°, 180°]$ by $[-3, 3]$, respectively.

30. $[0°, 720°]$ by $[-1, 1]$, $[0°, 720°]$ by $[-1, 1]$, $[-90°, 270°]$ by $[-4, 4]$, respectively.

31. Check by graphing the functions in $[-\pi, \pi]$ by $[-3, 3]$.

32. Check by graphing $y_1 = \cos x$, $y_2 = y_1^{-1}$ in $[-1.5\pi, 1.5\pi]$ by $[-4, 4]$.

33. Graph the functions in $[0, 2\pi]$ by $[-1, 1]$.

34. Graph $y_1 = \sin(x/4)$ and $y_2 = \sin x$ in $[0, 8\pi]$ by $[-1, 1]$.

35. Amplitude $= 2$, period $= 6\pi$, horizontal stretch by a factor of 3. To see one period of the function graph it in $[0, 6\pi]$ by $[-2, 2]$.

36. Amplitude $= 2$, period $= \frac{2\pi}{3}$, horizontal shrinking by a factor of $\frac{1}{3}$, vertical stretch by a factor of 2. To see one period of the function graph it in $[0, \frac{2\pi}{3}]$ by $[-2, 2]$.

37. $y = \cot(2x + \frac{\pi}{2}) = \cot[2(x + \frac{\pi}{4})]$. A horizontal shrinking by a factor of $\frac{1}{2}$ is applied to the graph of $y = \cot x$ followed by a horizontal shift left $\frac{\pi}{4}$ units. The period is $\frac{\pi}{2}$. Graphing the function in $[-\frac{\pi}{4}, \frac{3\pi}{4}]$ by $[-2, 2]$ shows two periods of the function.

38. Horizontal shift left $\frac{\pi}{4}$ units, vertical stretch by a factor of 3 followed by a vertical shift 2 units down. Amplitude $= 3$, period $= 2\pi$. Graph $y = 3\cos(x + \pi/4) - 2$ in $[-\frac{\pi}{4}, \frac{7\pi}{4}]$ by $[-5, 1]$ to see one period.

39. Period $= 2\pi/3$, domain is all real numbers except $n\pi/3$, n an integer, range $= (-\infty, -5] \cup [1, \infty)$. One period of the graph may be viewed in $[-\frac{\pi}{3}, \frac{\pi}{3}]$ by $[-11, 7]$. Start with the graph of $y = \csc x$, shrink horizontally by a factor of $1/3$, shift horizontally left $\pi/3$ units, stretch vertically by a factor of 3, shift vertically downward 2 units.

40. Start with the graph of $y = \sin x$. Shift left π units, shrink horizontally by a factor of $\frac{1}{4}$, stretch vertically by a factor of 2 and finally shift vertically up 3 units. Amplitude $= 2$, period $= \frac{\pi}{2}$, domain $= (-\infty, \infty)$, range $= [1, 5]$. Graph y in $[-\frac{\pi}{4}, \frac{\pi}{4}]$ by $[1, 5]$ to view one period.

41. Period $= \pi/3$, domain is all real numbers except odd multiples of $\pi/6$, range is all real numbers. One period of the graph may be viewed in $[-\frac{\pi}{6}, \frac{\pi}{6}]$ by $[-11, 15]$. Start with the graph of $y = \tan x$, shrink horizontally by a factor of $1/3$, shift horizontally left $\pi/3$ units, stretch vertically by a factor of 3, reflect across the x-axis, shift vertically upward 2 units.

42. Start with the graph of $y = \sin x$. Shift horizontally left $\frac{\pi}{3}$ units, shrink horizontally by a factor of $\frac{1}{2}$, stretch vertically by a factor of 2. Domain $= (-\infty, \infty)$, range $= [-2, 2]$, period $= \pi$, amplitude $= 2$. Graph $y = 2\sin(2x + \frac{\pi}{3})$ in $[-\frac{\pi}{6}, \frac{5\pi}{6}]$ by $[-2, 2]$ to view one period.

43. $\{\pm\cos^{-1}(-0.7) + 2n\pi\}$.

44. $\{x + 2n\pi$ where $x = 0.20$ and $x = 2.94\}$.

45. $\{(\tan^{-1} 4) + n\pi\}$

46. $x + 2n\pi$ where $x = -0.20$ and -2.94.

47. $\{-2.596, 0, 2.596\}$.

48. $\{-3.837, -1.977, 1.306\}$.

49. 2.219.   **50.** No solution.

51. $(-\infty, -2.596) \cup (0, 2.596)$.

52. $(-\infty, -3.837) \cup (-1.977, 1.306)$.

53. Graph $x_1 = \sqrt{5}\cos t$, $y_1 = \sqrt{5}\sin t$, $0 \leq t \leq 2\pi$ in $[-3.8, 3.8]$ by $[-\sqrt{5}, \sqrt{5}]$.

54. Graph $x_1 = 2\cos t$, $y_1 = 2\sin t$, $0 \leq t \leq 2\pi$ in $[-3.4, 3.4]$ by $[-2, 2]$.

55. Graph $x_1 = 2 + 3\cos t$, $y_1 = -3 + 3\sin t$, $0 \leq t \leq 2\pi$, in $[-3.1, 7.1]$ by $[-6, 0]$.

56. Graph $x_1 = -1 + 4\cos t$, $y_1 = -3 + 4\sin t$, $0 \leq t \leq 2\pi$ in $[-7.8, 5.8]$ by $[-7, 1]$.

57. $y = \sqrt{13}\sin(x + \alpha)$, where $\alpha = \sin^{-1}(3/\sqrt{13}) = 0.9828$.

58. $y = 2\sin(x + \frac{\pi}{3})$.

59. $y = \sqrt{2}\sin(2x + \frac{\pi}{4})$.

60. $y = 2\sqrt{2}\sin(3x + \frac{\pi}{4})$.

61. b) and d); c) and e)

62. c), g), h) all have the same graph as $y = -\sin x$. b), e), f) all have the same graph as $y = -\cos x$.

65. Graphs of cosine, sine and tangent are symmetric about the y-axis, the origin and the origin, respectively.

66. The graph of the secant is symmetric about the y-axis. The graphs of the cosecant and cotangent are symmetric with respect to the origin.

67. a) yes,   b) $-1 \leq \cos 2x \leq 1$,   c) $0 \leq \frac{1+\cos 2x}{2} \leq 1$,   d) The domain is the set of all reals; the range is the interval $[0, 1]$.

68. a) Exclude $(2k + 1)\frac{\pi}{2}$,   b) Exclude $(2k + 1)\pi$,   c) All real numbers, d) The domain consists of all real numbers except $(2k + 1)\pi$. The range is the set of all real numbers.

69. a) 37   b) 365   c) 101 units to the right   d) 25 units upward

70. a) $62°, -12°$.   b) $25°$. This is equal to the vertical shift because the range of the sine function is symmetric about $y = 0$.

71. We obtain $\cos(A - A) = \cos A \cos A + \sin A \sin A$ or $1 = \cos^2 A + \sin^2 A$ for the first equation. For the second equation we obtain $\sin(A - A) = \sin A \cos A - \cos A \sin A$ or $0 = 0$.

72. They become $\cos(A - \pi/2) = \sin A$ and $\sin(A - \pi/2) = -\cos A$.

73. $\cos(A + \frac{\pi}{2}) = \cos A \cos \frac{\pi}{2} - \sin A \sin \frac{\pi}{2} = -\sin A$. If we start the cosine curve, reflect it across the x-axis and shift horizontally $\frac{\pi}{2}$ units to the left, we obtain the sine curve. Similarly, $\sin(A + \frac{\pi}{2}) = \cos A$.

74. $\cos(A + \pi) = -\cos A$, $\sin(A + \pi) = -\sin A$, $\cos(A - \pi) = -\cos A$, $\sin(A - \pi) = -\sin A$.

75. $\frac{\sqrt{6}+\sqrt{2}}{4}$

76. $\frac{\sqrt{6}+\sqrt{2}}{4}$

77. $\frac{\sqrt{2}+\sqrt{6}}{4}$

78. $\frac{\sqrt{6}-\sqrt{2}}{4}$

79. $\frac{2+\sqrt{2}}{4}$

80. $\frac{2+\sqrt{3}}{4}$

81. $\frac{2-\sqrt{3}}{4}$

82. $\frac{2-\sqrt{2}}{4}$

84. Let $A = \sqrt{a^2 + b^2}$ and let α be the unique solution in $[0, 2\pi)$ of $\cos \alpha = a/A$, $\sin \alpha = b/A$. $(a/A, b/A)$ is a point on the unit circle so there is such an angle α. Then $A \sin(x + \alpha) = A \sin x \cos \alpha + A \cos x \sin \alpha = a \sin x + b \cos x$.

86. $\tan(A - B) = \frac{\tan A - \tan B}{1 + \tan A \tan B}$

87. a) Let $f(x) = \cot x$. $f(-x) = \frac{\cos(-x)}{\sin(-x)} = \frac{\cos x}{-\sin x} = -f(x)$, proving $f(x)$ is odd.

b) Let $g(x) = \frac{h(x)}{k(x)}$ where $h(x)$ is even and $k(x)$ is odd. $g(-x) = \frac{h(-x)}{k(-x)} = \frac{h(x)}{-k(x)} = -g(x)$ proving $g(x)$ is odd where defined.

c) The graph of $y = \cot(-x) = -\cot x$ can be obtained by reflecting the graph of $y = \cot x$ across the x-axis.

88. c) By reflecting it across the origin.

89. Use the method indicated in the solution of Exercise 87.

91. Fundamental period $= \frac{\pi}{30}$. Graph $y = \sin(60x)$ in the window $[0, \frac{\pi}{30}]$ by $[-1, 1]$.

92. Fundamental period $= \frac{1}{30}$. Graph $y = \cos(60\pi x)$ in $[0, \frac{1}{30}]$ by $[-1, 1]$.

94. $116.565°$

95. $41.186°$

96. $68.199°$

97. $18.435°$

PRACTICE EXERCISES, CHAPTER 1

1. a) $(1, -4)$ b) $(-1, 4)$ c) $(-1, -4)$ **2.** a) $(2, 3)$ b) $(-2, -3)$ c) $(-2, 3)$

3. a) $(-4, -2)$ b) $(4, 2)$ c) $(4, -2)$ **4.** a) $(-2, 2)$ b) $(2, -2)$ c) $(2, 2)$

5. a) origin only   b) y-axis only   **6.** a) origin only   b) y-axis only

7. a) both axes and the origin   b) none of the mentioned symmetries

8. a) origin only   b) y-axis only

9. $x = 1$, $y = 3$ $\qquad\qquad$ **10.** $x = 2$, $y = 0$

11. $x = 0$, $y = -3$ $\qquad\qquad$ **12.** $x = x_0$, $y = y_0$

13. $y = 2x - 1$. Intercepts: $x = \frac{1}{2}$, $y = -1$

14. $y = 3$. y-intercept 3.

15. $y = -x + 1$. Intercepts: $x = 1$, $y = 1$

16. $y = 1 - x$. x-intercept 1, y-intercept 1

17. $y + 6 = 3(x - 1)$ or $y = 3x - 9$. Intercepts: $x = 3$, $y = -9$.

18. $y = x + 2$. x-intercept -2, y-intercept 2.

19. $y - 2 = -\frac{1}{2}(x + 1)$ or $y = -\frac{1}{2}x + \frac{3}{2}$. Intercepts: $x = 3$, $y = \frac{3}{2}$.

20. $y = \frac{1}{3}x$. x-intercept 0, y-intercept 0

21. $3y = 5x + 4$ $\qquad\qquad$ **22.** $y = -2x$

23. $y = \frac{5}{2}x - 6$ $\qquad\qquad$ **24.** $y - 3 = -\frac{2}{5}(x - 3)$ or $2x + 5y = 21$

25. $y = \frac{1}{2}x + 2$ $\qquad\qquad$ **26.** $y = -3x + 3$

27. $y = -2x - 1$ $\qquad\qquad$ **28.** $y = 2x$

29. a) $2x - y = 12$ b) $x + 2y = 6$ c) $14\sqrt{5}/5$

30. a) $y = x - 2$ b) $y = -x + 4$ c) $2\sqrt{2}$

31. a) $4x + 3y = -20$ b) $y + 12 = \frac{3}{4}(x - 4)$ c) $\frac{32}{5}$

32. a) $y = -\sqrt{3}x + 1$ b) $y = \frac{1}{\sqrt{3}}x + 1$ c) 2

33. Domain = range = $(-\infty, \infty)$

34. Graph $y = |x| - 2$ in $[-6, 6]$ by $[-4, 4]$. Domain = $(-\infty, \infty)$, range = $[-2, \infty)$.

35. Check your sketch by graphing $y = 2 \operatorname{abs}(x - 1) - 1$ in $[-2, 4]$ by $[-1, 5]$. Domain = $(-\infty, \infty)$, range = $[-1, \infty)$

36. Graph one period of $y = \sec x$ in $[-\frac{\pi}{2}, 1.5\pi]$ by $[-4, 4]$. Domain = all reals except $(2k + 1)\frac{\pi}{2}$, range = $(-\infty, -1] \cup [1, \infty)$.

37. Domain = $(-\infty, \infty)$, range = $[-1, 1]$.

38. Domain = $(-\infty, \infty)$, range = all integers.

39. Domain = $(-\infty, 0]$, range = $(-\infty, \infty)$. Check your sketch by graphing $y = -\sqrt{-x}$ and $y = \sqrt{-x}$ in $[-9, 0]$ by $[-3, 3]$.

40. Graph $y = -2 + \sqrt{1 - x}$ in $[-10, 2]$ by $[-3.5, 3.5]$. Domain = $(-\infty, 1]$ range = $[-2, \infty)$.

41. Domain = range = $(-\infty, \infty)$. Graph $f(x)$ in $[-9, 4]$ by $[-100, 100]$.

42. Graph $y = -1 + \sqrt[3]{1 - x}$ in $[-4, 6]$ by $[-4.5, 3.2]$. Domain = range = $(-\infty, \infty)$.

43. Domain = $(1, \infty)$, range = $(-\infty, \infty)$. Graph $y = \ell n(x - 1)/\ell n(7) + 1$ in $[1, 3]$ by $[-3, 3]$, recalling that $x = 1$ is a vertical asymptote.

44. Graph $y = 3^{2-x} + 1$ in $[-1, 6]$ by $[0, 28]$. Domain = $(-\infty, \infty)$, range = $(1, \infty)$.

45. Domain = $(-\infty, \infty)$, range = $[5, \infty)$. Graph $y = \operatorname{abs}(x - 2) + \operatorname{abs}(x + 3)$ in $[-5, 4]$ by $[4, 9]$.

46. $f(x) = \frac{|x-2|}{x-2} = \begin{cases} -1, & x < 2 \\ 1, & x > 2 \end{cases}$.

Domain = all reals except 2, range = $\{-1, 1\}$.

47. Stretch vertically by a factor of 2, reflect across the x-axis, shift horizontally right one unit, shift vertically 5 units upward.

48. Shift horizontally left one unit, reflect across the y-axis, vertically stretch by a factor of 2, shift vertically upward 3 units.

49. Stretch vertically by a factor of 3, shrink horizontally by a factor of 1/3, shift horizontally $\pi/3$ units left.

50. Shift horizontally left 3 units, reflect across the y-axis, stretch vertically by a factor of 2, reflect across the x-axis, shift vertically 5 units up.

51. $y = -2(x-2)^2 + 3$

52. $-2(x+3) = (y+2)^2$

53. $y = \frac{3}{x+2} + 5$

54. $(x+3)^2 + (y-5)^2 = 1$

55.

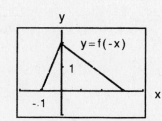

56.

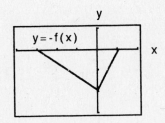

57.

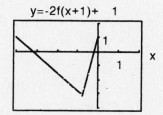

58.

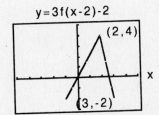

59. Vertex is $(2,3)$. $x = 2$ is the line of symmetry. Check your sketch by graphing y in $[-2, 5]$ by $[-6, 3]$.

60. Vertex: $(-5, -2)$, axis of symmetry: $y = -2$. In parametric mode graph $x = 2t^2 + 8t + 3$, $y = t$, $-5 \le t \le 1$ in $[-5, 10]$ by $[-6.5, 1.9]$.

61. all are even

62. a) odd b) odd c) neither

63. a) even b) odd c) odd

64. a) odd b) odd c) even

65. a) even b) odd c) odd

66. a) odd b) odd c) even

67. Graph y in $[-2, 2]$ by $[0, 2]$. The function is periodic of period 1.

68. The function has graph the same as the graph of $y = 1$ except at $x = n$, an integer, $y = 0$. The function is periodic of period 1.

69. Graph $y_1 = \sqrt{-x}$ and $y_2 = \sqrt{x}$ at the same time in $[-4, 4]$ by $[0, 2]$.

70. Graph $y_1 = -x - 2 + 0\sqrt{x + 2} + 0\sqrt{-(x + 1)}$, $y_2 = x + 0\sqrt{x + 1} + 0\sqrt{1 - x}$, $y_3 = -x + 2 + 0\sqrt{x - 1} + 0\sqrt{2 - x}$ in $[-3, 3]$ by $[-1, 1]$.

71. The graph consists of one period of the sine function on $[0, 2\pi]$ together with all points on the x-axis larger than 2π.

72. The graph consists of one period of the cosine function from 0 to 2π and the x-axis for $2\pi < x < \infty$.

73. $y = \begin{cases} 1 - x, & 0 \leq x < 1 \\ 2 - x, & 1 \leq x \leq 2 \end{cases}$ **74.** $f(x) = \begin{cases} \frac{5}{2}x, & 0 \leq x \leq 2 \\ -\frac{5}{2}x + 10, & 2 \leq x \leq 4 \end{cases}$

75. For $f(x)$, domain $=$ range $=$ all real numbers except 0. For the remaining functions, domain $=$ range $=$ all positive real numbers.

76. Domains and ranges: $f : [0, \infty), [0, \infty)$. $g : (-\infty, 1], [0, \infty)$. $f + g :$ $[0, 1], [1, \sqrt{2}]$. $f \cdot g : [0, 1], [0, 0.5]$. $f/g : [0, 1), [0, \infty)$. $g/f : (0, 1], [0, \infty)$. $f \circ g : (-\infty, 1], [0, \infty)$. $g \circ f : [0, 1], [0, 1]$.

77. $(x - 1)^2 + (y - 1)^2 = 1$ **78.** $(x - 2)^2 + y^2 = 25$

79. $(x - 2)^2 + (y + 3)^2 = \frac{1}{4}$ **80.** $(x + 3)^2 + y^2 = 9$

81. $(3, -5)$, 4 **82.** Center: $(0, 5)$. Radius: $\sqrt{2}$

83. $(-1, 7)$, 11 **84.** $(-4, -1)$, 9

85. a) $x^2 + y^2 < 1$ b) $x^2 + y^2 \leq 1$

86. a) $(x - 1)^2 + (y - 1)^2 > 4$ b) $(x - 1)^2 + (y - 1)^2 \geq 4$

87. $\{\frac{1}{2}, \frac{3}{2}\}$ **88.** $\{\frac{1}{3}, 1\}$

89. $\{-20, 15\}$ **90.** $\{-9, 19\}$

91. $-\frac{5}{2} \leq x \leq -\frac{3}{2}$ **92.** $2 \leq x \leq 5$

93. $-\frac{1}{5} < y < 1$ **94.** $14 < y < 18$

95. $\{0.19, 2.47, 4.34\}$ **96.** $\{-0.82, 1.5, 1.82\}$ or $\{\frac{3}{2}, \frac{1\pm\sqrt{7}}{2}\}$.

97. $\{\frac{15-\sqrt{5}}{6}, \frac{15+\sqrt{5}}{6}\}$ or $\{2.127, 2.873\}$.   **98.** $\{-0.775 + 2n\pi, 0.775 + (2n+1)\pi\}$.

99. $-1 < x < 2$

100. $-2 \leq x \leq 3$. We may support this graphically by graphing $y_1 = \text{abs}((2x - 1)/5)$ and $y_2 = 1$ and observing that y_2 is above y_1 on, and only on, $-2 < x < 3$.

101. $(-\infty, -1) \cup (5, \infty)$ **102.** $(-\infty, \frac{1}{3}) \cup (1, \infty)$ **103.** $(-\infty, 0.19) \cup (2.47, 4.34)$

104. $[-0.82, 1.5] \cup [1.82, \infty)$ or $[\frac{1-\sqrt{7}}{2}, 1.5] \cup [\frac{1+\sqrt{7}}{2}, \infty)$.

105. a) $\frac{\pi}{6}$ b) 0.122π c) -0.722π d) $-\frac{5\pi}{6}$

106. a) $270°$ b) $-51.57°$ c) $157.56°$ d) $-225°$

107. a) $0.891,\ 0.454,\ 1.965,\ 0.509,\ 2.205,\ 1.122$

b) $-0.891,\ 0.454,\ -1.965,\ -0.509,\ 2.205,\ -1.122$

c) $\sqrt{3}/2,\ -1/2,\ -\sqrt{3},\ -\sqrt{3}/3,\ -2,\ 2\sqrt{3}/3$

d) $-\sqrt{3}/2,\ -1/2,\ \sqrt{3},\ \sqrt{3}/3,\ -2,\ -2\sqrt{3}/3$

108. a) $\frac{\sqrt{2}}{2}, \frac{\sqrt{2}}{2}, 1, 1, \sqrt{2}, \sqrt{2}$ b) $-\frac{\sqrt{2}}{2}, \frac{\sqrt{2}}{2}, -1, -1, \sqrt{2}, -\sqrt{2}$ c) $0.43, -0.90,$ $-0.47, -2.12, -1.11, 2.34$ d) $-0.43, -0.90, 0.47, 2.12, -1.11, -2.34$

109. Graph the functions in $[0, 2\pi]$ by $[-1, 2]$.

110. Check your result by graphing $y_1 = \cos 2x$, $y_2 = -y_1$, $y_3 = 1 - \cos 2x$, $y_4 = (\sin x)^2$ in $[0, 2\pi]$ by $[-1, 2]$.

111. $\frac{3}{4}$ **112.** $\frac{1}{2}$ **113.** $f^{-1}(x) = \frac{2-x}{3}$

114. $f^{-1}(x) = -2 + \sqrt{x}$. Graph $y_1 = (x+2)^2 + 0\sqrt{x+2}$ and $y_2 = -2 + \sqrt{x}$ in $[-9.5, 13]$ by $[-3.5, 10]$.

115. The inverse relation is not a function. Its graph may be obtained using $x_1 = t^3 - t$, $y_1 = t$, $-2 \leq t \leq 2$ in $[-6, 6]$ by $[-2, 2]$.

116. Graph $f^{-1}(x) = \frac{x+2}{x-1}$, a function, in $[-10, 10]$ by $[-10, 10]$.

117. $0.775,\ 44.427°$ **118.** $-1.161,\ -66.501°$

119. Graph $y = |\cos x|$ in $[-\frac{\pi}{2}, \frac{\pi}{2}]$ by $[0,1]$. The graph is complete because the function has period π.

120. The graph of one period of y, $-\frac{\pi}{2} \leq x \leq \frac{3\pi}{2}$, coincides with the graph of $y = \cos x$ on $[-\frac{\pi}{2}, \frac{\pi}{2}]$ and with the x-axis on $[\frac{\pi}{2}, \frac{3\pi}{2}]$.

121. For x in the interval $[-\frac{\pi}{2}, \frac{3\pi}{2}]$, $y = \begin{cases} 0, & -\frac{\pi}{2} \leq x < \frac{\pi}{2} \\ -\cos x, & \frac{\pi}{2} \leq x \leq \frac{3\pi}{2} \end{cases}$. Graphing this part gives a complete graph because the function has period 2π.

122. The graph of one period of y, $-\frac{\pi}{2} \leq x \leq \frac{3\pi}{2}$, coincides with the x-axis on $[-\frac{\pi}{2}, \frac{\pi}{2}]$ and with the graph of $\cos x$ on $[\frac{\pi}{2}, \frac{3\pi}{2}]$.

123. a) $A(x) = (\frac{x}{4})^2 + (\frac{100-x}{4})^2$　　b) Graph this function in $[-50, 150]$ by $[300, 1000]$ c) Domain $= (-\infty, \infty)$, range $= [312.5, \infty)$　　d) $0 < x < 100$　　e) $50 - 10\sqrt{7}$in and $50 + 10\sqrt{7}$in　　f) The maximum $(\frac{100}{4})^2 = 625$in^2 cannot be attained. The minimum of 312.5in^2 is attained if both pieces are 50in.

124. a) $V = x(20 - 2x)(30 - 2x)$

b) Graph V in $[-5, 21]$ by $[-3800, 3200]$.

c) Domain = range = $(-\infty, \infty)$

d) $0 < x < 10$

e) $V_{\max} = V(3.9237) = 1056.31\text{in}^3$

f) $x = 1.70\text{in}$ by 16.6in by 26.6in or $x = 6.62\text{in}$ by 6.76in by 16.76in.

125. The graph is the square with vertices $(1, 0), (0, 1), (-1, 0), (0, -1)$.

CHAPTER 2

LIMITS AND CONTINUITY

2.1   LIMITS

1. 4   2. 0   3. 2   4. 0   5. 9   6. -9 7. 1

8. 1   9. -15 10. -16 11. -2 12. 5   13. 0   14. $\frac{11}{4}$

15. Limit does not exist.

16. The limit does not exist.

17. Function is not defined at $x = 0$ so substitution cannot be used. The limit does not exist because the left-hand limit -1 does not equal the right-hand limit 1.

18. 8   19. $\frac{1}{2}$ 20. -7 21. $-\frac{1}{2}$ 22. $\frac{1}{4}$ 23. $\frac{1}{2}$ 24. $-\frac{1}{2}$ 25. $-\frac{1}{4}$

26. 12   27. $\lim_{x \to 0} x \sin \frac{1}{x} = 0$

28. $\lim_{x \to 0} \frac{\sin x}{x} = 1$ 29. The limit does not exist.

30. $\lim_{x \to 0} \frac{10^x - 1}{x} = 2.30\ldots$ We will later be able to show that this limit is $\ln 10$.

31. $\lim_{x \to 0} \frac{2^x - 1}{x} = 0.693\ldots$ We will later be able to show that the limit is $\ln 2$.

32. $\lim_{x \to 0} x \sin(\ln|x|) = 0$

33. Limiting value of investment = \$106.18. There is not much advantage here in compounding more frequently than about 8 times.

34. In both cases the difference rounds to 0.001. To pocket a real difference you would have to invest at least \$1000 and hope the bank rounds to the nearest cent.

35. There appear to be no points of the graph very near to $(0,4)$. The actual graph is the graph of $y = x + 4$ with the point $(0,4)$ missing.

36. There appear to be no points of the graph near $(0,3)$. The graph is the graph of the parabola $y = x^2 + 3x + 3$ with the point $(0,3)$ missing.

37. $\lim_{x \to 2^+} f(x) = \infty$, $\lim_{x \to 2^-} f(x) = -\infty$

38. $\lim_{x \to 2^+} f(x) = -\infty, \ \lim_{x \to 2^-} f(x) = \infty$

39. a), b), d), e), f) **40.** All are true except b) and c)

41. a)

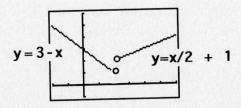

b) $\lim_{x \to 2^+} f(x) = 2, \ \lim_{x \to 2^-} f(x) = 1$

c) Does not exist because right-hand and left-hand limits are not equal.

42. a)

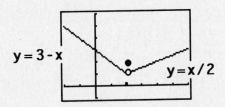

b) $\lim_{x \to 2^+} f(x) = 1, \ \lim_{x \to 2^-} f(x) = 1$.

c) The limit exists and $\lim_{x \to 2} f(x) = 1$

43. a) A complete graph of $f(x)$ can be obtained on a graphing calculator by graphing both $y = (x-1)^{-1} + 0\sqrt{(1-x)}$ and $y = x^3 - 2x + 5 + 0\sqrt{(x-1)}$ in the viewing rectangle $[-3, 5]$ by $[-25, 25]$.

b) $\lim_{x \to 1^+} f(x) = 4$ and $\lim_{x \to 1^-} f(x)$ does not exist.

c) No. For this limit to exist, the two limits in b) must be equal to the same finite number.

44. a) A complete graph of $f(x)$ can be obtained on a graphing calculator by graphing both $y = (2-x)^{-1} + 0\sqrt{(2-x)}$ and $y = 5 - x^2 + 0\sqrt{(x-2)}$ in the viewing rectangle $[-3,5]$ by $[-10,10]$.

b) $\lim_{x\to 2^+} f(x) = 1$ and $\lim_{x\to 2^-} f(x)$ does not exist.

c) $\lim_{x\to 2} f(x)$ does not exist because the two limits in b) are not equal to the same finite number.

45. $a = 15$ **46.** $a = 5$

47. a)

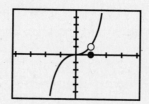

$[-4,4]$ by $[-6,6]$

b) $\lim_{x\to 1^-} f(x) = 1 = \lim_{x\to 1^+} f(x)$

c) $\lim_{x\to 1} f(x) = 1.$

48. a)

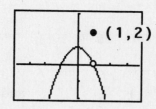

b) $\lim_{x\to 1^+} f(x) = 0$, $\lim_{x\to 1^-} f(x) = 0$

c) Yes, $\lim_{x\to 1} f(x) = 0$

49.

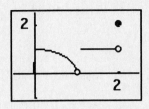

a) All points c except $c = 0, 1, 2.$ b) $x = 2$ c) $x = 0$

50.

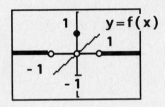

a) $\lim_{x \to c} f(x)$ exists at all points c except $c = \pm 1.$ b) None   c) None

51. 0   **52.** -1 **53.** 0   **54.** 1   **55.** 1   **56.** -1 **57.** 1   **58.** -1

59. a) 10   b) 20   **60.** a) 6   b) 0   c) 9   d) -3

61. a) 4   b) -21 c) -12 d) $-7/3$ **62.** a) 1   b) 0   **63.** 0

64. A complete graph of $\sin x/x$ can be seen in the viewing rectangle $[-20, 20]$ by $[-1, 1]$. $\lim_{x \to 0} \frac{\sin x}{x} = 1.$

65. 0

66. The graph can be viewed in the rectangle $[-5, 5]$ by $[-3, 3]$ and, for an indication of the behavior as $x \to 0$, in $[-10^{-7}, 10^{-7}]$ by $[-10^8, 10^8]$. As $x \to 0$, values of $|\frac{1}{x} \sin \frac{1}{x}|$ can be made arbitrarily large; the limit does not exist.

67. 0

68. $\text{Lim}(1+x)^{3/x} = L$ where $L \approx 20.085$

69. $\lim_{x \to 0}(1+x)^{4/x} = 54.598$ with error less than 0.01.

70. 2

71. $\lim_{x \to 0} \frac{2^x - 1}{x} = 0.6931$ with error less than 0.0001.

72. $\lim_{x \to 0} \frac{3^x - 1}{x} = 1.0986$ with error less than 0.0002

74. It can be shown that the limit is $\frac{1}{2}$. When x is too close to 0, the calculator cannot give meaningful results.

75. Graph the function in $[1.49\pi, 1.51\pi]$ by $[-0.00001, 0.00001]$ and use TRACE. This suggests the limit is about 9.536×10^{-7}. This is close to the actual limit which can be shown to be $\frac{1}{2^{20}}$.

76. The graph of the function in $[0.9\pi, 1.1\pi]$ by $[-0.00001, 0.00001]$ and TRACE suggest the limit is about 9.5363×10^{-7}. The actual limit is $\frac{1}{2^{20}} \approx 9.5367 \times 10^{-7}$

77. $b \to \frac{1}{2}$

2.2 CONTINUOUS FUNCTIONS

1. a) Yes, $f(-1) = 0$ b) Yes, $\lim_{x \to -1+} f(x) = 0$ c) Yes d) Yes

2. a) Yes, $f(1) = 1$ b) Yes, $\lim_{x \to 1} f(x) = 2$ c) No d) No

3. a) No b) No

4. All points in $[-1, 3]$ except $0, 1, 2$.

5. a) $\lim_{x \to 2} f(x) = 0$ b) Define $g(x) = f(x)$, $x \neq 2$, $g(2) = 0$. Then g is an extension of f which is continuous at $x = 2$.

6. $h(x) = f(x)$, $x \neq 1$, $h(1) = 2$

7. $f(x)$ is continuous at all points of $[-1, 2]$ except $x = 0$ and $x = 1$.

8. $f(x)$ is continuous at all points of $[-1, 3]$ except $x = 1$ and $x = 2$.

9. $f(x)$ is continuous at all points except $x = 2$.

10. $f(x)$ is continuous at all points except $x = 2$.

11. $f(x)$ is continuous at all points except $x = 1$.

12. $f(x)$ is continuous at all points except $x = 2$.

13. $f(x)$ is continuous at all points except $x = 1$.

14. $f(x)$ is continuous at all points except $x = 1$.

15. a) b) All points except $x = 0$ and $x = 1$

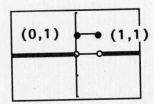

16. a)

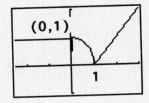

b) f is continuous at all points. In particular, at $x = 0$ and $x = 1$ the right-hand limit and the left-hand limit are equal even though they must be determined by different formulas.

17. $x = 2$ **18.** -2 **19.** $x = 1$ and 3 **20.** $x = -2, 5$ **21.** $x = \pm 1$

22. No discontinuities **23.** There are no points of discontinuity.

24. No discontinuities **25.** $x = 0$

26. $x = 0$ **27.** All x with $x < -3/2$.

28. $x < 1/3$ **29.** No points of discontinuity

30. No discontinuities

31. $\lim_{x \to 1} \frac{x^2 - 1}{x - 1} = \lim_{x \to 1} (x + 1) = 2$. Hence $f(1) = \lim_{x \to 1} f(x)$ and f is continuous at $x = 1$.

32. $g(3) = 6$ **33.** $h(2) = 7$ **34.** $f(1) = 3/2$ **35.** $g(4) = 8/5$ **36.** $g(2) = 1$

37. $a = 4/3$

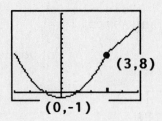

(3,8)

(0,-1)

38. $b = 1/2$. For a graph of $g(x)$ on a graphing calculator we graph $y = x^3 + 0\sqrt{(0.5 - x)}$ and $y = x^2/2 + 0\sqrt{(x - 0.5)}$ in $[-10, 10]$ by $[-10, 10]$. For more detail we can zoom into the point $(1/2, 1/8)$.

39. $\lim_{x \to 0} \sec x = 1$ **40.** 0 **41.** 1 **42.** 1 **43.** 1 **44.** 0

45. $-\sqrt[3]{2} \approx -1.2599$ **46.** $-\sqrt[3]{3} \approx -1.442$ **47.** Both methods give 1.324717957

48. a) -1.7693 b) The same value is obtained.

49. The maximum value of f occurs when $x = 2$ and $x = 3$. f does not take on its minimum value 0 but only approaches it arbitrarily closely. Theorem 7 is not contradicted because of the discontinuities.

50. The function on the domain $(-\infty, \infty)$ takes on neither a maximum value nor a minimum value.

51. The maximum value 1 is not attained but is only approached as x approaches ± 1. The minimum value 0 is attained at $x = 0$. Theorem 7 is not contradicted because the interval $(-1, 1)$ is not closed.

52. No. By the theorem, continuity on $0 \leq x \leq 1$ is sufficient for the attainment of extreme values. The theorem does not state that continuity is necessary.

53. We are given $f(0) < 0 < f(1)$. By Theorem 8 there exists some c in $[0, 1]$ such that $f(c) = 0$. A possible graph is

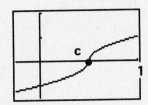

54. Let $f(x) = \cos 3x - x$. Then $f(x)$ is continuous being the difference of two continuous functions. $f(0) = 1$ is positive and $f(\frac{\pi}{2}) = -\pi/2$ is negative. By the Intermediate Value Theorem there exists a c between 0 and $\pi/2$ such that $f(c) = 0$, $\cos 3c - c = 0$ or $\cos 3c = c$. Therefore $\cos 3x = x$ has at least one solution.

2.3   THE SANDWICH THEOREM AND $(\sin\theta)/\theta$

1. 1   **2.** 3   **3.** $\frac{1}{2}$ **4.** 1   **5.** 1

6. 1   **7.** 2   **8.** $\frac{1}{3}$ **9.** 1   **10.** 2

11. -1 **12.** 2   **13.** 0   **14.** 0

15. 4   **16.** $\frac{5}{2}$ **17.** a) Approximately 0.6   b) Very close   c) $\frac{3}{5}$.

18. a) 0.6666666666   b) Extremely close   c) $\frac{2}{3}$.   **19.** 1

20. a) We graph $y_1 = 1 - \frac{x^2}{6}$, $y_2 = \frac{x \sin x}{2 - 2 \cos x}$ and $y_3 = 1$ in the viewing window $[-0.12, 0.12]$ by $[0.998, 1.002]$ which supports the inequality.   b) 1

21. a) We graph $y_1 = \frac{1}{2} - \frac{x^2}{24}$, $y_2 = \frac{1 - \cos x}{x^2}$ and $y_3 = \frac{1}{2}$ (y_1 and y_2 are extremely close near $x = 0$) in the window $[-6, 6]$ by $[-0.1, 0.6]$ supporting the inequality.   b) $\frac{1}{2}$

22. a) Graph $y_1 = 1$, $y_2 = \frac{\tan x}{x}$ and $y_3 = 1 + x^2$ in $[-0.1, 0.1]$ by $[0.9995, 1.0025]$ to support the inequality.   b) 1

23. The numerator $\cos x$ approaches 1 as $x \to 0$ while the denominator approaches 0. Thus the fraction can be made arbitrarily large in absolute value if x is sufficiently close to 0. Therefore the fraction cannot approach any finite number and so the limit does not exist.

24. $A = \frac{\pi}{360} r^2 \theta$ **25.** $\frac{\pi}{180}$

26. $f(x) = \frac{\sin 2x}{x}$.

x	± 0.1	± 0.01	± 0.001
$f(x)$	1.987	1.999	1.9999

Conjecture: $\lim_{x \to 0} f(x) = 2$.

27. $f(x) = \frac{\tan 3x}{x}$.

x	± 0.1	± 0.01	± 0.001
$f(x)$	3.0934	3.0009	3.0000

Conjecture: $\lim_{x \to 0} f(x) = 3$.

28. $f(x) = \frac{\cos x - 1}{x}$.

x	± 0.1	± 0.01	± 0.001
$f(x)$	∓ 0.04996	∓ 0.00500	∓ 0.00050

Conjecture: $\lim_{x \to 0} f(x) = 0$.

29. $f(x) = \frac{x - \sin x}{x^2}$.

x	-0.01	0.01	-0.001	0.001
$f(x)$	-0.00167	0.00167	-0.00017	0.00017

Conjecture: $\lim_{x \to 0} f(x) = 0$.

2.4   LIMITS INVOLVING INFINITY

1. a) $\frac{2}{5}$ b) $\frac{2}{5}$ **2.** a) 2   b) 2   **3.** a) 0   b) 0

4. a) 0   b) 0   **5.** a) ∞ b) $-\infty$ **6.** a) ∞ b) $-\infty$

7. a) 0   b) 0   **8.** a) 0   b) 0   **9.** a) $-\frac{2}{3}$ b) $-\frac{2}{3}$

10. a) -1 b) -1 **11.** a) -1 b) -1 **12.** a) 5   b) 5

13. ∞ **14.** $-\infty$ **15.** ∞ **16.** $-\infty$ **17.** ∞

18. $-\infty$ **19.** $-\infty$ **20.** ∞

21. $y = 0$ is the end behavior asymptote. Vertical asymptotes at $x = -\frac{5}{2}$ and $x = 1$.

22. EBA: $T = 0$. Vertical asymptotes at $y = \pm 2$ in the (y, T)-plane.

23. EBA: $y = 3$; VA: $x = \pm 2$ **24.** EBA: $y = \frac{1}{2}$; VA: $x = \frac{1 \pm \sqrt{31}}{6}$

25. EBA: $y = x - 4$; VA: $x = -2$ **26.** EBA: $y = x - 6$; VA: $x = -3$

27. EBA: $y = x^2 + 2x + 2$; VA: $x = 2$ **28.** EBA: $y = x^2 + 2$; VA: $x = \pm 2$

29. EBA: $y = 1$; VA: $x = \frac{1 \pm \sqrt{5}}{2}$ **30.** EBA: $y = x - 1$; VA: $x = -1, 1, 2$

31. a) ∞ b) $-\infty$ c) $-\infty$ d) ∞

32. a) ∞ b) $-\infty$ c) ∞ d) $-\infty$

33. a) ∞ b) $-\infty$ **34.** a) ∞ b) $-\infty$ **35.** 0 **36.** ∞

37. 1 **38.** -1 **39.** ∞ **40.** $-\infty$ **41.** $-\infty$ **42.** ∞

43. $0, -\infty, -1, -1$, respectively **44.** $1, 2, \infty, 0$, respectively

45. 2 **46.** 0 **47.** 2 **48.** 1 **49.** 0 **50.** 1

51. Both limits are equal to 2. **52.** 1

53. Each graph satisfies $y \to \infty$ as $x \to \infty$ and $y \to -\infty$ as $x \to -\infty$. As the power of x increases, the vertical steepness of the graph increases for $|x| > 1$.

54. Each graph satisfies $y \to -\infty$ as $x \to \pm\infty$. For $|x| > 1$, the vertical steepness of the graph increases as the power of x increases.

55. Carrying out the hint proves that $y = -\frac{1}{7}$ is an end behavior model for $f(x)$ by definition of end behavior model.

57. One such function is $f(x) = \begin{cases} x + 1, & x \leq 2 \\ \frac{1}{5-x}, & 2 < x < 5 \\ -1, & x \geq 5 \end{cases}$. Graph $y_1 = x + 1 + 0\sqrt{2-x}$, $y_2 = \frac{1}{5-x} + 0\sqrt{x-2} + 0\sqrt{5-x}$ and $y_3 = -1 + 0\sqrt{x-5}$ in $[-5, 10]$ by $[-10, 10]$.

58. One such function is $f(x) = \begin{cases} 2 - \frac{15}{x^2+1}, & x \leq 4 \\ x + \frac{1}{4-x}, & x > 4 \end{cases}$. Graph $y_1 = 2 - \frac{15}{x^2+1} + 0\sqrt{4-x}$, and $y_2 = x + \frac{1}{4-x} + 0\sqrt{x-4}$ in $[-10, 9]$ by $[-20, 20]$.

59. Does not exist, 0, 1, respectively.

60. Does not exist, 0, -8, respectively.

61. Does not exist, 0, 0, respectively.

62. $\infty, 0, \infty$, respectively,

63. Let $f(x) = x^3$, $g(x) = \frac{1}{x^2}$. Then $\lim_{x \to 0}(fg) = \lim_{x \to 0} x = 0$.
Let $f(x) = 5x^2$, $g(x) = \frac{1}{x^2}$. Then $\lim_{x \to 0}(fg) = \lim_{x \to 0} 5 = 5$.
Let $f(x) = x^2$, $g(x) = \frac{1}{x^4}$. Then $\lim_{x \to 0}(fg) = \lim_{x \to 0} \frac{1}{x^2} = \infty$.

64. Yes, $\lim_{x \to c}(f \pm g) = \pm \lim_{x \to c} g(x)$ because the values of $f(x) \pm g(x)$ are dominated by $\pm g(x)$ as $x \to c$. The values of $f(x)$ tend toward L but the values of $g(x)$ become numerically arbitrarily large as $x \to c$.

65. $\lim_{x \to \pm\infty} \frac{f(x)}{a_n x^n} = \lim_{x \to \pm\infty} \left(1 + \frac{a_{n-1}}{a_n} \frac{1}{x} + \cdots + \frac{a_1}{a_n} \frac{1}{x^{n-1}} + \frac{a_0}{a_n} \frac{1}{x^n}\right) = 1 + 0 + \cdots + 0 = 1$

66. a) 1   b) 1   c) 2   d) $\ell n\ 10$

67. Using graphs, support $(1 + \frac{1}{x})^x \to e$ as $x \to \pm\infty$.

68. Using graphs, we can support $(1 + \frac{5}{x})^x \to e^5$ as $x \to \pm\infty$.

69. Using graphs, we can support $(1 + \frac{0.07}{x})^x \to e^{0.07}$ as $x \to \pm\infty$.

70. Using graphs, we can support $(1 + \frac{1}{x})^{1/x} \to 1$, as $x \to \pm\infty$.

71. $xe^{-x} = \frac{x}{e^x} \to 0$ as $x \to \infty$. $xe^{-x} \to -\infty$ as $x \to -\infty$.

72. $y = x^2 e^{-x} = \frac{x^2}{e^x} \to 0$ as $x \to \infty$. $y \to \infty$ as $x \to -\infty$.

73. $y = xe^x \to \infty$ as $x \to \infty$. $y \to 0$ as $x \to -\infty$.

74. $y = x^2 e^x \to \infty$ as $x \to \infty$. $y \to 0$ as $x \to -\infty$.

76. We assume that the numerator and denominator of the rational function have no common factor of the form $x - a$. Then the number of vertical asymptotes is the number of distinct factors of the denominator of the form $x - a$. If the degree of the numerator is larger than the degree of the denominator, there is no horizontal asymptote. If the degree of the numerator equals the degree of the denominator, there is one horizontal asymptote $y = k \neq 0$. If the degree of the denominator exceeds the degree of the numerator $y = 0$ is the one and only horizontal asymptote.

2.5 CONTROLLING FUNCTION OUTPUTS

1. All are equivalent except a), e) and g).

2. All are equivalent except c), d) and h).

3. g)   **4.** c)   **5.** e)   **6.** b)   **7.** h)   **8.** d)   **9.** i)   **10.** a)

11. $-3 \leqq y \leqq 7$ **12.** $-4 < y < -2$ **13.** $2 < y < 3$

14. $-3 < y < -2$ **15.** $0 \leqq y \leqq 4$ **16.** $3 < y < 5$

17. $\frac{9}{5} < y < \frac{11}{5}$ **18.** $1 < y < 4$ **19.** $|x - \frac{9}{2}| < \frac{7}{2}$

20. $|x - \frac{5}{2}| < \frac{9}{2}$ **21.** $|x + \frac{3}{2}| < \frac{5}{2}$ **22.** $|x + \frac{9}{2}| < \frac{7}{2}$

23. $-1.22 < x < -0.71$

24. $\pi - \sin^{-1} 0.7 < x < \pi - \sin^{-1} 0.3$ or, rounding appropriately, $2.37 < x < 2.83$

25. $0.93 < x < 1.36$

26. $\tan^{-1} 1.8 < x < \tan^{-1} 2.2$ or, rounding appropriately, $1.07 < x < 1.14$

27. $-1.36 < x < -0.93$ **28.** $-1.14 < x < -1.07$

29. $9.995 < x < 10.004$ rounding to thousandths appropriately

30. $-10.004 < x < -9.995$ **31.** $22.21 < x < 23.81$ **32.** $3 < x < 15$

33. $20 < x < 30$ **34.** $\frac{1}{6} < x < \frac{1}{2}$ **35.** $-\frac{1}{9} < x < \frac{1}{11}$

36. $-3.05 < x < -2.96$ **37.** $3.94 < x < 4.06$ **38.** $-4.06 < x < -3.94$

39. $-2.68 < x < -2.66$ rounding to hundredths appropriately

40. $0.72 < x < 0.74$

41. $\ln 0.4 < x < \ln 0.6$ or rounding to hundredths appropriately $-0.91 < x < -0.52$

42. $6.69 < x < 8.16$ **43.** $|x - 3| < 0.5$ **44.** $|x + 2| < \frac{1}{2}$

45. $|x - 1| < 0.04$ **46.** $|x - 3.5| < 0.38$

47. $\lim_{x \to 1} x^2 = 1$, $\lim_{x \to 1} x^2 = 1$, $\lim_{x \to \pi/6} \sin x = 0.5$, $\lim_{x \to 3} \frac{x+1}{x-2} = 4$, respectively.

48. $\lim_{x \to -1} x^2 = 1$, $\lim_{x \to 5\pi/6} \sin x = 0.5$, $\lim_{x \to x_0} \cos x = 0.4$ where $x_0 = \cos^{-1} 0.4$, $\lim_{x \to x_0} \tan x = 2$ where $x_0 = \tan^{-1} 2$, $\lim_{x \to x_0} \cos x = 0.4$ where $x_0 = \cos^{-1} 0.4$, $\lim_{x \to x_0} \tan x = -2$ where $x_0 = \tan^{-1}(-2)$, respectively.

49. $\lim_{x \to 10} x^2 = 100$, $\lim_{x \to -10} x^2 = 100$, $\lim_{x \to 23} \sqrt{x - 7} = 4$, $\lim_{x \to 10} \sqrt{19 - x} = 3$, $\lim_{x \to 24}\left(\frac{120}{x}\right) = 5$, $\lim_{x \to 1/4}\left(\frac{1}{4x}\right) = 1$, $\lim_{x \to 0} \frac{3-2x}{x-1} = -3$, $\lim_{x \to -3} \frac{3x+8}{x+2} = 1$, respectively.

50. $\lim_{x \to 4}(x^2 - 5) = 11$, $\lim_{x \to -4}(x^2 - 5) = 11$, $\lim_{x \to x_0}(x^3 - 9x) = 5$ where x_0 is a solution of $x^3 - 9x = 5$ near -3, $\lim_{x \to x_0}(x^4 - 10x^2) = -5$ where x_0 is the solution of $x^4 - 10x^2 = -5$ near 1, $\lim_{x \to x_0} e^x = 0.5$ where $x_0 = \ln 0.5$, $\lim_{x \to e^2} \ln x = 2$, $\lim_{x \to 3}(x + 1) = 4$, $\lim_{x \to -2}(2x - 1) = -5$, $\lim_{x \to 1}(2x^2 + 1) = 3$, $\lim_{x \to 3.5} \sqrt{2x - 3} = 2$, respectively.

51. $3.384 < x < 3.387$ or, in symmetric form, $|x - x_0| < 0.001$.

52. $23.6 < R < 24.4$ **53.** $x > 702$ **54.** $x > 157.4$

55. $x > 50 + \sqrt{1504} \approx 88.781$ **56.** $x > 9.2186...$ by use of ZOOM-IN

57. Let $x_1 = 0.65241449628$, $x_2 = 0.93923517764$. x must satisfy $x_1 + 2n\pi < x < x_2 + 2n\pi$ or $(2n + 1)\pi - x_2 < x < (2n + 1)\pi - x_1$.

58. At most 0.25 cm, assuming the middle of the stripe corresponds to exactly one liter.

59. $x < -175.5$ **60.** $x < -274.5$

61. $x < -\frac{1097}{9}$ **62.** $x < -701$

2.6 DEFINING LIMITS FORMALLY WITH EPSILONS AND DELTAS

1. $\delta = 2$ **2.** $\delta = 1$ **3.** $\delta = \frac{1}{2}$ **4.** $\delta = 1$

5. $\delta = 0.1$ **6.** $\delta = 0.1$ **7.** $\delta = 0.23$

8. $(\sqrt{5}/2) - 1 \approx 0.11$ rounded to hundredths appropriately

9. $\delta = \frac{7}{16}$ **10.** $\delta = 0.39$ **11.** $L = 5$. $\delta = 0.005$

12. $L = -3$. $\delta = 0.01$ **13.** $L = 4$. $\delta = 0.05$ **14.** $L = -4$. $\delta = 0.05$

15. $L = 2$. $\delta = 0.0399$ or any other smaller positive number.

16. $L = 4$. $\delta = 0.75$

17. $L = 2.\ \delta = 1/3$

18. $L = 8.\ \delta = 1/402 \approx 0.0024$ rounding to ten thousandths appropriately.

19. $\delta = \varepsilon$ in each case   **20.** $0.001,\ 0.0001,\ \varepsilon/3$, respectively

21. $\lim_{x\to\infty} f(x) = 1$ **22.** $\lim_{x\to\infty} f(x) = \frac{1}{2}$

23. $\lim_{x\to-1+} \frac{x+2}{x+1} = \infty$ **24.** $\lim_{x\to\frac{\sqrt{2}}{2}+} \frac{x^2}{2x^2-1} = \infty$

25. $L = \sin 1 \approx 0.84.\ \delta = \varepsilon/0.54 = 1.85\varepsilon$, using the method of Example 6 and rounding down δ to hundredths to be safe.

26. $L = \tan 1 \approx 1.56.\ \delta = 0.29\varepsilon$

27. 1.17ε **28.** 0.56ε **29.** 0.30ε **30.** $\varepsilon/11$ **31.** 1.78ε **32.** $4\varepsilon/3$

33. $I = (5, 5 + \varepsilon^2).\ \lim_{x\to5+} \sqrt{x-5} = 0$

34. $I = (4 - \varepsilon^2, 4).\ \lim_{x\to4-} \sqrt{4-x} = 0$

35.

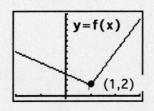

$$[-2, 3]\ \text{by}\ [-1, 16]$$

$\delta = \varepsilon/6$ and $I = (1 - \varepsilon/6, 1 + \varepsilon/6)$

36. If $\varepsilon = 4$, it is all $x \neq 5$. In the remaining cases it is all $x > 5$.

37. $\lim_{x\to2} f(x) = 5$ means corresponding to any radius $\varepsilon > 0$ about 5, there exists a radius $\delta > 0$ about 2 such that $0 < |x - 2| < \delta$ implies $|f(x) - 5| < \varepsilon$.

38. $\lim_{x \to 0} g(x) = k$ means corresponding to each radius $\varepsilon > 0$ about k, there exists a radius $\delta > 0$ about 0 such that $0 < |x - 0| < \delta$ implies $|g(x) - k| < \varepsilon$, x in the domain of g.

39. $\delta = \sqrt{4 + \varepsilon} - 2$. $\lim_{x \to 2} x^2 = 4$ or $\lim_{x \to 2}(x^2 - 4) = 0$. $\delta \to 0$ as $\varepsilon \to 0$. The graph of δ as a function of ε can be viewed by graphing $y = \sqrt{4 + x} - 2$ in the rectangle $[0, 4]$ by $[0, 1]$ and excluding the endpoints.

40. $\delta = 2\varepsilon/(1 + \varepsilon)$. This implies $\lim_{x \to 3} \frac{2}{x-1} = 1$ or $\lim_{x \to 3}(\frac{2}{x-1} - 1) = 0$.

42. a) The inequality is supported by graphing $y_1 = \frac{1}{2+x}$, $y_2 = \frac{1}{2}$, $y_3 = \frac{1}{2-x}$ in $[0, 2]$ by $[-1, 3]$. b) If $\varepsilon > 2$, $\frac{1}{2} < \frac{1}{2-\varepsilon}$ fails because $\frac{1}{2-\varepsilon}$ is negative.

44. a) Graph $y_1 = x^3 + 1.001 + 0\sqrt{x}$ and $y_2 = x^3 + 0.009 + 0\sqrt{-x}$ in $[-1, 1]$ by $[-0.9, 1.6]$. b) The limit does not exist.

45. a)

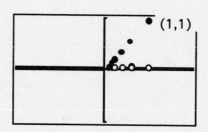

$[-2, 2]$ by $[-1, 1]$

b) $\lim_{x \to 0} f(x) = 0$

PRACTICE EXERCISES, CHAPTER 2

1. Exists **2.** Exists **3.** Exists **4.** Does not exist. **5.** Exists **6.** Exists

7. Continuous at $x = a$ **8.** Not continuous at $x = b$.

9. Not continuous at $x = c$.   **10.** Continuous at $x = d$.

11. -4 **12.** -10 **13.** 0 **14.** $\frac{1}{5}$ **15.** -1 **16.** 1

17. Does not exist   **18.** Does not exist

19. 2   **20.** -7 **21.** $\frac{1}{5}$ **22.** 1   **23.** 3

24. $-\frac{1}{4}$ **25.** $\frac{2}{5}$ **26.** $\frac{2}{5}$ **27.** 0   **28.** 0

29. $-\infty$ **30.** ∞ **31.** ∞ **32.** $-\infty$ **33.** ∞

34. ∞ **35.** $\frac{1}{2}$ **36.** 2   **37.** 8   **38.** $\frac{6}{5}$

39. a) 0.78   b) all close to 0.78   c) f appears to have a minimal value at $x = 0$.
d) 7/9

40. a) 1.60   b) quite close for x in the range $[-0.1, 0.1]$ c) f appears to have a minimal value at $x = 0$.   d) 8/5

41. a) ∞ b) $-\infty$ **42.** a) ∞ b) $-\infty$ c) ∞ d) ∞

43. a)

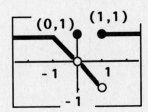

b) $\lim_{x \to -1+} f(x) = 1$, $\lim_{x \to -1-} f(x) = 1$, $\lim_{x \to 0+} f(x) = 0$, $\lim_{x \to 0-} f(x) = 0$, $\lim_{x \to 1+} f(x) = 1$, $\lim_{x \to 1-} f(x) = -1$

c) $\lim_{x \to -1} f(x) = 1$, $\lim_{x \to 0} f(x) = 0$ but $\lim_{x \to 1} f(x)$ does not exist because the right-hand and left-hand limits of f at 1 are not equal.

d) Only at $x = -1$

44. a)

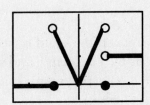

b) $\lim_{x \to -1-} f(x) = 0$, $\lim_{x \to -1+} f(x) = 2$, $\lim_{x \to 0-} f(x) = 0$, $\lim_{x \to 0+} f(x) = 0$, $\lim_{x \to 1-} f(x) = 2$, $\lim_{x \to 1+} f(x) = 1$

c) $\lim_{x \to 0} f(x) = 0$ but $\lim_{x \to -1} f(x)$ and $\lim_{x \to 1} f(x)$ do not exist because the left-hand and right-hand limits at $x = -1$ are not equal and the same is true at $x = 1$.

d) Only at $x = 0$.

45. a) A graph of f may be obtained by graphing the functions $y = abs(x^3 - 4x) + 0\sqrt{1 - x}$ and $y = x^2 - 2x - 2 + 0\sqrt{x - 1}$ in the viewing rectangle $[-5, 7]$ by $[-4, 10]$.

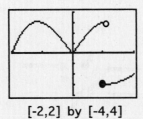

[-2,2] by [-4,4]

b) $\lim_{x \to 1+} f(x) = \lim_{x \to 1+} (x^2 - 2x - 2) = -3$.

$\lim_{x \to 1-} f(x) = \lim_{x \to 1-} |x^3 - 4x| = 3$

c) f does not have a limit at $x = 1$ because the right-hand and left-hand limits at $x = 1$ are not equal.

d) $x^3 - 4x$ is continuous by 2.2 Example 5 and $|x|$ is continuous by 2.2 Example 8. Thus $|x^3 - 4x|$ is continuous by Theorem 5 and so f is continuous for $x < 1$. For $x > 1$, $f(x) = x^2 - 2x - 2$, a polynomial, is continuous. Thus $f(x)$ is continuous at all points except $x = 1$.

e) f is not continuous at $x = 1$ because the two limits in b) are not equal and so $\lim_{x \to 1} f(x)$ does not exist.

46. a) A good idea of the graph is obtained by graphing $y = 1 - \sqrt{3 - 2x} + 0\sqrt{1.5 - x}$ and $y = 1 + \sqrt{2x - 3} + 0\sqrt{x - 1.5}$ in the rectangle $[-2, 4]$ by $[-3, 5]$.

b) Both limits are equal to 1

c) $\lim_{x \to 3/2} f(x) = 1$

d) f is continuous at all points because $f(c) = \lim_{x \to c} f(x)$ for all points c.

e) There are no points of discontinuity because of d)

47. a) A graph of f is obtained by graphing $y = -x + 0\sqrt{1 - x}$ and $y = x - 1 + 0\sqrt{x - 1}$ in the rectangle $[-2, 4]$ by $[-2, 4]$.

b) $\lim_{x \to 1+} f = \lim_{x \to 1+} x - 1 = 0$. $\lim_{x \to 1-} f = \lim_{x \to 1-} -x = -1$.

c) No value assigned to $f(1)$ makes f continuous at $x = 1$.

48. a) The idea of a complete graph of f can be obtained by graphing $y = 3x^2 + 0\sqrt{1 - x}$ and $y = 4 - x^2 + 0\sqrt{x - 1}$ in the viewing rectangle $[-2, 4]$ by $[-2, 4]$.

b) $\lim_{x \to 1+} f(x) = \lim_{x \to 1-} f(x) = 3$

c) b) shows that $\lim_{x \to 1} f(x) = 3$ so define $f(1) = 3$.

49. $x = \pm 2$ **50.** None   **51.** $y = 0$ **52.** $y = 2$ **53.** $x^2 - x$ **54.** x

55. a) -21 b) 49 c) 0 d) 1 e) 1 f) 7

56. a) $-\sqrt{2}$ b) $\sqrt{2}/2$ c) $\frac{1}{2} + \sqrt{2}$ d) 2 e) $\frac{1}{2}$ f) $\frac{1}{2}$

57. 0 **58.** 0 **59.** 1 **60.** 1 **61.** 0 **62.** 0 **63.** Set $k = 8$

64. $\lim_{x \to 0+} x^x = 1$. The limit must be approached from the right-hand side only because x^x is defined only for $x > 0$.

65. a) $\lim_{x \to 0-} f(x) = 0$ b) $\lim_{x \to 0+} f(x) = \infty$

c) The limit does not exist. To exist both one-sided limits must exist and be equal.

66. Set $k = \frac{1}{2}$

67. This is not a contradiction because $0 < x < 1$ is not a *closed* interval.

68. Let $y = f(x) = |x|$ on $-1 \le x < 1$. This function attains its minimum $(f(0) = 0)$ and its maximum $(f(-1) = 1)$. This is not a contradiction of the theorem which is only a sufficient (not necessary) condition for the attainment of extreme values.

69. True because $0 = f(1) < 2.5 < f(2) = 3$ and so by Theorem 7, $2.5 = f(c)$ for some c in $[1, 2]$.

70. Let $f(x) = x + \cos x$. Then $f(x)$ is continuous. $f(-\pi/2) = -\frac{\pi}{2}$ and $f(0) = 1$. Thus $f(-\pi/2) < 0 < f(0)$. By Theorem 7, $f(c) = 0$ for some c in $[-\pi/2, 0]$.

72. $\lim_{x \to 1} f(x) = 3$ means given any radius $\varepsilon > 0$ about 3 there exists a radius $\delta > 0$ about 1 such that for all x $0 < |x - 1| < \delta$ implies $|f(x) - 3| < \varepsilon$.

73. $\lim_{x \to 0} \frac{\sin x}{x} = 1$ means given any radius $\varepsilon > 0$ about 1 there exists a radius $\delta > 0$ about 0 such that for all x $0 < |x - 0| < \delta$ implies $|f(x) - 1| < \varepsilon$.

74. Let $f(x) = x^2$. $f(x)$ gets closer to -1 as x approaches 0 but -1 is not equal to $\lim_{x \to 0} f(x)$.

75. This "definition" puts a requirement on $f(x)$ but not necessarily for x near x_0. Thus for any given $\varepsilon > 0$ there is an x such that $|x^2 - 0| < \varepsilon$ but this does not imply $\lim_{x \to x_0} x^2 = 0$ in general.

76. $7 < x < 23$, $|x - 15| < 8$ **77.** $-\frac{1}{2} < x < \frac{7}{2}$, $|x - \frac{3}{2}| < 2$

78. $4.82 < x < 5.22$. Taking $x_0 = 5$, $|x - 5| < 0.18$.

79. $2.31 < x < 2.35$ or taking $x_0 = 7/3$, $|x - 7/3| < 0.02$.

80. $2.38 < x < 2.39$. If we take $x_0 = 2.383$ (near the root of $f(x) = 4$), we can say $|x - 2.383| < 0.003$ implies $|f(x) - 4| < 0.1$.

81. $-0.280 < x < -0.228$. $|x + 0.254| < 0.026$ **82.** $0 < \delta \le \varepsilon/2$

83. $0 < \delta \le \varepsilon$ **84.** $\lim_{x \to \infty} \frac{1 - 2x}{3x - 1} = -\frac{2}{3}$

85. $\lim_{x \to \frac{1}{3}^+} \frac{1 - 2x}{3x - 1} = \infty$ **86.** $L = 5$, $\delta = 0.01$

87. $L = 0$, $\delta = 0.01$ **88.** $L = 2$, $\delta = 3$

89. $L = 1$, $\delta = 3/8$ **90.** 1.13ε

91. 3.12ε **92.** $2.56 < x < 5.76$, $3.24 < x < 4.84$ **93.** $65° < t < 75°$

94. The exact positive solution is $\frac{-1 + \sqrt{1 + 4(10^{-12})}}{2000} \approx 10^{-15}$.

CHAPTER 3
DERIVATIVES

3.1   SLOPES, TANGENT LINES, AND DERIVATIVES

1. a) 0   b) -4 **2.** a) 0   b) -3 **3.** a) 1   b) -0.75 **4.** a) $\frac{5}{16}$ b) $-\frac{5}{16}$

5. a) April 15; $\frac{2}{3}$ degree per day.

b) Yes. Near Feb. 1, July 1 and Dec. 1   c) Postivie Feb. 1–July 1 and Dec. 1–Dec. 31; negative Jan. 1–Feb. 1 and July 1–Dec. 1.

6. a) April 7; 10 min/day   b) Yes. Near Jan. 1 and July 1   c) Positive Jan. 1–July 1, negative July 1–Dec. 31.

7. $f'(x) = 4x$. When $x = 3$, $m = 12$ and the tangent is $y = 12x - 23$.

8. $f'(x) = 2x - 6$. $f'(3) = 0$. Tangent line: $y = -9$

9. $f'(x) = 4x - 13$. $f'(3) = -1$. Tangent line: $y = -x - 13$

10. $f'(x) = -6x + 4$. $f'(3) = -14$. Tangent line: $y = -14x + 27$

11. $f'(x) = -2/x^2$. At $x = 3$ the slope is $-2/9$ and the tangent has equation $2x + 9y = 12$.

12. $f'(x) = -1/(x+1)^2$. At $x = 3$ the slope is $-1/16$ and an equation of the tangent is $x + 16y = 7$.

13. $f'(x) = \frac{1}{(x+1)^2}$. $f'(3) = \frac{1}{16}$. Tangent line: $16y - x = 9$.

14. $f'(x) = \frac{-2}{(2x+1)^2}$. $f'(3) = \frac{-2}{49}$. Tangent line: $49y + 2x = 13$.

15. $f'(x) = 1 - 9/x^2$. At $x = 3$ the slope is 0 and the tangent has equation $y = 6$.

16. $f'(x) = 1 + 1/x^2$. At $x = 3$ the slope is 10/9 and the tangent has equation $9y = 10x - 6$.

17. $f'(x) = \frac{1}{2\sqrt{x}}$. $f'(3) = \frac{1}{2\sqrt{3}}$. Tangent line: $y - (1 + \sqrt{3}) = \frac{1}{2\sqrt{3}}(x - 3)$.

18. $f'(x) = \frac{1}{2\sqrt{x+1}}$. $f'(3) = \frac{1}{4}$. Tangent line: $4y - x = 5$.

19. $f'(x) = 1/\sqrt{2x}$. At $x = 3$ the slope is $1/\sqrt{6}$ and the tangent has equation $\sqrt{6}y = x + 3$.

20. $f'(x) = 1/\sqrt{2x + 3}$. At $x = 3$ the slope is $1/3$ and the tangent has equation $3y = x + 6$.

21. Tangent line: $y = 2x + 5$. Graph $y_1 = 4 - x^2$ and $y_2 = 2x + 5$ in $[-5, 5]$ by $[-10, 10]$.

22. Tangent line: $y = 1$. Graph $y_1 = (x - 1)^2 + 1$ and $y_2 = 1$ in $[-3, 5]$ by $[0, 10]$.

23. Tangent line: $y = \frac{1}{2}(x + 1)$. Graph $y_1 = \sqrt{x}$ and $y_2 = 0.5x + 0.5$ in $[-3, 5]$ by $[-1, 3]$.

24. Tangent line: $y = 2x + 3$. Graph $y_1 = \frac{1}{x^2}$ and $y_2 = 2x + 3$ in $[-3, 3]$ by $[-1, 10]$.

25. $f'(\frac{1}{2}) = 0$ 26. $f'(2) = -5$ 27. $f'(-1) = -1$

28. $f'(2) = -2$ 29. $f'(4) = -\frac{1}{16}$ 30. $f'(-2) = -\frac{1}{27}$

31. The right-hand and left-hand derivatives at $x = 0$ are, respectively, 1 and 0. Since these are unequal, the function is not differentiable at $x = 0$.

32. The right-hand and left-hand derivatives at $x = 1$ are, respectively, 2 and 0. Since these are unequal, the function is not differentiable at $x = 1$.

33. Left- and right-hand derivatives at $x = 1$ are, respectively, $\frac{1}{2}$ and 2. Since they are not equal, f is not differentiable at $x = 1$.

34. The left- and right-hand limits at $x = 1$ are, respectively, 1 and -1. Hence f is not differentiable at $x = 1$.

35. a) $f'(x) = -2x$.   b) Graph $y_1 = -x^2$ and $y_2 = -2x$ in $[-3, 3]$ by $[-10, 5]$. c) $y' > 0$ for $x < 0$ and $y' < 0$ for $x > 0$. $f'(0) = 0$.   d) y increases on $(-\infty, 0)$ and decreases on $(0, \infty)$. The interval on which $y' > 0(y' < 0)$ is the interval on which y increases (decreases).

36. a) $f'(x) = \frac{1}{x^2}$.   b) Graph $y_1 = -\frac{1}{x}$ and $y_2 = \frac{1}{x^2}$ in $[-3, 3]$ by $[-5, 5]$. c) $f' > 0$ on $(-\infty, 0)$ and $(0, \infty)$. $f'(x)$ is never zero.   d) f is increasing on the same intervals.

37. a) $f'(x) = x^2$.   b) Graph $y_1 = \frac{x^3}{3}$ and $y_2 = x^2$ in $[-3, 3]$ by $[-5, 5]$. c) $f' > 0$ on $(-\infty, 0)$ and $(0, \infty)$. $f'(0) = 0$.   d) f is increasing on the same intervals.

38. a) $f'(x) = x^3$. b) Graph $y_1 = \frac{x^4}{4}$ and $y_2 = x^3$ in $[-3, 3]$ by $[-5, 5]$. c) $f' > 0$ on $(0, \infty)$ and $f' < 0$ on $(-\infty, 0)$. $f'(0) = 0$. d) f is increasing on the interval where $f' > 0$ and decreasing on the interval where $f' < 0$.

3.2 NUMERICAL DERIVATIVES

1. $y = 4x - 3$. The graphs of $y = x^2 + 1$ and $y = 4x - 3$ can be viewed in the rectangle $[-10, 10]$ by $[-10, 20]$.

2. $y = -2.75 + 8.5(x - 1.5)$. The graphs may be viewed in the rectangle $[-4, 4]$ by $[-50, 50]$.

3. $y = \sqrt{3} + 0.58(x + 1)$. The graphs can be viewed in the rectangle $[-6, 6]$ by $[-4, 4]$.

4. $y = 4.375 + 6.75(x - 2.5)$. For a good idea of the graphs one can view them in the two rectangles $[-4, 4]$ by $[-10, 10]$ and $[-6, 6]$ by $[-60, 60]$.

5. $y = 0.8(x - 2)$. The graphs can be viewed in the rectangle $[-8, 8]$ by $[-8, 8]$.

6. $y = 1.82 + 0.08(x - 2)$. View the graphs in the rectangle $[-4, 4]$ by $[-3, 3]$ and then zoom out.

7. a) Only. We can draw the graph without lifting our pencil so the function is continuous. But the function is not differentiable at each of the points which are peaks or low points. At these points the left-hand and right-hand derivatives are not equal (there is not a *unique* tangent line).

8. c). The function is continuous and differentiable because its graph has a unique tangent line at each point.

9. c). $x = 0$ is not a point of the domain. At every other point there is a unique tangent line so the function is both continuous and differentiable.

10. d). The function is not continuous (hence not differentiable) at each of the x-intercepts where there is a jump discontinuity.

11 through 18. In these exercises one may evaluate $D(h)$ and $S(h)$ directly using a calculator, or one may first algebraically simplify $D(h)$ and $S(h)$. If the calculator is used, meaningful results may not be obtained when $h = \pm 10^{-15}$ due to the limits of machine accuracy. This answers part c) of these exercises.

11. b) Conjectures: $f'(2) = 10$, $f'(0) = -2$. $S(h)$ is closer in both cases (in fact exact).

12. b) Conjectures: $f'(2) = 28$, $S(h)$ is closer. $f'(0) = 4$, $D(h) = S(h)$.

13. b) $f'(2) = -0.25$, $S(h)$ is closer. $f'(0)$ and $D(h)$ for $a = 0$ are not defined but $S(h) = 0$ for all h.

14. b) $f'(2) = -0.25$, $S(h)$ is closer. When $a = 0, f(a)$ and $D(h)$ are not defined, and $f'(0)$ is not defined. $S(h) = \frac{f(h)}{h} \to \infty$ as $h \to 0$.

15. a) If $a = 2$, $D(h) = S(h) = 1$ for all the h's considered. If $a = 0$, $D(h) = \begin{cases} -1, & \text{if } h < 0 \\ 1, & \text{if } h > 0 \end{cases}$ and $S(h) = 0$ for all h.   b) $f'(2) = 1$; both $S(h)$ and $D(h)$ are exact. $f'(0)$ does not exist.

16. a) If $a = 2, D(h) = \begin{cases} -1, & \text{if } h < 0 \\ 1, & \text{if } h > 0 \end{cases}$ and $S(h) = 0$ for all h's considered. If $a = 0$, $D(h) = S(h) = -1$ for the h's considered.   b) $f'(2)$ does not exist. $f'(0) = -1$.

17. a) If $a = 2$, $D(h) \to 0$ as $h \to 0$ while $S(h) = 0$ for those h's considered. If $a = 0$, $D(h)$ is undefined for $h < 0$ while $D(h) \to \infty$ as $h \to 0^+$.   b) $f'(2) = 0$, $S(h)$ is closer. $f'(0)$ does not exist.

18. a) If $a = 2$, $D(h) \to -\infty$ as $h \to 0^-$ while $D(h)$ is undefined for $h > 0$. If $a = 0$, $D(h) \to 0$ as $h \to 0$ while $S(h) = 0$ for those h's considered.   b) $f'(2)$ does not exist. $f'(0) = 0$.

19. Even though the derivative may not exist, the values of $S(h)$ may be defined giving meaningless approximations of the derivative.

20. See the comment for Exercise 19.   **21.** See the comment for Exercise 19.

22. $f'(2)$ does not exist. See the comment for Exercise 19.

23. $S(h)$ is undefined for all $h \neq 0$ when $a = 0$ because either $(0 - h)$ or $(0 + h)$ is out of f's domain, and is undefined for $h = 0$.

24. $S(h)$ is undefined for all $h \neq 0$ when $a = 2$ because either $(2 - h)$ or $(2 + h)$ is out of f's domain, and is undefined for $h = 0$.

25. a) We agree that $f'(a) = \text{NDER}(f(x), a)$ (with $h = 0.01$) rounded to two decimal places and obtain $f'(-1) = 0.14$, $f'(0) = -14.94$, $f'(1.5) = -9.69$ and $f'(3.5) = 0.13$.   b) $\text{NDER}(f(x), a)$ may give results even though $f'(a)$ does not exist. This was the case for $f'(0)$.

26. a) Using the understanding of Exercise 23, we obtain $g'(0) = -0.03$, $g'(1.5) = 0.03$ and $g'(5) = -0.06$. b) We are confident about the results of part a).

27. a) Graph $y_1 = -x^2$ and $y_2 = $ NDER y_1 in $[-3,3]$ by $[-10,7]$. b) y_1' exists for all x. e) y_1 is increasing over the interval $(-\infty, 0)$ where y_1' is positive. y_1 is decreasing over the interval $(0, \infty)$ where y_1' is negative.

28. a) Graph $y_1 = -\frac{1}{x}$ and $y_2 = $ NDER y_1 in $[-3,3]$ by $[-8,9]$. b) y_1' does not exist at $x = 0$ because even y_1 does not exist at $x = 0$. This is suggested by the graph of y_2 since $y_2 \to \infty$ as $x \to 0$. y_1' is positive, tangent lines have positive slope and y_1 is increasing for all x except $x = 0$.

29. a) Graph $y_1 = \sqrt[3]{x-2}$ and $y_2 = $ NDER y_1 in $[0,3]$ by $[-2.2, 3.8]$. b) y_1' does not exist at $x = 2$ because the tangent line is vertical there. This is suggested by the graph because $y_2 \to \infty$ as $x \to 2$. y_1' is positive, tangent lines have positive slope and y_1 is increasing for all x except $x = 2$.

30. This function is the negative of the function in Exercise 27. The graphs may be obtained by reflecting the preceding graphs across the x-axis. Use the preceding solution but change positive to negative and increasing to decreasing. Also here $y_2 \to -\infty$ as $x \to 2$.

31. a) Graph $y_1 = \sqrt{1-x}$ and $y_2 = $ NDER y_1 in $[-2,1]$ by $[-2.2, 2.5]$. b) y_1' does not exist for $x > 1$ because $(1, \infty)$ is not part of the domain of y_1. y_1' does not exist at $x = 1$ because the graph has a vertical tangent there. This is suggested by the graph because $y_1 \to -\infty$ as $x \to 1^-$. y_1' is negative, slopes of tangent lines are negative and y_1 is decreasing on the interval $(-\infty, 1)$.

32. Graph $y_1 = \sqrt[4]{x-1}$ and $y_2 = $ NDER y_1 in $[0,2]$ by $[-3,3]$. b) y_1' does not exist on $(-\infty, 1)$ because this interval is not in the domain of y_1. y_1' does not exist at $x = 1$ because there is a vertical tangent there. This is suggested by the graph because $y_2 \to \infty$ as $x \to 1^+$. y_1' is positive, slopes of tangent lines are positive and y_1 is increasing on $(1, \infty)$.

33. $[0.25895206, 0.25895208]$ by $[0.135, 0.145]$ is one possibility.

34. $[0.13231095, 0.13231302]$ by $[0.184, 0.196]$ is one possibility.

35. a) Let $y_1 = -x^2(x < 0) + (4 - x^2)(x \geq 0)$. Graph NDER$(y_1, x)$ in the given window. b) We see the graph of $y = -2x$, $x \neq 0$. c) With $h = 0.01$, NDER$(f(x), 0) = 200$. $f'(0)$ does not exist.

36. a) Let $y_1 = x^2(x < 0) + x(x \geq 0)$. Graph $y_2 = $ NDER(y_1, x) in the given window. b) We see the graph of $\begin{cases} 2x, & x < 0 \\ 1, & x \geq 0 \end{cases}$. c) NDER$(f(x), 0) = 0.495$ if $h = 0.01$ but $f'(0)$ does not exist.

37. a) Let $y_1 = -\frac{x^2}{2} + 0\sqrt{-x}$, $y_2 = \frac{x^2}{2} + 0\sqrt{x}$, $y_3 = \text{NDER}(y_1, x)$, $y_4 = \text{NDER}(y_2, x)$. Graph y_3, y_4 in the given viewing window.   b) This is the graph of $y = \begin{cases} -x, & x < 0 \\ x, & x \geq 0 \end{cases}$.   c) $\text{NDER}(f(x), 0) = 0.005$ if $h = 0.01$ but $f'(0)$ does not exist.

39. Graph $y_1 = (x^3 + 6x^2 + 12x)(x < 0) + (-x^2)(x > 0)$ and $y_2 = \text{NDER}(y_1, x)$ in $[-5, 5]$ by $[-10, 10]$. Since the two one-sided derivatives at $x = 0$ are unequal, $f'(0)$ does not exist.

40. Graph $y_1 = -3\sqrt{-x}(x < 0) + (3 - 0.2x^2)(x > 0)$ and $y_2 = \text{NDER}(y_1, x)$ in $[-5, 5]$ by $[-10, 10]$. $f'(0)$ does not exist.

41. Graph $y_1 = -5(abs\,x)^{1/3}$ and $y_2 = \text{NDER}(y_1, x)$ in $[-5, 5]$ by $[-10, 10]$. $f'(0)$ does not exist.

42. b) In the given rectangle, if $a \approx 2.7$, the two graphs appear to coincide.   c) From part b), $f(x) \approx 2.7^x$. All solutions to this problem are determined in Chapter 7.

43. b) $D_x(\sin x) = \cos x$

44. $f'(0)$ does not exist while $\text{NDER}(f(x), 0) = 39.81$. Thus the numerical derivative at a point may exist even if the function is not differentiable at the point.

45. By Example 6 of 3.1, $f'(0)$ does not exist.   But $\text{NDER}(|x|, 0) = 0$. $\text{NDER}(f(x), a)$ may exist even if $f'(a)$ does not exist.

46. e) $g(x) = \begin{cases} -1, & x < -0.01 \\ 100x, & -0.01 \leq x < 0.01 \\ 1, & x \geq 0.01 \end{cases}$

48. 1

3.3 DIFFERENTIATION RULES

1. $1, 0$ **2.** $-1, 0$ **3.** $-2x, -2$ **4.** $x^2 - 1, 2x$ **5.** $2, 0$ **6.** $2x + 1, 2$

7. $x^2 + x + 1, 2x + 1$ **8.** $-1 + 2x - 3x^2, 2 - 6x$ **9.** $4x^3 - 21x^2 + 4x, 12x^2 - 42x + 4$

10. $15x^2 - 15x^4, 30x - 60x^3$ **11.** $8x - 8, 8$ **12.** $x^3 - x^2 + x - 1, 3x^2 - 2x + 1$

13. $y' = 2x - 1$, $y'' = 2$, $y^{(n)} = 0$ for $n \geq 3$

14. $y' = x^2 + x$, $y'' = 2x + 1$, $y''' = 2$, $y^{(n)} = 0$ for $n \geq 4$

15. $y' = 2x^3 - 3x - 1$, $y'' = 6x^2 - 3$, $y''' = 12x$, $y^{(4)} = 12$, $y^{(n)} = 0$ for $n \geq 5$

16. $y' = \frac{x^4}{24}$, $y'' = \frac{x^3}{6}$, $y''' = \frac{x^2}{2}$, $y^{(4)} = x$, $y^{(5)} = 1$, $y^{(n)} = 0$ for $n \geq 6$

17. $3x^2 + 2x + 1$ **18.** $-3x^2 - 2x + 3$ **19.** $3x^2$ **20.** $2x + \frac{2}{x^3}$ **21.** $12x + 13$

22. $12x - 22$ **23.** $5x^4 - 2x$ **24.** $3x^2 + 10x + 1$ **25.** $\frac{8}{(x+7)^2}$ **26.** $\frac{-19}{(3x-2)^2}$

27. $\frac{2x^3 - 7}{x^2}$ **28.** $\frac{2-5x}{x^3}$ **29.** $\frac{3}{x^4}$ **30.** $\frac{-3}{x^4}$ **31.** $\frac{x^2 - 2x - 1}{(1+x^2)^2}$ **32.** $\frac{-17}{(2x-7)^2}$

33. $\frac{x^4 + 2x}{(1-x^3)^2}$ **34.** With $y = \frac{x^2 - 1}{x^2 + x - 2} = \frac{x+1}{x+2}$, $y' = \frac{1}{(x+2)^2}$.   **35.** $\frac{-5}{\sqrt{x}(\sqrt{x}-4)^2}$

36. $\frac{\sqrt{x}-7}{(2\sqrt{x}-7)^2}$ **37.** $\frac{1}{\sqrt{x}(\sqrt{x}+1)^2}$ **38.** $-\frac{1}{x^2} + 2x^{-3/2}$ **39.** $-\frac{4x^3 + 3x^2 - 1}{(x^2-1)^2(x^2+x+1)^2}$

40. $\frac{-6(x^2-2)}{(x^2-3x+2)^2}$.   **41.** $y' = -\frac{6}{x^3}$, $y'' = \frac{18}{x^4}$ **42.** $y' = \frac{1}{x^2}$, $y'' = -\frac{2}{x^3}$

43. $y' = -\frac{20}{x^5}$, $y'' = \frac{100}{x^6}$ **44.** $y' = \frac{21}{x^8}$, $y'' = -\frac{168}{x^9}$ **45.** $y' = 1 - \frac{1}{x^2}$, $y'' = \frac{2}{x^3}$

46. $y' = -\frac{12}{x^2} + \frac{12}{x^4} - \frac{4}{x^5}$, $y'' = \frac{24}{x^3} - \frac{48}{x^5} + \frac{20}{x^6}$

47. $y - 3^{-0.2} = 0.63(x - 1)$. The result is confirmed by viewing $y = x3^{-0.2x}$ and $y = 3^{-0.2} + 0.63(x-1)$ in the rectangle $[-10, 10]$ by $[-10, 10]$.

48. $y = -0.32(x - \pi)$. The result is confirmed by graphing $y = \sin x/x$ and $y = -0.32(x - \pi)$ in $[2, 4]$ by $[-0.5, 0.5]$.

49. $y = (3/5) + 0.44x$. The result is confirmed by graphing $y = f(x)$ and $y = (3/5) + 0.44x$ in the rectangle $[-1, 1]$ by $[0.3, 0.9]$.

50. $y = (\sqrt[3]{3}/3) + 0.09(x - 2)$. The result can be confirmed by viewing $y = f(x)$ and $y = (\sqrt[3]{3}/3) + 0.09(x - 2)$ in the rectangle $[-12, 12]$ by $[-1, 1]$.

51. The graphs can be viewed in the two rectangles $[-10, 10]$ by $[-10, 10]$ and $[-50, 50]$ by $[-50, 50]$.

52. These graphs can be viewed in the rectangles $[-5, 5]$ by $[-25, 25]$ and $[-50, 50]$ by $[-2500, 2500]$.

53. $y = f'(x)$ or $y = \text{NDER}(f(x))$ can be viewed in the rectangle $[-2, 8]$ by $[-4, 4]$. $y = f''(x)$ or $y = \text{NDER2}(f(x))$ can be viewed in $[-2, 10]$ by $[-4, 10]$.

54. Both $y = \text{NDER}(f(x), x)$ and $y = \text{NDER2}(f(x), x)$ can be viewed in $[-3, 5]$ by $[-5, 5]$.

55. $y = \text{NDER}(f(x))$ can be viewed in the rectangle $[-8, 8]$ by $[-2, 0]$. $y = \text{NDER2}(f(x))$ can be viewed in $[-6, 8]$ by $[-1, 1]$.

56. $y = \text{NDER}(f(x))$ can be viewed in the rectangle $[-10, 10]$ by $[-0.1, 0.2]$. To obtain an idea of the complete graph of $y = \text{NDER2}(f(x))$ it is necessary to view the graph in two rectangles, for example, $[-10, 10]$ by $[-0.1, 0.1]$ and $[-5, 2]$ by $[-1, 1]$.

57. The graph of $y = \text{NDER}(f(x))$ oscillates, appears to cross the x-axis infinitely often and to be symmetric with respect to the origin. The three solutions of $f'(x) = 0$ of smallest absolute value are -2.029, 0, 2.029. The graph of $y = \text{NDER2}(f(x))$ appears to cross the x-axis infinitely often. The solution set of $f''(x) > 0$ consists of an infinite sequence of intervals. The three closest to the origin are $(-6.578, -3.644)$, $(-1.077, 1.077)$ and $(3.644, 6.578)$ rounding appropriately.

58. The graph of $y = f'(x)$ is symmetric with respect to the y-axis. It crosses the x-axis infinitely many times. The three numerically smallest solutions to $f'(x) = 0$ are -2.29, 0, 2.29. The graph of $y = f''(x)$ is symmetric with respect to the origin, crosses the x-axis infinitely often. The solution set of $f''(x) > 0$ consists of an infinite sequence of intervals, of which the two closest to the origin are $(-3.99, -1.52)$ and $(0, 1.51)$ rounding appropriately.

59. We use zoom-in and the graphs of Exercise 53. $f'(x) = 0$ for $x = -0.313$ and $x = 3.198$. $f''(x) > 0$ for x in the set $(-\infty, -1) \cup (1, \infty)$.

60. $f'(x) = 0$ has solution set $\{-1.287, 3.108\}$. The solution set of $f''(x) > 0$ is the interval $(-2, 2)$.

61. $f'(x) = 0$ has no solution. $f''(x) > 0$ has solution set $(-3, -0.333) \cup (5, \infty)$.

62. The solution set of $f'(x) = 0$ is $\{-2.732, 0.732\}$. The solution set of $f''(x) > 0$ is $(-4.648, -1) \cup (1.804, \infty)$ rounding appropriately to be sure.

63. $f''(x) = 6(6x^3 - 45x^2 - 24x + 20)/(3x^2 + 4)^3$. We cannot solve $f''(x) > 0$ exactly by a convenient method. The approximate solution set is $(-0.911, 0.460) \cup (7.950, \infty)$.

66. $\left(\frac{1}{f(x)}\right)' = -\frac{f'(x)}{f^2(x)}$ **67.** a) 13   b) -7 c) 7/25   d) 20

68. a) 2   b) -10 c) $\frac{10}{9}$ d) -12 **69.** c)   **70.** c)   **71.** $x + 9y = 29$

72. $y = 4x - 2$ and $y = 4x + 2$ are the tangents at $x = 1$ and $x = -1$, respectively. The smallest slope on the curve is 1 and it occurs at $x = 0$.

73. $(-1, 27), (2, 0)$ **74.** $-4/3$, 16   **75.** $y = 4x$, $y = 2$

76. $x + 2y = 4$ **77.** $\frac{dP}{dV} = -\frac{nRT}{(V-nb)^2} + \frac{2an^2}{V^3}$

78. $\frac{ds}{dt} = 9.8t$, $\frac{d^2s}{dt^2} = 9.8$ **79.** $\frac{dR}{dM} = CM - M^2$

80. The derivative of $Kf(x)$ is $Kf'(x)$ so $f'(x)$ and $(Kf(x))'$ have the same zeros. For the case mentioned $x = 1.12$ is the only solution to $f'(x) = 0$. The graphs of $y = K2^x/(2 + 3^x)$, $K = 1, 2, 3$ can be viewed in $[-10, 15]$ by $[0, 1.5]$.

83. a) $x = 1.442695\ldots$ b) $(1.442695\ldots, 0.5307378\ldots)$ c) very close

84. a) $x = 2.88543\ldots$ b) $(2.88539\ldots, -0.135335\ldots)$ c) very close

85. a) 0.0424   b) $y_2 = \frac{y_1(x+0.01) - y_1(x-0.01)}{0.02}$

c) About 0.01. NOTE: The answers for a) and c) depend on the h used in the NDER algorithm. We used $h = 0.01$ here.

3.4   VELOCITY, SPEED, AND OTHER RATES OF CHANGE

1. a) The particle first moves left then right.   b) $(2, 3)$ at $t = 0$, $(0, 3)$ at $t = 1$, $(0, 3)$ at $t = 2$, $(2, 3)$ at $t = 3$.   c) The particle changes direction at $(-0.25, 3)$ when $t = 1.5$. When $t = 1.5$, $v = 0$ and $a = 2$.   d) 14.5meters f) The particle is at rest when $t = 1.5$sec.

2. The particle moves first right, then left. b) $(5, 3)$ when $t = 0$, $(7, 3)$ when $t = 1$, $(7, 3)$ when $t = 2$, $(5, 3)$ when $t = 3$.   c) The particle changes direction at $(7.25, 3)$ when $t = 1.5$. At this time $v = 0$ and $a = -2$.   d) 14.5 meters. f) The particle is at rest when $v = 3 - 2t = 0$, i.e., when $t = 1.5$ sec.

3. We use Tstep 0.05 in the viewing rectangle $[-10, 10]$ by $[-15, 25]$.   a) The particle first moves to the right, then to the left and then to the right again.   b) $(-3, 3), (-1, 3), (-5, 3), (-9, 3)$ c) $(-0.70, 3)$ when $t = 0.7$, $v = 0$, $a = -7.7$; $(-9.30, 3)$ when $t = 3.3$, $v = 0$, $a = 7.7$ d) 27.2 meters f) Approximately when $t = 0.7$ and $t = 3.3$ sec.

4. a) The particle first moves left, then right and then left again.   b) $(4,3)$, $(2,3)$, $(6,3)$, $(10,3)$ c) Using TRACE, we get $(1.70,3)$ when $t = 0.7$, $v = -0.07$, $a = 7.8$; $(10.30,3)$ when $t = 3.3$, $v = -0.07$, $a = -7.8$. d) 27.2meters   e) $t = 0.7$, 3.3 approximately.

5. We use $x_1 = t \sin t$, $y_1 = 3$, $x_2 = t$, $y_2 = \mathrm{NDER}(x_1, t, t)$, $x_3 = t$, $y_3 = \mathrm{NDER}(y_2, t, t)$ with $0 \le t \le 15$, Tstep 0.05 in $[-15, 15]$ by $[-15, 15]$ and TRACE approximations.   a) The particle moves right, left, right, left, right, and finally left slightly.   b) $(0,3)$, $(0.84,3)$, $(1.82,3)$, $(0.42,3)$ c) $(1.82,3)$ when $t = 2.05$, $v = -0.06$, $a = -2.7$; $(-4.814,3)$ when $t = 4.90$, $v = -0.07$, $a = 5.19$; $(7.91,3)$ when $t = 8$, $v = -0.17$, $a = -8.2$; $(-11.04,3)$ when $t = 11.1$, $v = 0.16$, $a = 11.2$; $(14.17,3)$ at $t = 14.2$, $v = 0.106$, $a = -14.3$ d) 69.75meters.   f) $t = 0$, 2.05, 4.9, 8, 11.1 and 14.2.

6. We use $x_1(t) = 5\sin(\frac{2t}{\pi})$, $y_1(t) = 3$, $x_2(t) = t$, $y_2(t) = \mathrm{NDER}(x_1, t)$ and $x_3(t) = t$, $y_3(t) = \mathrm{NDER}(y_2, t)$ with $0 \le t \le 2\pi$, Tstep .05 in $[-5, 7]$ by $[-4, 4]$. Results are TRACE approximations.   a) The particle moves to the right and then to the left.   b) $(0,3)$, $(2.97,3)$, $(4.78,3)$, $(4.72,3)$ c) $(5.00,3)$ when $t = 2.45$, $v = .03$, $a = -2.03$ d) 13.71meters   e) $t = 2.45\mathrm{sec}$

7. 4.46sec on Mars, 0.73sec on Jupiter.

8. a) $v(t) = 24 - 1.6t$, $a(t) = -1.6$ b) 15sec   c) 180meters   d) 4.39sec   e) 30sec

9. One possibility: Graph $x_1(t) = t$, $y_1(t) = 24t - 0.8t^2$, $0 \le t \le 30$, in $[0, 30]$ by $[0, 180]$. Then use TRACE and zoom-in if more accuracy is desired.

10. 29.39meters.   11. 320sec, 52sec

13. a) 10^4 per hour   b) 0   c) -10^4 per hour   14. 8000gal/min, 10000gal/min

15. a) The average cost of one washing machine when producing the first 100 washing machines is $c(100)/100 = \$110$. During production of the first 100 machines the average increase in producing one more machine is: average increase $= \frac{c(100)-c(0)}{100-0} = \$90$; the fixed cost $c(0) = \$2000$ is omitted with this method.   b) \$80   c) \$79.90.

16. a) A graph of $r(x)$, $x \ge 0$ can be viewed in $[0, 50]$ by $[0, 2000]$. Only non-negative integral values of x make sense in this problem situation.   b) $r'(x) = 2000/(x+1)^2$ c) \$55.56   d) $\lim_{x \to \infty} 2000(1 - \frac{1}{x+1}) = 2000(1-0) = \$2000$. As more and more desks are made, the revenue gets arbitrarily close

to \$2000. Note that the marginal revenue $r'(x) \to 0$ as $x \to \infty$ so that it does not pay to produce many desks.

17. $a = -6\text{m/sec}^2$ when $t = 1\text{sec}$ and $a = 6\text{m/sec}^2$ when $t = 3\text{sec}$.

18. At $t = 1\text{sec}$ the speed is 0m/sec and at $t = 2\text{sec}$ the speed is 1m/sec.

19. a) We use $-12 \leq t \leq 12$, Tstep 0.05 in the viewing rectangle $[-35, 35]$ by $[-3, 10]$.   b) For this graph we can use $0 \leq t \leq 6.29 \approx 2\pi$, Tstep 0.05 in $[-3, 8]$ by $[-3, 3]$.   c) This line segment can be viewed using $0 \leq t \leq 6.29$, Tstep 0.05 in $[-6, 10]$ by $[-6, 2]$.

20. Only c) is the graph of a function.

21. a) All have derivative $3x^2$.   c) The result of a) suggests that the family consists of all functions of the form $x^3 + C$ where C can be any constant. d) Yes, $f(x) = x^3$.   e) Yes, $g(x) = x^3 + 3$.

22. a) A graph of $P(x)$ can be obtained in the viewing rectangle $[0, 200]$ by $[0, 11]$.   b) Only non-negative integral values of x make sense in the problem situation.   c) The graph of $y = P'(x) = \text{NDER}(P(x))$ is the same as the graph of $y = M(x)$ in $[0, 200]$ by $[0, 0.2]$.   d) Using only integral values of x and zoom-in and TRACE, we find a maximal marginal profit of 0.1732 at $x = 106$ and 107. Returning to the graph of $P(x)$, using zoom-in and TRACE, we find $P(106) = 4.93$ and $P(107) = 5.10$. We estimate the remaining values of $P'(x)$ using TRACE and the viewing rectangle $[0, 330]$ by $[0, 0.2]$: $P'(50) = 0.01$, $P'(100) = 0.17$, $P'(125) = 0.12$, $P'(150) = 0.03$, $P'(175) = 0.006$, $P'(300) = 1.1 \times 10^{-6}$.   e) Since $2^{5-0.1x} = \frac{1}{2^{0.1x-5}} \to 0$ as $x \to \infty$, $\lim_{x \to \infty} P(x) = \frac{10}{1+0} = 10$. The profit can approach 10 (thousand dollars) arbitrarily closely but cannot attain it exactly. But $P(316)$ rounds out to \$10,000.00.   f) More information is needed but since $P(240)$ is about \$999 not much is lost by cutting product at $x = 240$.

23. a) 190ft/s b) 2   c) At $8s$ when $v = 0$ d) At $10.8s$ when it was falling at 90ft/s e) From $t = 8s$ to $t = 10.8s$, i.e., $2.8s$ f) Just before burnout, i.e., just before $t = 2s$. The acceleration was constant from $t = 2s$ to $t = 10.8s$ during free fall.

24.

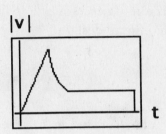

25. a) 0, 0   b) 1700, 1400   c) Rabbits per day and foxes per day

27. (b)   **28.** (a)   **29.** (d)   **30.** (c)

31. a)

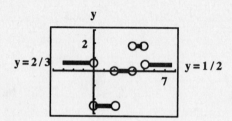

b) $x = 0, 2, 4, 5$

32. a)

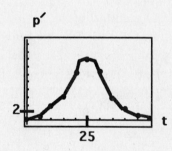

The horizontal axis is measured in days, the vertical axis in fruit flies per day.

b) Growing fastest around day 25, slowest near the beginning day 0 and near the end day 50.

33. $t = 2.832$

34. Our results are approximations using TRACE when we graph $x_1(t) = 2t^3 - 13t^2 + 22t - 5$, $y_1(t) = 2$, $0 \leq t \leq 5$, tStep $= 0.05$ in $[-6, 30]$ by $[-1, 3]$. Parts a), c), d), e): We find that the particle starts $(t = 0)$ at $(-5, 2)$, moves right until $t = 1.15$ when the particle is at $(6.149, 2)$, then moves left until $t = 3.2$ at which time its location is $(-2.184, 2)$ and then it moves right for $t > 3.2$. The particle is at rest $(v = 0)$ at the turning points, i.e., at $t = 1.15$ and $t = 3.2$. We graph v and the speed $|v|$. Here $v = \frac{ds}{dt} = 6t^2 - 26t + 22$.

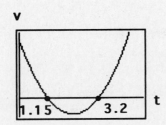

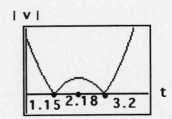

These graphs describe the velocity and speed of the particle.   b) $|v|$ is increasing for $1.15 < t < 2.18$ and for $t > 3.2$. $|v|$ is decreasing for $0 < t < 1.15$ and for $2.18 < t < 3.2$.   f) $x_1(t) \approx 5$ when $t = 0.75, 1.6, 4.15$.

35.

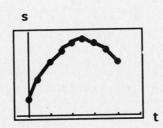

a) $v \approx 18\text{ft/sec}$ b) $v \approx 0\text{ft/sec}$ c) $v \approx -12\text{ft/sec}$

36.

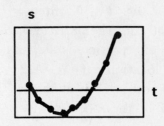

a) $v \approx -6$ftsec   b) $v \approx 12$ft/sec   c) $v \approx 24$ft/sec

3.5   DERIVATIVES OF TRIGONOMETRIC FUNCTIONS

1. $1 + \sin x$ **2.** $2\cos x - \sec^2 x$ **3.** $-\frac{1}{x^2} + 5\cos x$

4. $2x - \sec x \tan x$ **5.** $-\csc x \cot x - 5$ **6.** $2 - \csc^2 x$

7. $\sec x (x \tan x + 1)$ **8.** $\csc x (1 - x \cot x)$ **9.** $x(2\cot x - x\csc^2 x)$

10. $-x(x\cos x + 2\sin x)$ **11.** $3 + x\sec^2 x + \tan x$ **12.** $x\cos x$

13. $\sec^2 x$ **14.** $\sec x \csc x (\tan x - \cot x) = \sec^2 x - \csc^2 x$ **15.** 0

16. $-\sin x$ **17.** $4\sec x \tan x$ **18.** $-\csc^2 x$

19. $-\frac{x\sin x + \cos x}{x^2}$ **20.** $2\cos x + \sin x$ **21.** $\frac{1+\cos x + x\sin x}{(1+\cos x)^2}$

22. $\sec^2 x$ **23.** $-\frac{\csc^2 x}{(1+\cot x)^2}$ **24.** $-(1 + \sin x)^{-1}$

25. $\csc x (\csc^2 x + \cot^2 x)$ **26.** a) $\sin x$ b) $\cos x$

27. Tangent: $y = x$. Normal: $y = -x$. We may graph the three functions $y = \sin x$, $y = x$ and $y = -x$ in the viewing rectangle $[-3, 3]$ by $[-2, 2]$.

28. Tangent: $y = x$. Normal: $y = -x$. We may graph $y = \tan x$, $y = x$ and $y = -x$ in $[-3, 3]$ by $[-2, 2]$.

29. Tangent: $y = 2\sin^2 2 + 4\sin 2\cos 2(x - 2)$.

Normal: $y = 2\sin^2 2 - (4\sin 2\cos 2)^{-1}(x - 2)$. We may view $y = 2(\sin x)^2$, the tangent and the normal in $[0, 4]$ by $[0, 2.7]$.

30. Let $m = -(\csc^2 1 + \cot 1 + 2)$. Then the tangent is $y = 2 + \cot 1 + m(x-1)$ and the normal is $y = 2 + \cot 1 - m^{-1}(x-1)$. The result may be confirmed by viewing the graphs of $y = f(x)$, the tangent and the normal in $[-1,3]$ by $[2, 4.7]$.

33. $(\tan x)' = \sec^2 x = \frac{1}{\cos^2 x}$ and $(\cot x)' = -\csc^2 x = -\frac{1}{\sin^2 x}$ cannot be 0 for any value of x.

34. (π, π) is the only point where there is a horizontal tangent.

35. $y' = 0$ is equivalent to $\cos x = -2$. Since the latter equation has no solution, the graph has no horizontal tangent.

36. $(\frac{\pi}{2}, \frac{\pi}{2})$ is the only point on the graph where there is a horizontal tangent.

37. There are horizontal tangents at the points $(\pi/6, (\pi/6) + \sqrt{3})$, $(5\pi/6, (5\pi/6) - \sqrt{3})$.

38. a) $v(\frac{\pi}{4}) = -\sqrt{2}$, $|v(\frac{\pi}{4})| = \sqrt{2}$, $a(\frac{\pi}{4}) = \sqrt{2}$.

   b) $v(\frac{\pi}{4}) = 0$, $|v(\frac{\pi}{4})| = 0$, $a(\frac{\pi}{4}) = -\sqrt{2}$

39. $y = -x + 1 + \pi/4$, $y = x + 1 - \pi/4$ 40. $(-\pi/4, -1)$, $(\pi/4, 1)$

41. $y = -1$ is the tangent line at $(\pi/4, -1)$, the only point at which the tangent is horizontal.

42. $y = 2\sqrt{3} - 3$ is the tangent line at $(\pi/3, 2\sqrt{3} - 3)$, the only point at which the tangent is horizontal.

43. The graph of $\tan x$ and its derivative $\sec^2 x$, $-\pi/2 < x < \pi/2$ may be viewed in the rectangle $[-1.57, 1.57]$ by $[-5, 5]$.

44. The graph of $\cot x$ and its derivative $-\csc^2 x$, $0 < x < \pi$ may be viewed in the rectangle $[0, 3.14]$ by $[-5, 5]$.

45. $1/2$

3.6 THE CHAIN RULE

1. $3\cos(3x+1)$ 2. $-5\cos(7-5x)$ 3. $-\frac{1}{3}\sin(x/3)$

4. $-\sqrt{3}\sin(\sqrt{3}x)$ 5. $(2-3x^2)\sec^2(2x-x^3)$ 6. $10\sec^2[5(2x-1)]$

7. $1+2x\sec(x^2+\sqrt{2})\tan(x^2+\sqrt{2})$ 8. $\sec(3-8x)[1-8x\tan(3-8x)]$

9. $(2x+7)\csc(x^2+7x)\cot(x^2+7x)$ 10. $\frac{1}{2\sqrt{x}}+2\csc(1-2x)\cot(1-2x)$

11. $\frac{10}{x^2}\csc^2(\frac{2}{x})$ 12. $-\frac{1}{x^2}\csc^2(\pi-\frac{1}{x})$

13. $[-\sin(\sin x)]\cos x$ 14. $[\sec(\tan x)\tan(\tan x)]\sec^2 x$

15. $y=(2x+1)^5.$ $y'=5(2x+1)^4(2)=10(2x+1)^4.$ We support this result by graphing $10(2x+1)^4$ and $\text{NDER}((2x+1)^5,x)$ in $[-2,1]$ by $[0,810]$ and seeing that the two graphs coincide.

16. $-27(4-3x)^8$ 17. $-6x(x^2+1)^{-4}$ 18. $-2(x+\sqrt{x})^{-3}(1+\frac{1}{2\sqrt{x}})$

19. $(1-\frac{x}{7})^{-8}$ 20. $-5(\frac{x}{2}-1)^{-11}$ 21. $y'=4(\frac{x^2}{8}+x-\frac{1}{x})^3(\frac{x}{4}+1+\frac{1}{x^2})$

22. $(1-\frac{1}{x^2})(\frac{x}{5}+\frac{1}{5x})^4$ 23. $\csc x(\csc x+\cot x)^{-1}$ 24. $\sec x(\sec x+\tan x)^{-1}$

25. $2\sin x(2\sin^2 x\cos x+\cos^{-3} x)$ 26. $-5\sin^{-6} x\cos x+3\cos^2 x\sin x$

27. $x^2(2x-5)^3(14x-15)$ 28. $(3x^2-5)^4(5+30x-33x^2)$

29. $(4x+3)^3(x+1)^{-4}[-3(4x+3)+16(x+1)]=(4x+3)^3(x+1)^{-4}(4x+7)$

30. $2(x^2-5x)^5[3-(2x-5)^{-2}(x^2-5x)]$

31. $\frac{2\sin x}{(1+\cos x)^2}$ 32. $\frac{1}{1+\cos x}$ 33. $3(\frac{x-1}{x})^2\frac{1}{x^2}$ 34. $\frac{2(x-2)}{(x-1)^3}$

35. $\sin^2 x(4\sin x\sec^2 4x+3\cos x\tan 4x)$

36. $-\cos^3 x(7\cos x\csc^2 7x+4\sin x\cot 7x)$

37. $\frac{\cos x}{2\sqrt{\sin x}}$ 38. $-\frac{\sin x}{2\sqrt{\cos x}}$ 39. $2\sec x\sqrt{\sec x+\tan x}$

40. $-\csc x\sqrt{\csc x+\cot x}$ 41. $-\frac{3}{(2x+1)^{3/2}}$ 42. $\frac{1}{(1+x^2)^{3/2}}$

43. $\frac{3x+7}{\sqrt{x+5}}$ 44. $\frac{2x^2-3x}{\sqrt{x^2-2x}}$ 45. $3\sin(\frac{\pi}{2}-3t)=3\cos 3t$

46. $4t\sin(\pi-4t)+\cos(\pi-4t)$ 47. $\frac{4}{\pi}(\cos 3t-\sin 5t)$

48. $\frac{3\pi}{2}\cos\left(\frac{3\pi}{2}t\right) - \frac{7\pi}{4}\sin\left(\frac{7\pi}{4}t\right)$

49. $-\sec^2(2-\theta)$

50. $2\sec 2\theta(sec^2 2\theta + \tan^2 2\theta)$

51. $\frac{\theta\cos\theta + \sin\theta}{2\sqrt{\theta\sin\theta}}$

52. $\sqrt{\sec\theta}(\theta\tan\theta + 2)$

53. $6\sin(3x-2)\cos(3x-2)$

54. $10(\sec^2 5x)\tan 5x$

55. $-4(\sin 2x)(1+\cos 2x)$

56. $\sec^2(x/2)(1-\tan(x/2))^{-3}$

57. $-2[\sin(2x-5)]\cos(\cos(2x-5))$

58. $-42(\sin 7x)(\cos 7x)(1+\cos^2 7x)^2$

59. $-\frac{\csc^2\sqrt{2x}}{\sqrt{2x}}$

60. $\frac{5\sec^2 5x}{2\sqrt{\tan 5x}}$

61. $2(\sec^2 x)\tan x$

62. $2(\csc^2 x)\cot x$

63. $18\csc^2(3x-1)\cot(3x-1)$

64. $2\sec^2(x/3)\tan(x/3)$

65. $\frac{5}{2}$

66. 1

67. $-\frac{\pi}{4}$

68. 5π

69. 0

70. -8

71. In both cases we get $-6\sin(6x+2)$.

72. $\frac{dy}{dx} = 2x\cos(x^2+1)$ in both cases.

73. $\frac{dy}{dx} = 1$ in both cases.

74. $\frac{dy}{dx} = 2[\cos(\sin 2x)]\cos 2x$ in both cases.

75. 5

76. 3

77. $\frac{1}{2}$

78. $y = mx$

79. Tangent: $y - 2 = \pi(x-1)$. Normal: $y - 2 = -\frac{1}{\pi}(x-1)$.

80. Graph the functions in $[-6,6]$ by $[-3.53, 3.53]$.

81. a) $\frac{2}{3}$ b) $2\pi + 5$ c) $15 - 8\pi$ d) $\frac{37}{6}$ e) -1

     f) $\frac{\sqrt{2}}{24}$ g) $\frac{5}{32}$ h) $\frac{-5\sqrt{17}}{51}$

82. a) 1 b) 6 c) 1 d) $-\frac{1}{9}$ e) $-\frac{40}{3}$

     f) -6 g) $-\frac{4}{9}$

83. $s = A\cos(2\pi bt)$, $V = s' = -2\pi bA\sin(2\pi bt)$ and $a = v' = -4\pi^2 b^2 A\cos(2\pi bt)$. Now let $s_1 = A\cos[2\pi(2b)t] = A\cos(4\pi bt)$. Then the new velocity and acceleration are given by $v_1 = -4\pi bA\sin(4\pi bt) = 2(-2\pi bA)\sin(4\pi bt)$ and $a_1 = -16\pi^2 b^2 A\cos(4\pi bt) = 4(-4\pi^2 b^2 A)\cos(4\pi bt)$. Thus the amplitude of v is doubled and the amplitude of a is quadrupled.

85. a) Graph y in $[0, 365]$ by $[-12, 62]$.

b) When $t = 101$ or April 12 in a non-leap year.

c) About $0.637°F$ per day.

86. a) Graph y in $[0, 365]$ by $[4, 21]$.

b) On March 25 in a non-leap year.

c) About 0.146 hours per day.

3.7 IMPLICIT DIFFERENTIATION AND FRACTIONAL POWERS

1. $(9/4)x^{5/4}$ **2.** $-(3/5)x^{-8/5}$ **3.** $(1/3)x^{-2/3} = \frac{1}{3\sqrt[3]{x^2}}$

4. $(1/4)x^{-3/4} = \frac{1}{4\sqrt[4]{x^3}}$ **5.** $-(2x+5)^{-3/2}$ **6.** $-4(1-6x)^{-1/3}$

7. $\frac{2x^2+1}{\sqrt{x^2+1}}$ **8.** $\frac{1}{(x^2+1)^{3/2}}$ **9.** $-(2xy + y^2)/(x^2 + 2xy)$

10. $(6y - x^2)/(y^2 - 6x)$ **11.** $(1 - 2y)/(2x + 2y - 1)$ **12.** $(y - 3x^2)/(3y^2 - x)$

13. $x(1 - y^2)/[y(x^2 - 1)]$ **14.** $\frac{3x+7}{y^2}$ **15.** $1/[y(x + 1)^2]$

16. First multiplying by $x + y$: $y' = (1 - 3x^2 - 2xy)/(x^2 + 1)$.

Immediately differentiating: $y' = \frac{y}{x} - (x + y)^2$.

First solving for y explicitly: $y' = (1 - 4x^2 - x^4)/(x^2 + 1)^2$.

17. $\frac{-1}{4\sqrt{x}\sqrt{1-\sqrt{x}}}$ **18.** $x^{-3/2}(2x^{-1/2} + 1)^{-4/3}$ **19.** $-(9/2)\csc^{3/2} x \cot x$

20. $(5/4)[\sin(x + 5)]^{1/4}\cos(x + 5)$ **21.** $\cos^2 y$ **22.** $\sec y$

23. $-\frac{[\cos^2(xy)+y]}{x}$ **24.** $(y - 1)/(\cos y - x)$

25. $y' = y/[\frac{1}{y}\cos(\frac{1}{y}) - \sin(\frac{1}{y}) - x]$

26. $y' = 2/[\sin(\frac{1}{y}) + 2y\cos(\frac{1}{y}) - 2]$

27. b), c), d).

28. a) possible   b) impossible   c) possible   d) impossible.

29. $-x/y, \ -(y^2 + x^2)/y^3 = -1/y^3$

30. $-x^{-1/3}y^{1/3}, (1/3)[x^{-2/3}y^{-1/3} + x^{-4/3}y^{1/3}]$

31. $(x+1)/y, [y^2 - (x+1)^2]/y^3$

32. $\frac{1}{y+1}, -\frac{1}{(y+1)^3}$ **33.** $\frac{\sqrt{y}}{\sqrt{y}+1}, \frac{1}{2(\sqrt{y}+1)^3}$

34. $-y/(x+2y), 2y(x+y)/(x+2y)^3$

35. a) $7x - 4y = 2$ b) $4x + 7y = 29$

36. a) $3x - 4y = 25$ b) $4x + 3y = 0$

37. a) $y - 3x = 6$ b) $x + 3y = 8$

38. a) $x + y = -1$ b) $y = x + 3$

39. a) $y = \frac{6}{7}(x+1)$ b) $y = -\frac{7}{6}(x+1)$

40. a) $y = 2$ b) $x = \sqrt{3}$

41. a) $y = -\frac{\pi}{2}x + \pi$ b) $y = \frac{2}{\pi}x + \frac{\pi^2-4}{2\pi}$

42. a) $y = 2x$ b) $y = -\frac{1}{2}x + \frac{5\pi}{8}$

43. a) $y = 2\pi(x-1)$ b) $y = -\frac{1}{2\pi}(x-1)$

44. a) $y = \pi$ b) $x = 0$

45. $-\pi/2$ **46.** $y = 2x$

47. a) At $(\frac{\sqrt{3}}{4}, \frac{\sqrt{3}}{2})$, the slope is -1, at $(\frac{\sqrt{3}}{4}, \frac{1}{2})$ it is $\sqrt{3}$.

b) Graph $x_1 = \sqrt{t^2 - t^4}$, $y_1 = t$ and $x_2 = -x_1$, $y_2 = t$, $-1 \leq t \leq 1$ in $[-0.5, 0.5]$ by $[-1, 1]$.

48. a) Tangent line: $y = 2x - 1$. Normal line: $x + 2y = 3$.

b) Setting $y = tx$, one may obtain $x = 2t^2/(1+t^2)$, $y = 2t^3/(1+t^2)$. This curve along with $x = t$, $y = 2t - 1$ and $x = 3 - 2t$, $y = t$, can be graphed with $-2 \leq t \leq 2$, Tstep $= 0.05$, $-1 \leq x \leq 8$ and $-3 \leq y \leq 3$. Alternatively, $y = \pm\sqrt{x^3/(2-x)}$ may be used.

49. b) $\frac{3}{2}$ **50.** b) $f'(2) = 1$, $f''(2) = -4$

51. x-intercepts are $\pm\sqrt{7}$. The tangents at $(\pm\sqrt{7}, 0)$ both have slope -2.

52. a) $(\sqrt{7/3}, -2\sqrt{7/3})$, $(-\sqrt{7/3}, 2\sqrt{7/3})$.

b) $(-2\sqrt{7/3}, \sqrt{7/3})$, $(2\sqrt{7/3}, -\sqrt{7/3})$.

53. Graph $y_1 = \sqrt{(5-2x^2)/3}$, $y_2 = -y_1$, $y_3 = x^{1.5}$, $y_4 = -y_3$ $y_5 = -(2/3)x + 5/3$, $y_6 = (3/2)x - 1/2$, $y_7 = (2/3)x - 5/3$, $y_8 = -(3/2)x + 1/2$ in $[-6, 6]$ by $[-3.5, 3.5]$.

54. $(2/5)$m/sec, $(-4/125)$m/sec^2.   **55.** $a = \frac{k^2}{2}$

56. The graph of the relation $x = \pm\sqrt{2t - \sin t}$, $y = t$, $0 \leq t \leq 10$, suggests that it passes the vertical line test and hence that the relation is a function. The domain is $(-\infty, \infty)$. The derivative may be graphed using $x = \pm\sqrt{2t - \sin t}$, $y = \pm 2\sqrt{2t - \sin t}/(2 - \cos t)$.

57. b) $xy = \sin^{-1}(-y^5) + 2k\pi$ or $xy = (2k+1)\pi + \sin^{-1}(y^5)$.   c) Domain: $[-\frac{\pi}{2}, 0)$, range of graphed relation: $[-1, 0) \cup (0, 1]$.   d) Domain: $(-\infty, \frac{-5\pi}{2}] \cup [\frac{3\pi}{2}, \infty)$, range: $[-1, 0) \cup (0, 1]$.

58. a) $x = -0.06251\ldots$ b) $\frac{dy}{dx} = \frac{-y\cos xy}{5y^4 + x\cos xy}$ using $y^5 + \sin xy = 0$; $1.9988\ldots$ c) The tangent line has approximate equation $y = -0.5 + 2(x + 0.06251)$ which can be graphed in $[-2, 2]$ by $[-4, 4]$.

59. $(-2\sqrt{\frac{7}{3}}, -\sqrt{\frac{7}{3}})$, $(2\sqrt{\frac{7}{3}}, \sqrt{\frac{7}{3}})$.

60. Graph $y = x^{1/3}$ in $[-8, 8]$ by $[-2, 2]$; domain $=$ range $= (-\infty, \infty)$. Graph $y' = \frac{1}{3}|x|^{-2/3}$ in $[-3, 3]$ by $[0, 2]$; domain $= (-\infty, 0) \cup (0, \infty)$, range $= (0, \infty)$.

3.8   LINEAR APPROXIMATIONS AND DIFFERENTIALS

1. $4x - 3$ **2.** $1 - \frac{x}{4}$ **3.** $2(x - 1)$

4. $10x - 13$ **5.** $\frac{x}{4} + 1$ **6.** $\frac{(9-4x)}{5}$

7. $2x$ **8.** $2 - x$ **9.** -5

10. $1 + x$ **11.** $2 + (1/12)(x - 8)$ **12.** $(x + 1)/4$

13. $L(x) = x$ **14.** $L(x) = 1$ **15.** $L(x) = \pi - x$

16. $x + \pi/2$ **17.** $L(x) = 1 + 2(x - \pi/4)$ **18.** $\sqrt{2}[1 + (x - \pi/4)]$

19. a) $1 + 2x$ b) $1 - 5x$ c) $2(1 + x)$ d) $1 - 6x$ e) $3 + x$ f) $1 - (1/2)x$

20. a) 1.2, calculator: 1.22   b) 1.003, calculator: 1.00299

21. $L(x) = 1 + (3/2)x$ is the sum of the linearizations of $\sqrt{x + 1}$ and $\sin x$.

23. c), d) the sequence of numbers always approaches 1.

24. b) The square roots approach 1.   c) The linearization of $(1+x)^{1/10}$ is $1 + \frac{x}{10}$. If $m > 1$, this leads to $m^{1/10^n} \approx 1 + \frac{m-1}{10^n}$. Thus the part of m greater than 1, is divided by 10 each time we take another tenth root.

25. a) 0.21   b) 0.2   c) 0.01

26. a) 0.02   b) 0   c) 0.02

27. a) 0.231   b) 0.2   c) 0.031

28. a) 0.4641   b) 0.4   c) 0.0641

29. a) $-1/3$ b) $-2/5$ c) $1/15$

30. a) 1.061   b) 1   c) 0.061

31. $4\pi r_0^2 dr$ **32.** $8\pi r_0 dr$ **33.** $3x_0^2 dx$

34. $12x_0 dx$ **35.** $2\pi r_0 h dr$ **36.** $2\pi r dh$

37. a) $0.08\pi \approx 0.2513 m^2$ b) 2.000%

38. 0.6366 in; 10 in^2 **39.** 3%

40. With an error equal to at most 1% of its length.   **41.** 3%

42. The error in the measurement of the diameter should be at most 1% of its length.

43. $1/3$ of 1% **44.** a) $1/2$ of 1% b) 5%

45. The variation of the radius should not exceed $1/2000$ of its ideal value, that is, 0.05% of the ideal value.

46. 12.5% **48.** Approximately 37.9

49. b) $x = 28\sqrt{3} - 45$ c) $g(28\sqrt{3} - 45) \approx -0.009$ d) $x = 3.156$ with error at most 0.01 e) $\frac{225}{64}$

50. a) $f(0) = 1, f(\frac{\pi}{2}) = -\sqrt{1 + \frac{\pi}{2}} < 0.$ b) The linearization $L_1(x)$ of $2\cos x$ at $x = \pi/4$ is $L_1(x) = \sqrt{2}\,(1 + \pi/4 - x)$. The linearization $L_2(x)$ of $\sqrt{1 + x}$ at $x = 0.69$ is $L_2(x) = 1.3 + (1/2.6)(x - 0.69)$. c) The equation $L_1(x) = L_2(x)$ leads to $x \approx 0.8285$. $f(0.8285) \approx -2.6 \times 10^{-4}$. d) $x = 0.82836$ e) We have no method to find an exact solution.

51. $3(x^2 - 1)dx$

52. $\frac{(1 - 2x^2)dx}{\sqrt{1 - x^2}}$

53. $\frac{2(1 - x^2)dx}{(1 + x^2)^2}$

54. $9x(3x^2 - 1)^{1/2}dx$

55. $y = \frac{x}{1 + x}$, $dy = \frac{dx}{(1 + x)^2}$

56. $-\frac{(y^2 + 2xy)dx}{2xy + x^2}$

57. $5\cos(5x)dx$

58. $-2x\sin(x^2)dx$

59. $2\sec^2(x/2)dx$

60. $2x\sec(x^2 - 1)\tan(x^2 - 1)dx$

61. $\csc(1 - (x/3))\cot(1 - (x/3))dx$

62. $-\frac{(\csc^2\sqrt{x})dx}{\sqrt{x}}$

63. b) The slope of the straight line should be $f'(0) = 0.5$ or very close to it.

64. Similar to Exercise 64. Here $L(x) = \frac{3}{5} - \frac{13}{25}(x - 3)$.

PRACTICE EXERCISES, CHAPTER 3

1. $5x^4 - \frac{1}{4}x + \frac{1}{4}$

2. $21x^2(x^4 - 1)$

3. $2(x + 1)(2x^2 + 4x + 1)$

4. $\frac{3}{(4 - x)^2}$

5. $2\cos 2x$

6. $x\sin x$

7. $\frac{1}{(x + 1)^2}$

8. $\frac{-4}{(2x - 1)^2}$

9. $-4x^2(x^3 + 1)^{-7/3}$

10. $-(x - 4)(x^2 - 8x)^{-3/2}$

11. $2\sin(1 - 2x)$

12. $\frac{2}{x^2}\csc^2(\frac{2}{x})$

13. $3(x^2 + x + 1)^2(2x + 1)$

14. $(1 + x)(1 + \frac{x}{2} + \frac{x^2}{4})$

15. $\frac{4(x + 2)}{\sqrt{4x^2 + 16x + 15}}$

16. $(\frac{u}{1 + u})^2 = \frac{1}{(x + 1)^2}$

17. $\frac{-y}{x + 2y}$

18. $\frac{-7}{(x + 3)^2}$

19. $\frac{5 - 2x - y}{x + 2y}$

20. $\frac{3x^2 + 4y}{2(3y - 2x)}$

21. $\frac{-1}{3(xy)^{1/5}}$

22. $-\frac{y}{x}$

23. $\frac{1}{2y(x + 1)^2}$

24. $\frac{1}{2y(1 - x)^2}\sqrt{\frac{1 - x}{1 + x}} = \frac{1}{2y^3(1 - x)^2}$

25. $(5x + 1)(5x^2 + 2x)^{1/2}/2y$

26. $\frac{-9(5x + 1)}{(5x^2 + 2x)^{5/2}}$

27. $\frac{x - 1}{2x\sqrt{x}}$

28. $\frac{3x+1}{\sqrt{2x+1}}$ **29.** $3\sec(1+3x)\tan(1+3x)$

30. $6\sec^2(1+3x)\tan(1+3x)$ **31.** $-2x(\csc x^2)^2$

32. $x(2\cos 5x - 5x\sin 5x)$ **33.** $\frac{x^2-2x-1}{2(1-x)^{1/2}(1+x^2)^{3/2}}$ **34.** $\frac{2x}{y(x^2+1)^2}$

35. a)

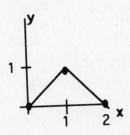

b) Yes.   c) f is not differentiable at $x = 1$ because its left-hand derivative (1) is not equal to its right-hand derivative (-1) at $x = 1$.

36. a) 2 and m, respectively   b) $m = 2$ **37.** $(-1, 27)$, $(2, 0)$

38. $(-13/4, 17/16)$

39. b) $5\sqrt{2}$.   c) -10, 10   d) at -10, $v = 0$, $a = 10$; at 10, $v = 0$, $a = -10$. e) The particle first reaches the origin at $t = \pi/4$. At that time velocity $= -10$, speed $= 10$, acceleration $= 0$.

40. b) 2 sec; 64 ft/sec   c) 12.308 sec; 393.846 ft.

41. a) $(4/7)$ sec; 280 cm/sec   b) 560 cm/sec; 980 cm/sec^2

42.

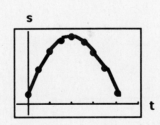

a) 32 ft/sec   b) -16 ft/sec   c) 0 ft/sec

43. a) (iii)   b) (i)   c) (ii)

44. a)

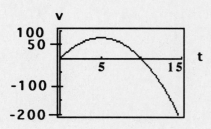 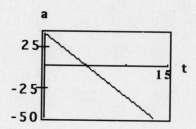

b) $|v|$ is least at $t = 0$ and $t = 10$. $|v|$ is highest at $t = 15$.

c) Compare with the graphs of $s'(t) = 30t - 3t^2$ and $s''(t) = 30 - 6t$ in the viewing window $[0, 15]$ by $[-200, 100]$.

45.

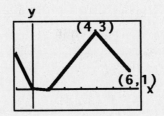

46.

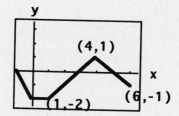

47.

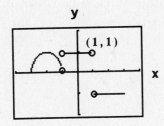

48.

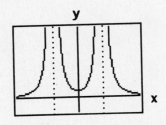

49. $\pi(20x - x^2)$

50. $r(x) = x[3 - (x/40)]^2,\ 0 \leqq x \leqq 60.$ 40 people make marginal revenue zero with corresponding fare 4 dollars.

51. a) $(\pm\frac{\pi}{3} + 2k\pi,\ 4 \mp \sqrt{3})$.   b) $y - 2 = -(x - \frac{\pi}{2})$

52. a) $(\frac{3\pi}{4} + 2k\pi, 2)$ and $(-\frac{3\pi}{4} + 2k\pi, 0)$.   b) $y + 4x = \pi + 4$

53. Yes, at the points $(2n\pi, 0)$ for all integers n.

54. a) $x = \tan\theta$ b) $dx/dt = -(3/5)\sec^2\theta$ km/sec   c) 600 m/sec   d) $18/\pi \approx$ 5.73 rev/min

55. a) 1   b) 6   c) 1   d) $-1/9$ e) $-40/3$ f) 2   g) $-4/9$

56. No. The Chain Rule gives a sufficient condition for the composites to be differentiable. It does not state that it is necessary for f and g to be differentiable.

57. Differentiating both sides of the identity $\sin(x+a) = \sin x \cos a + \cos x \sin a$ with respect to x, we obtain the identity $\cos(x+a) = \cos x \cos a - \sin x \sin a$. We cannot do the same with $x^2 - 2x - 8 = 0$ because this is not an identity between two functions.

58. 0   **59.** 9/2   **60.** $\sqrt{3}$

61. $(0,1)$ and $(-4,0)$ **62.** $y = 1/2$

63. a) $x + 4y = 9$, $4x - y = 2$ b) $3x + 2y = 5$, $3y - 2x = 1$ c) $y = 2x - 4$, $x + 2y = 7$

64. d)   **65.** 3 ft

66. $y'(r) = -\frac{1}{2r^2\ell}\sqrt{\frac{T}{\pi d}}$, $y'(\ell) = -\frac{1}{2r\ell^2}\sqrt{\frac{T}{\pi d}}$, $y'(d) = -\frac{1}{4r\ell}\sqrt{\frac{T}{\pi d^3}}$, $y'(T) = \frac{1}{4r\ell\sqrt{\pi d T}}$

67. a) $y'' = \frac{-2x(x^3+y^3)}{y^5} = -\frac{2x}{y^5}$ b) $y'' = \frac{-(1+2xy^2)}{x^4 y^3} = \frac{3-2x}{x^4 y^3}$ replacing y^2 by its given value

69. a) $-\frac{1}{(2x+7)^{3/2}}$ b) $-\frac{1}{y^3}$ **70.** -6

71. a) $L(x) = 2x + (\pi/2) - 1$. Graph $y = \tan x$ and $y = L(x)$ in the viewing rectangle $[-5,5]$ by $[-8,8]$.   b) $L(x) = \sqrt{2} - \sqrt{2}(x + \pi/4)$. Graph $y = \sec x$ and $y = L(x)$ in the viewing rectangle $[-8,8]$ by $[-10,10]$.

73. b) $L(x) = 0.5 + 1.5x = 0$ leads to $x = -1/3$ c) $f(-1/3) \approx -0.01$ d) By zoom-in, $x = -0.326\ldots$

74. b) $L(x) = -0.1 + 2.5x$ leads to $x = 0.04$ c) $f(0.04) \approx 0.003$. d) $\{0.0388196\ldots, 10.031939\ldots\}$. We cannot find the exact solutions with the tools at hand.

75. $\frac{2}{3}\pi r_0 h dr$ **76.** $\frac{\pi r h_0 dh}{\sqrt{r^2 + h_0^2}}$

77. a) With an error of no more than 1%   b) With an estimated error of no more than 3%

78. a) 4%   b) 8%   c) 12%   **79.** 2.33 ft

80. The height is 14 ft with a possible error of about 0.04 ft.

81.

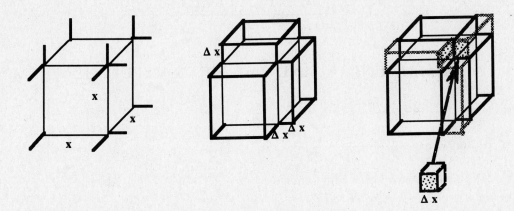

CHAPTER 4

APPLICATIONS OF DERIVATIVES

4.1 MAXIMA, MINIMA, AND THE MEAN VALUE THEOREM

1. $4/3$, -2 2. $-5/3$, 3 3. 0 4. $-\frac{\pi}{2}$, $\frac{\pi}{2}$ 5. -1, 1, 3 6. -5, -2, 1 7. 0

8. Inflection point at $x = 0$.

9. a) Between two zeros of a function lies a zero of its derivative.

10. f is not continuous on $[0, 1]$.

11. Between zeros of $f(x) = \sin x$ there is a zero of $f'(x) = \cos x$.

12. Use the window $[-5, 5]$ by $[-13, 3]$. Rolle's Theorem can be used only to prove the existence of the positive zero of y'.

13. a) Use the window $[-5, 5]$ by $[-1, 15]$.   b) no   c) no   d) local maxima at $(\pm 1.73, 10.39)$; local minima at $(\pm 3, 0), (0, 0)$.   f) increasing on $[-3, -1.73] \cup [0, 1.73] \cup [3, \infty)$ decreasing on $(-\infty, -3] \cup [-1.73, 0] \cup [1.73, 3]$

14. a) $[-20, 20]$ by $[-20, 20]$ b) no   c) local min at $x = 2$ e) increasing $[2, \infty)$, decreasing $(-\infty, 2]$

15. Local maximum at $(5/2, 6.25)$; increasing on $[0, 5/2]$, decreasing on $[5/2, 6]$; absolute maximum at $(5/2, 6.25)$, absolute minimum at $(6, -6)$. Local minimum at $(0, 0)$.

16. Local min at $(1/2, -12.25)$, absolute min $= -12.25$, absolute maximum $= 8$, decreasing on $[-4, 1/2]$, increasing on $[1/2, 4]$. Local maximum at $(4, 0)$.

17. Absolute maximum at $(8, 2)$; absolute minimum at $(4, 0)$; increasing on $[4, 8]$.

18. f decreasing on $[-2, 5]$. $f(5) = 1.35 \ldots \leq f \leq 4 = f(-2)$

19. Local and absolute minima at $(\pm\sqrt{5}, -16)$; absolute maximum at $(0, 9)$, local maxima at $(\pm 3, 0)$. Increasing on $[-\sqrt{5}, 0] \cup [\sqrt{5}, 3]$, decreasing on $[-3, -\sqrt{5}] \cup [0, \sqrt{5}]$.

20. Absolute maxima at $(\pm\sqrt{\frac{5}{2}}, 2.25)$, local minimum at $(0, -4)$; absolute minima at $(\pm 3, -40)$. Increasing on $[-3, -\sqrt{\frac{5}{2}}]$ and $[0, \sqrt{\frac{5}{2}}]$, decreasing on $[-\sqrt{\frac{5}{2}}, 0]$ and $[\sqrt{\frac{5}{2}}, 3]$.

21. Absolute minimum at $(-5, -115.567)$, absolute maximum at $(5, 114.433)$; local minimum at $(0.559, -2.639)$, local maximum at $(-1.126, -0.036)$. Increasing on $[-5, -1.126] \cup [0.559, 5]$; decreasing on $[-1.126, 0.559]$.

22. On $[0, 2\pi]$ local minima at: $(0, 2)$, $(1.571, -1)$, $(4.712, -3)$; local maxima at $(0.125, 2.063)$, $(3.016, 2.063)$, $(2\pi, 2)$. Absolute minimum is -3, absolute maximum is 2.063. Increasing on $[0, 0.125] \cup [1.571, 3.016] \cup [4.712, 2\pi]$; decreasing on $[0.125, 1.571] \cup [3.016, 4.712]$.

23. $1/2$ **24.** $8/27$ **25.** 1 **26.** $3/2$

27. $s'(c) = v(c) = 79.5$ **28.** $T'(c) = 10.1°\text{F/sec}$

29. $v(c) = 7.66$ knot   **30.** $v_{\max} > 11$

31. $[-2, 9]$ by $[-7, 3]$

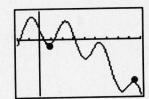

32. Let $g(x) = f(x) - K$.

33. $0, \pm 2.029$ **34.** $0, \pm 3.644, \pm 1.077$ **35.** 1 **36.** 1.5

37. $y' = -1/x^2 < 0$. By Cor 1, y is decreasing.

38. $y' > 0$ for $x < 0$, $g' < 0$ for $x > 0$.

39. By Mean Value Thm., $\frac{f(1) - f(0)}{1 - 0} = f'(c)$ for some $c \in (0, 1)$. $f(1) \neq f(0)$ because $f'(c) \neq 0$.

40. $|\sin b - \sin a| = |\cos c||b - a| \leq |b - a|$.

41. $a \neq b$ because $f(a) \neq f(b)$, so $a < b$. By Mean Value Thm., $f'(c) = \frac{f(b) - f(a)}{b - a}$ for some $c \in (a, b)$. $f'(c) < 0$ because $f(b) - f(a) < 0$ while $b - a > 0$.

42. By the Intermediate Value Theorem, $f(c) = 0$ for some $c \in (a, b)$. Suppose $f(d) = f(e) = 0$ for some $d, e \in (a, b)$, $d \neq e$. Then by Rolle's Theorem, $f'(k) = 0$ for some $k \in (d, e)$, which contradicts $f' \neq 0$ on (a, b). Thus there is exactly one zero on (a, b).

43. $f(-2) = 11$, $f(-1) = -1$. $f'(x) \neq 0$ on $(-2, -1)$.

44. $f(0) = 1$, $f(1) = -3$; $f'(x) = -3(x^2 + 1)$ which is never 0.

45. $f(1) = -1$; $f(3) = 7/3$. $f'(x) = 1 + \frac{2}{x^2}$ which is never zero.

46. $f(-\pi) = -2\pi + 1$; $f(\pi) = -(-2\pi + 1)$. $f'(x) = 2 + \sin x > 0$.

47. Select $b \neq 3$. By the M.V.T. $f(b) - 3 = 0 \cdot (b - 0) = 0$.

48. $\frac{f(x)-5}{x-0} = 2$ **49.** a) $(2,5)$ b) $(-2,2)$ c) $x = 2$

50. a) $(-1.25, 1.25)$, b) $(-2, -1.25)$ and $(1.25, 2.5)$, c) $x = -1.25$, $x = 1.25$

51. $f(x) = \sqrt{(x-a)(b-x)}$, for example

52.

a

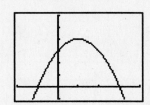

b

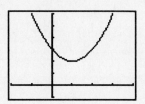

c

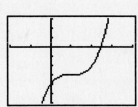

d

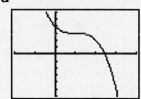

53.

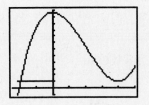

54.

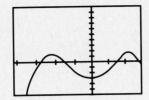

55. a) 1.000

b)

a	$f(a)$	b	area
0.5	0.303	1.762	0.382
0.8	0.359	1.238	0.157
1.0	0.368	1.0	0
1.2	0.361	0.817	0.138
1.5	0.335	0.627	0.292

c) near 0.3, 0.459

4.2 ANALYZING HIDDEN BEHAVIOR

1. $f' > 0$ on $(-\infty, -1) \cup (1, \infty)$; $f' < 0$ on $(-1, 1)$; $f' = 0$ for $x = \pm 1$.

2. $f' > 0$ on $(-1.2, 0)$ and $(1.2, \infty)$; $f' < 0$ on $(-\infty, -1.2)$ and $(0, 1.2)$. $f'(-1.2) = f'(0) = f'(1.2) = 0$.

3. Rising on $(-\infty, -2]$ and $[0, 2]$; falling on $[-2, 0]$ and $[2, \infty)$. Local maxima at $x = -2$, $x = 2$; local minimum at $x = 0$.

4. f is rising on $[-2, 0]$ and $[0, 2]$, falling on $(-\infty, 2]$ and $[2, \infty)$; local minimum at $x = -2$, local maximum at $x = 2$.

5. Falling on $(-\infty, 1/2]$, rising $[1/2, \infty)$; concave up everywhere, local minimum at $(1/2, -5/4)$.

6. Falling for $x \leq -1$, rising for $x \geq -1$, local minimum at $(-1, -3)$, always concave up.

7. Local maximum at $(1,5)$; local minimum at $(3,1)$, inflection point at $(2,3)$. Rising $(-\infty,1] \cup [3,\infty)$, falling on $[1,3]$, concave down for $x < 2$, concave up for $x > 2$.

8. Rising on $[0,2]$, falling on $(-\infty,0]$ and $[2,\infty)$; local minimum at $(0,-3)$, local maximum at $(2,5)$; inflection point at $(1,1)$; concave up for $x < 1$; concave down for $x > 1$.

9. Local minima $(\pm 1,-1)$, local maximum $(0,1)$, inflection points $(\pm 1/\sqrt{3}, -1/9)$. Rising on $[-1,0] \cup [1,\infty)$; falling on $(-\infty,-1] \cup [0,1]$; concave down on $(-1/\sqrt{3}, 1/\sqrt{3})$; concave up otherwise.

10. Falling on $(-\infty,-1]$ and $[0,1]$; rising on $[-1,0]$ and $[1,\infty)$; local minima at $(\pm 1,-1)$; local maximum at $(0,0)$; inflection points at $(\pm\sqrt{1/3}, -0.5\bar{5})$; concave down on $(-1/\sqrt{3}, 1/\sqrt{3})$, concave up elsewhere.

11. Falling on $[2/3, 1]$; rising on $(-\infty, 2/3]$ and $[1,\infty)$; local minimum at $(1,11)$; local maximum at $(2/3, 11.037)$; inflection point at $(5/6, 11.019)$; concave down for $x < 5/6$; concave up for $x > 5/6$.

12. Rising on $(-\infty,-2]$ and $[-3/2, \infty)$; falling on $[-2,-3/2]$; local maximum at $(-2,-40)$, local minimum at $(-3/2, -40.25)$ inflection point at $(-1.75, -40.125)$. Concave down for $x < -1.75$, concave up for $x > 1.75$.

13. Local minima at $(\pm 1/\sqrt{6}, -121/12)$, local maximum at $(0,-10)$. Inflection points occur when $x = \pm 1/\sqrt{18}$. Concave up for $x < -1/\sqrt{18}$ and $x > 1/\sqrt{18}$, concave down on $(-1/\sqrt{18}, 1/\sqrt{18})$. Falling on $(-\infty, -1/\sqrt{6}] \cup [0, 1/\sqrt{6}]$; rising elsewhere.

14. Increasing on $(-\infty,-1/3]$ and $[0,1/3]$; decreasing on $[-1/3,0]$ and $[1/3,\infty)$; local minimum at $(0,20)$; local maxima at $(\pm 1/3, 20.111)$, inflection points at $(\pm 0.192, 20.06)$. Concave up on $(-0.192, 0.192)$, concave down otherwise.

15. Inflection point (π,π); always rising, minimum at $(0,0)$, maximum at $(2\pi, 2\pi)$ concave down for $0 < x < \pi$, concave up $\pi < x < 2\pi$.

16. y is always rising; local minimum at $(0,0)$, local maximum at $(2\pi, 2\pi)$; inflection point at (π,π). Concave up for $x < \pi$, concave down for $x > \pi$.

17. Local minima at $(-2.115, -22.236)$ and $(1.861, -6.268)$; local maximum at $(0.254, 2.504)$; inflection points at $(-2/\sqrt{3}, -11.508)$ and $(2/\sqrt{3}, -2.270)$. Concave down on $(-2/\sqrt{3}, 2/\sqrt{3})$, concave up elsewhere. Falling on $(-\infty, -2.135] \cup [0.254, 1.861]$, rising elsewhere.

18. Graph on $[-4, 4]$ by $[-10, 20]$; concave up between inflection points at $(0, 1)$ and $(2, 9)$; local maxima at $(-0.532, 2.446)$ and $(2.880, 16.234)$; local minimum at $(0.653, -0.680)$; rising on $(-\infty, 0.532] \cup [0.653, 2.880]$; falling elsewhere.

19. Local maximum at $(-1.263, 2.435)$; inflection points at $(-\sqrt{1/3}, 0.288)$ and $(\sqrt{1/3}, -3.176)$. Rising on $(-\infty, -1.263]$, falling thereafter, concave up on $(-1/\sqrt{3}, 1/\sqrt{3})$, concave down elsewhere.

20. Graph on $[-1.5, 1.5]$ by $[0, 10]$; local minimum at $(0.836, 2.770)$, inflection points at $(-0.289, 5.797)$ and $(0.289, 4.065)$. Concave down on $(-0.289, 0.289)$; falling for $x \leq 0.836$.

21. Graph is always rising; inflection point at $(0, 3)$; concave up for $x < 0$, concave down for $x > 0$.

22. Concave down for $x < 0$; inflection point at $(0, 5)$; concave up for $x > 0$. Always falling.

23. Defined for $x \geq 0$; always rising and concave down; local minimum at $(0, -1)$.

24. Defined for $x \geq 0$; always rising and concave down; local minimum at $(0, 0)$.

25. The graph is always rising, concave up for $x < 2$, inflection point at $(2, 2.5)$.

26. Graph on $[-5, 10]$ by $[-10, 0]$; graph is always falling, inflection point at $(2, -3.5)$. Concave down for $x < 2$.

27. Local minimum at $(0, 1)$. Always rising, concave down for $x < 0$, concave up for $x > 0$, but $x = 0$ is not an inflection point.

28. Local maximum at $(1, 1)$; concave down for $x \geq 1$. No concavity for $x < 1$. Rising for $x < 1$, falling for $x \geq 1$.

29. Local minimum at $(0, 0)$; local maximum at $(1.200, 2.033)$, inflection point at $(-0.6, 2.561)$. Concave up for $x < -0.6$, concave down on $(-0.6, 0)$ and $(0, \infty)$. Rising on $[0, 1.2]$.

30. Defined for $x \geq 0$; local minimum at $(0, 0)$; local maximum at $(2.143, 5.060)$. Rising on $[0, 2.143]$. Concave down for $x > 0$.

31. Local minimum at $(1, -3)$; inflection points at $(-2, 7.560)$ and $(0, 0)$; falling on $(-\infty, 1]$, rising thereafter. Concave down on $(-2, 0)$. Concave up elsewhere.

32. Defined for $x \geq 0$; local minimum at $(0,0)$; inflection point at $(1.800, 5.560)$; concave down for $0 < x < 1.800$, concave up for $x > 1.800$. Always rising.

33.

time	$a(t) = 2$	$\nu(t) = 2t - 4$	speed	direction
$t < 2$	pos	neg, inc	slowing	to the left
$t = 2$	pos	0		stopped
$2 < t$	pos	pos, inc	gaining	to the right

34.

time	$a(t)$	$\nu(t)$	speed	direction
$t < -1$	neg	pos, dec	dec	to the right
$t = -1$	neg	0, dec	0	stopped
$-1 < t$	neg	neg, dec	inc	to the left

35.

time	$a(t)$	$\nu(t)$	speed	direction
$t < -1$	neg	pos, dec	dec	to the right
$t = -1$	neg	0	0	stopped
$-1 < t < 0$	neg	neg, dec	inc	to the left
$0 < t < 1$	pos	neg, inc	dec	to the left
$1 < t$	pos	pos	inc	to the right

36.

time	$a(t)$	$\nu(t)$	speed	direction
$t < 0$	pos	neg, inc	dec	to the left
$0 < t < 1/2$	pos	pos, inc	inc	to the right
$1/2 < t < 1$	neg	pos, dec	dec	to the right
$1 < t$	neg	neg, dec	inc	to the left

37. Local minimum at $x = 2$; inflection points at $x = 1, 5/3$.

38. Local minimum at 4, local maximum at 2; inflection points at $1, 1.634, 3.366$.

39. Local maximum at $(-1, -2)$; local minimum at $(1, 2)$.

40. Local minimum at $(3/2, 1.25)$; local maximum at $(-1/2, -.75)$.

41. No, f might have an inflection point.

42. No.   **43.** True.   **44.** True.

45. a) $t = 2, 6, 9.5,$ b) $t = 4, 8, 11.5.$

46. a) $t = 0, 4, 12, 16,$ b) $t = 1.5, 5.5, 7, 10.5, 13.5.$

47.

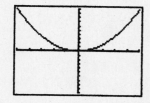

48.

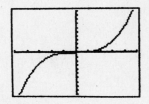

49.

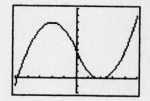

50.

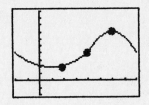

51. Viewing rectangle: $[-1, 1]$ by $[-1, 1]$.

53. Viewing rectangle: $[-0.5, 0.5]$ by $[-5, 5]$.

55. $y_2 = (-2a^3) + (3a^2 - 9)x$; locally y_2 is below y_1 for $x > 0$.

56. b) $(-0.317, -1.299)$

57. Graph in $[0, 300]$ by $[-20, 150]$ using $0 \le t \le 10$.

58. Airtime $= (V_0 \sin \alpha)/16$; maximum height $= (V_0^2 \sin^2 \alpha)/64$; range is $(V_0^2 \sin \alpha \cos \alpha)/16$.

59. $75.964°$

4.3 POLYNOMIAL FUNCTIONS, NEWTON'S METHOD, AND OPTIMIZATION

1. 0.618033988, −1.618033989

2. +0.682327

3. 1.16403514, −1.452626879

4. −0.4142135..., 2.4142135...

5. 0.6301153962, 2.5732719864

6. ±0.5411961001, ±1.30656296

7. 3.216451347, −1.564587289

8. −2.153634878

9. 1.189207115

10. $x_2 = -1.193500.., x = -1.1892...$

11. If $f'(x_0) \neq 0$, all $x_n = x_0$.

12. x_0 must be close to $\pi/2$.

13. $x_0 = h > 0 \Rightarrow x_1 = x_0 - \sqrt{x_0}/(\frac{1}{2\sqrt{x_0}}) = -h.$

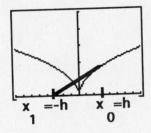

14. $x_1 = -2,\ x_2 = 4,\ x_3 = -8,\ x_4 = 16,\ x_{n+1} = -2x_n$

15. Always rising; concave down $x < 1$, concave up $x > 1$. Inflection point $(1, -1)$. One real root.

16. Graph is always rising, concave down until inflection point at $(2, 10.667)$. One real root.

17. Rising to local maximum $(\frac{2-\sqrt{13}}{3}, 8.879)$, then falling to local minimum at $(\frac{2+\sqrt{13}}{3}, 1.9354)$, then rising; inflection point at $(\frac{2}{3}, 5.407)$; concave down for $x < 2/3$, concave up for $x > 2/3$. One real root.

18. Rising on $(-\infty, -23/3]$ and $[1, \infty)$, falling on $[-23/3, 1]$, concave down on $(-\infty, -10/3)$, concave up on $(-10/3, \infty)$. Local maximum at $(-23/3, 325.48)$, local minimum at $(1, 0)$; inflection point at $(-10/3, 162.7)$. Two distinct roots.

19. Local minimum $(-1/\sqrt{12}, 11.808)$; local maximum at $(1/\sqrt{12}, 12.192)$; inflection point at $(0, 12)$; one real root. Rising on $[-1/\sqrt{12}, 1/\sqrt{12}]$, falling elsewhere. Concave up for $x < 0$, concave down for $x > 0$.

20. Rising to a local maximum at $(-1.37, 0.160)$, falling to a local minimum at $(1.70, -28.864)$, inflection point at $(1/6, -14.352)$; three real roots. Concave down for $x < 1/6$, concave up for $x > 1/6$.

21. Use $[-10, 10]$ by $[-60, 60]$. Graph is always falling; inflection point $(0, 20)$. Concave up for $x < 0$, concave down for $x > 0$. One real root.

22. Graph on $[-5, 5]$ by $[-60, 60]$, falling to local minimum at $(-2/\sqrt{27}, -16.03)$, then rising to local maximum at $(2/\sqrt{27}, -13.97)$, then falling; inflection point at $(0, -15)$; concave up for $x < 0$, concave down for $x > 0$.

23. Falling to local minimum at $(-0.383, 7.785)$, then rising; concave up everywhere; no real roots.

24. 4 real zeros. Local minima at $(4.056, -25.057)$ and $(0.399, -2.766)$; local maximum at $(1.545, 0.324)$; inflection points at $(0.920, -1.325)$ and $(3.080, -14.286)$. Concave down on $(0.920, 3.080)$, concave up elsewhere. Falling on $(-\infty, 0.399] \cup [1.545, 4.056]$, rising elsewhere.

25. Use $[-1, 6]$ by $[-30, 10]$. Local maximum $(0.259, 0.001)$; inflection point $(1.417, -12.412)$; local minimum $(2.574, -24.825)$; three zeros. Rising on $(-\infty, 0.259] \cup [2.574, \infty)$, falling on $[0.259, 2.574]$; concave down for $x < 1.417$, concave up for $x > 1.417$.

26. Use $[-10, 5]$ by $[-40, 15]$, 3 real roots; falling to a local minimum at $(-3.082, -27, 041)$, rising to a local maximum at $(1.082, 9.041)$; inflection point at $(-1, -9)$; concave up for $x < 1$, concave down for $x > 1$.

27. Use $[-5, 5]$ by $[-17, 17]$. Graph rises to a local maximum at $(2.000, 15.333)$, then falls. Concave up on $(0, 1.33)$. Concave down elsewhere. Inflection points $(0, 10)$ and $(1.333, 13.160)$; two real roots.

28. Use $[-5, 5]$ by $[-12, 4]$; 2 real roots. Falling to a minimum at $(-1.793, -11.397)$, then rising. Always concave up.

29. Use $[-3, 3]$ by $[0, 34]$. Falling to a local minimum at $(-1.107, 17.944)$; rising to a local maximum at $(0.270, 20.130)$; falling to a local minimum at $(0.837, 19.927)$; rising thereafter. Concave down between inflection points $(-0.577, 18.867)$ and $(0.577, 20.022)$; concave up elsewhere. No real roots.

30. $[-5, 5]$ by $[-10, 30]$ shows a complete graph; 2 real roots. Rising to a maximum at $(-0.667, 22.222)$, falling to a local minimum at $(0.667, 18.667)$, rising to a local maximum at $(1.000, 18.750)$, falling thereafter. Concave up between inflection points at $(-0.176, 20.747)$ and $(0.843, 18.710)$.

31. Use $[-8, 4]$ by $[-20, 35]$. Rising to a local maximum at $(-4.023, 32.012)$; falling to a local minimum at $(-1.514, -0.189)$, rising to a local maximum at $(0.287, 13.095)$. Concave up between inflection points $(-3, 18)$ and $(-0.5, 7.063)$; concave down elsewhere. Four real roots.

32. $[-2, 7]$ by $[-10, 30]$ shows a complete graph. Falling to a local minimum at $(-0.236, -6,000)$, then rising to a local maximum at $(2.000, 19.000)$, falling to a local minimum at $(4.236, -6.000)$ then rising. Concave down between inflection points at $(0.709, 5.111)$ and $(3.291, 5.111)$, concave up elsewhere. Four real roots.

33. Falling to local minimum at $(-2.601, -7.580)$; rising to local maximum at $(-1.097, 21.196)$; falling to local minimum at $(0.534, -0.495)$; rising to $(2.364, 53.006)$, falling thereafter. Concavity: up until $(-2.016, 4.530)$, down until $(-0.266, 10.206)$, up until $(1.681, 31.029)$, down thereafter. Five real roots.

34. $[-3, 6]$ by $[-40, 20]$ shows a complete graph. Rising to a local maximum at $(0, 1)$, falling to a local minimum at $(2.359, -31.191)$, rising thereafter; inflection point at $(1.678, -19.587)$; concave down for $x < 1.678$, concave up for $x > 1.678$. Three real roots.

35. Use $[-2, 2]$ by $[-50, 50]$. Always rising; inflection point at $(-0.288, -2.922)$ where concavity changes from concave down to concave up. One real root.

36. $[-6, 6]$ by $[-20, 20]$ combined with $[4, 5]$ by $[43, 44]$ show a complete graph of y. Rising to a local maximum at $(-0.929, 12.856)$, falling to a local minimum at $(0.835, -6.548)$, rising to a local maximum at $(4.340, 43.742)$, falling to a local minimum at $(4.755, 43.500)$, thereafter rising. Concave down on $(-\infty, -0.206)$ and $(2.399, 4.557)$, concave up elsewhere. Inflection points at $(-0.206, 4.424), (2.399, 17.322)$, and $(4.557, 43.617)$. Three real roots.

37. 0 and 20   **38.** $w = \ell = 2$ ft   **39.** $5/3 \times 14/3 \times 35/3$ inches

40. 80000 m^2 **41.** a) $y = 1 - x$, b) $A(x) = 2x(1 - x)$, c) $1/2$

42. 32   **43.** a) $v(0) = 100$ ft/sec, b) 356.25 feet, c) -150.997 feet/sec.

44. a) 96 ft/sec b) 256 ft c) -128 ft/sec.   **45.** $18 \times 18 \times 36$ inches

46. a) $D^2 = (x - 2)^2 + (x^2 + 1/2)^2$ b) 0.68233

47. a) $x = 12, y = 6$ b) $x = 12, y = 6$

48. $r = \sqrt{2}, \ h = 1, \ v = 2\pi/3$　　　　**49.** 0.653　　　　**50.** 0.774

51. a) $a = -3, \ b = -9;$　b) $a = -3, \ b = -24$

52. a) $t = 4, \ t = 8/5,$　b) $8/5 < t < 4,$　c) $-17.496 (\max |v| = 17.496, 8/5 < t < 4)$

53. $32\pi/3$　　　　**54.** $4\sqrt{3}$ wide $\times 4\sqrt{6}$ inches deep.

55. 6 inches wide by $6\sqrt{3}$ inches deep.　**56.** $v = ka^2/4$ when $x(t) = a/2$

57. $p = K/2$　　**58.** Maximum v at $r = \frac{2}{3}r_0$　　　**59.** $M = c/2$

60. Degree 7; local maximum at $x = -1$, local minimum at $x = 5$; concave up on $(-0.48, 1)$ and $(2.81, \infty)$.

61. Answer depends on technology used; 1.003 is common.

63. c) $1.879, \ -0.347, \ -1.532$　　　　**64.** 1.16556

65. Use $x - (\tan x) \times (\cos x)^2 \to x$　　**66.** 1.49870

67. b) $v = 2x(24 - 2x)(18 - 2x),$　c) $0 < x < 9$　e) $x = 3.394$ in, $v = 1309.955$ in^3　f) $x = 2$ or $x = 5$

68. Squares cut from 10" side: $x = 1.962$ in, $V = 66.019$ in^3.

69. Square cut from 15 inch end: $x = 1.962$ in, $v_{\max} = 66.019$ in^3.

71. f and g will have extrema at the same values of x-although their nature may be reversed.

73. 0　　　　　　　**74.** $y'(-L) = 3aL^2 - 2bL = 0$

75. Solve $3aL - 2b = 0$ and $-aL^3 + bL^2 = H$ for a and b.

76. Use $[-90, 0]$ by $[-1, 25000/5280]$

4.4 RATIONAL FUNCTIONS AND ECONOMIC APPLICATIONS

1. No extrema or inflection points; always rising; concave up if $x < 0$, concave down if $x > 0$. $[-5, 5]$ by $[-5, 5]$ shows a complete graph.

2. Graph on $[-6, 6]$ by $[-4, 4]$; local maximum at $(-2, -2)$; local minimum at $(2, 2)$. Rising on $(-\infty, -2] \cup [2, \infty)$, falling on $[-2, 0) \cup (0, 2]$; concave down for $x < 0$, concave up for $x > 0$.

3. Local minima at $(\pm 1, 2)$. $[-5, 5]$ by $[0, 5]$ shows a complete graph. Always concave up. Rising on $[-1, 0) \cup [1, \infty)$, falling on $(-\infty, -1] \cup (0, 1]$.

4. Local minimum at $x = 2^{1/3} = 1.260$, no inflection points. Graph on $[-6, 6]$ by $[-4, 4]$. Rising on $(-\infty, 0)$ and $[1.260, \infty)$; falling on $(0, 1.260]$. Always concave up.

5. Concavity: down $(-\infty, -2)$, up $(-2, 0)$, down $(0, 2)$, up $(2, \infty)$. Falling on $(-\infty, -2) \cup (-2, 2) \cup (2, \infty)$.

6. Inflection point at $(1.223, -0.192)$ no extrema, graph on $[-4, 4]$ by $[-4, 4]$. Rising on $(-\infty, 0)$; falling on $(0, 2) \cup (2, \infty)$; concave up for $x < 0$, $x > 2$ and on $(0, 1.223)$; concave down on $(1.223, 2)$.

7. $[-5, 5]$ by $[-5, 5]$ shows a complete graph. $(0, -1)$ is a local maximum. No inflection points. Concave up for $|x| > 1$, concave down on $(-1, 1)$. Rising on $(-\infty, -1) \cup (-1, 0]$. Falling on $[0, 1) \cup (1, \infty)$.

8. Local maximum at $(0, 0)$; no inflection points; graph on $[-3, 3]$ by $[-10, 10]$. Rising on $(-\infty, -1) \cup (-1, 0]$; falling on $[0, 1) \cup (1, \infty)$; concave up for $|x| > 1$, concave down on $(-1, 1)$.

9. Local maximum at $(0, -2)$. The graph is that of #7, decreased by 1. $[-5, 5]$ by $[-5, 5]$ shows a complete graph.

10. Local minimum at $x = 0$; no inflection points; graph on $[-3, 3]$ by $[-10, 10]$; concave up on $(-\sqrt{2}, \sqrt{2})$, concave down for $|x| > \sqrt{2}$, rising on $[0, \sqrt{2}) \cup (\sqrt{2}, \infty)$, falling on $(-\infty, -\sqrt{2}) \cup (-\sqrt{2}, 0]$.

11. $[-10, 10] \times [-10, 10]$ shows a complete graph. Concave up for $x < 1$, rising on $(-\infty, 1) \cup (1, \infty)$.

12. y is decreasing on $(-\infty, -1) \cup (-1, \infty)$; no inflection points. Graph on $[-3, 3]$ by $[-10, 10]$. Concave down for $x < -1$, concave up for $x > -1$.

13. $[-5, 4]$ by $[-10, 25]$ shows a complete graph. Local minimum at $(0.575, 0.144)$. Inflection point at $(-3, 11)$. Concave up on $(-\infty, -3) \cup (-2, \infty)$, concave down on $(-3, -2)$; falling on $(-\infty, -2) \cup (-2, 0.575]$, rising on $[0.575, \infty)$.

14. Local minimum at $(2, 3)$; no inflection points. Graph on $[-3, 3]$ by $[-10, 10]$. Concave up on $(-\infty, 0) \cup (0, \infty)$; rising on $(-\infty, 0) \cup [2, \infty)$, falling on $(0, 2]$.

15. Use $[-4, 4]$ by $[-0.5, 1.5]$. $(-2.414, -0.207)$ is a local minimum, $(-0.268, 0.683)$ is an inflection point, $(0.414, 1.207)$ is a local maximum, $(1, 1)$ is an inflection point. Rising on $[-2.414, 0.414]$, falling on $(-\infty, 2.414]$ and $[0.414, \infty)$; concave down on $(-0.268, 1)$, concave up elsewhere.

16. Local minimum at $(-0.729, 0.606)$; local maximum at $(0.729, -0.606)$; graph on $[-5, 5]$ by $[-10, 10]$. Falling on $(-\infty, -2) \cup (-2, -0.729] \cup [0.729, 2) \cup (2, \infty)$; rising on $[-0.729, 0) \cup (0, 0.729]$; concave down on $(-\infty, -2) \cup (0, 2)$, concave up on $(-2, 0) \cup (2, \infty)$.

17. $[-4, 4]$ by $[-10, 10]$ shows a complete graph. $(-0.475, -3.331)$ local maximum, $(0.490, 0.800)$ local minimum. Rising on $(-\infty, -2) \cup (-2, -0.475] \cup [0.490, \infty)$; falling on $[-0.475, 0) \cup (0, 0.490]$. Concave up on $(-\infty, -2) \cup (0, \infty)$; concave down on $(-2, 0)$.

18. Local minimum at $(0.323, 4.499)$; local maximum at $(-0.327, 0.400)$; falling only on $[-0.327, 0) \cup (0, 0.323]$, rising on $(-\infty, -0.327] \cup [0.323, 3) \cup (3, \infty)$; concave up on $(0, 3)$, concave down on $(-\infty, 0)$ and $(3, \infty)$; graph on $[-5, 5]$ by $[-10, 20]$.

19. Graph needs both $[-2, 6]$ by $[-10, 30]$ and $[-2, 2]$ by $[-2, 2]$ to be seen completely. Local minima at $(0.243, -1.589)$ and $(2.543, 18.459)$; local maximum at $(1.214, -0.869)$; inflection point at $(0.855, -1.158)$. Rising on $[0.243, 1.214] \cup [2.543, \infty)$; falling on $(-\infty, 0.243] \cup [1.214, 2) \cup (2, 2.543]$. Concave up on $(-\infty, 0.855) \cup (2, \infty)$, concave down on $(0.855, 2)$.

20. Local maxima at $(-0.121, 1.680)$ and $(-3.532, -15, 234)$; local minimum at $(-2.347, -1.446)$; inflection point at $(-1.740, -0.440)$; graph on $[-5, 5]$ by $[-30, 10]$. Concave down on $(-\infty, -3) \cup (-1.740, \infty)$, concave up on $(-3, -1.740)$; rising on $(-\infty, -3.532] \cup [-2.347, -0.121]$, falling on $[-3.532, -3) \cup (-3, -2.347] \cup [-0.121, \infty)$.

21. $[-5, 5]$ by $[-15, 15]$ shows a complete graph. Inflection points at $(0.037, -0.582)$ and $(-3.005, 10.792)$; local minimum at $(1.666, 2.884)$. Falling on $(-\infty, -2) \cup (-2, 1) \cup (1, 1.666]$; rising on $[1.666, \infty)$; concave down on $(-3.005, -2)$ and $(0.037, 1)$, concave up on $(-\infty, -3.005)$, $(-2, 0.037)$ and $(1, \infty)$.

22. Local minimum at $(-0.457, 13.892)$; inflection points at $(-2.206, 5.572)$ and $(1.070, 2.486)$; graph on $[-4, 4]$ by $[-20, 30]$. Falling on $(-\infty, -1) \cup (-1, -0.457]$, rising on $[-0.457, 0)$ and $(0, \infty)$; concave up on $(-\infty, -2.206) \cup (-1, 0) \cup (1.070, \infty)$, concave down on $(-2.206, -1) \cup (0, 1.070)$.

23. Three views are necessary: $[-5, 5]$ by $[-100, 100]$, $[-3.2, -2.8]$ by $[-100, 100]$ and $[2.8, 3.2]$ by $[-100, 100]$. Local maximum at $(2.919, 45.572)$, and a local minimum at $(3.077, 62.540)$. Inflection points at $(-3.257, -67.885)$, $(0.004, -0.222)$ and $(2.727, 39.274)$. Rising on $(-\infty, -3) \cup (-3, 2.919] \cup [3.077, \infty)$, falling on $[2.919, 3) \cup (3, 3.077]$; concave up on $(-3.257, -3) \cup (0.004, 2.727) \cup (3, \infty)$; concave down on $(-\infty, -3.257) \cup (-3, 0.004) \cup (2.727, 3)$.

24. Local maximum at $(-0.535, 0.688)$; local minimum at $(0.460, 0.168)$; inflection points at $(-5.209, -135.337)$, $(-0.036, 0.426)$ and $(2.486, 11.099)$. Rising on $(-\infty, -5) \cup (-5, -0.535] \cup [0.460, 2) \cup (2, \infty)$, falling on $[-0.535, 0.460]$; concave down on $(-\infty, -5.209) \cup (-5, -0.036) \cup (2, 2.486)$; concave up on $(-5.209, -5) \cup (-0.036, 2) \cup (2.486, \infty)$.

25. $[-4, 4]$ by $[-1, 2]$ shows a complete graph. Inflection points at $(\pm 1.155, 1.5)$, maximum at $(0, 2)$. Rising on $(-\infty, 0]$, falling on $[0, \infty)$; concave down for $|x| < 1.155$, concave up for $|x| > 1.55$.

26. Local minimum at $(-2, -1)$; local maximum at $(2, 1)$; inflection points at $(0, 0)$, $(\pm 3.464, \pm 0.866)$; graph on $[-15, 15]$ by $[-1.4, 1.3]$. Rising on $[-2, 2]$, falling elsewhere, concave down on $(-\infty, -3.464) \cup (0, 3.464)$; concave up elsewhere.

27. 16

28. Side of base is 4.642, height $= 2.321$.

29. 12×18 m, 72 m

30. Base $= 10$, height $= 5$.

31. $x = 15$ ft, $y = 5$ ft.

32. 18 in. wide by 9 in. high.

33. $h = r = \frac{10}{\sqrt[3]{\pi}}$ cm.

34. $r = 5$ cm, $\frac{h}{r} = \frac{8}{\pi}$.

35. Minimum value occurs when $x = 51/8$; minimum $L = 11.04$ inches.

36. $d'(c) = 0 \Rightarrow f'(c) = g'(c)$.

37. a) 16,   b) -1

39. $y \le -\frac{49}{3}$, its absolute maximum

40. $f(x) \ge f(1/2) > 0$

41. $50 + c/2$

42. 67 people

43. $(2km/h)^{1/2}$

44. $(2km/h)^{1/2}$

45. maximum of p is $p(3) = 0$ **46.** 13 items

47. The denominators of f, f', f'' have the same zeros.

49. Diameter and height are the same.

50. $r = 0.497$ ft, $h = 1.288$ ft, $C = \$5.97$.

4.5   RADICAL AND TRANSCENDENTAL FUNCTIONS

Exercises 1-48. For all problems, local extrema and inflection points are given. If intervals for rising, falling and/or concavity are not specified and there are no discontinuities, the graph rises as y goes from a local minimum to a local maximum, etc. Concavity changes at an inflection point. Normally, if y is differentiable at a local maximum (minimum) $x = c$, the graph is concave down (up) on a neighborhood of c.

1. Always rising; concave up for $x < 0$, concave down for $x > 0$; inflection point at $(0,0)$.

2. y is always concave up. y has a local minimum at $(0,0)$; y is decreasing for $x \le 0$, increasing for $x \ge 0$.

3. Local minimum at $(0,0)$, increasing and concave up for $x \ge 0$.

4. Inflection point at $(1,0)$, always decreasing.

5. For $x > -3/2$, y is rising and concave down; local minimum at $(-1.5,0)$.

6. For $x \ge 2$, increasing, concave down; local minimum at $(2,5)$.

7. The interval $-0.096 \le x \le 1.999$ (between $3x + 5 = 3\pi/2$ and $3x + 5 = 7\pi/2$) is one period; $y = 1$, a minimum at the endpoints. $y = 5$, a maximum, at $x = 0.951$. Inflection points at $(0.428, 3)$, $(1.475, 3)$.

8. Falling on $[0, \pi/2]$, rising on $[\pi/2, \pi]$. Inflection points at $\pi/4, 3\pi/4$, local maximum at $(0,4)$, local minimum at $(\pi/2, -2)$.

9. Local maximum at $(\pi/12, \sqrt{2})$, inflection point $(3\pi/12, 0)$, local minimum $(5\pi/12, -\sqrt{2})$, inflection point $(7\pi/12, 0)$, local maximum $(9\pi/12, \sqrt{2})$.

10. Rising on $[0, 0.515]$, and $[2.086, \pi]$. Inflection points at $(1.301, 0)$ and $(2.871, 0)$, local maximum at $(0.515, 5.831)$, local minimum at $(2.086, -5.831)$.

11. Always increasing, concave down for $x < 0$, inflection point at $x = 0$, concave up for $x > 0$.

12. Increasing from a minimum at $(0,0)$ and concave up.

13. Concave down and increasing from a minimum at $(\frac{3}{2}, 0)$.

14. Always decreasing; concave down $x < 3$, concave up $x > 3$; inflection point at $(3,5)$.

15. Use $[0,50]$ by $[-3,4]$. Increasing from a minimum of $(4,-2)$, concave down.

16. Graph on $[-5,8]$ by $[-4,4]$. Local minimum at $(1.500, -1.310)$; $(0,0)$ and $(3,0)$ are inflection points.

17. Local minimum at $(3\pi/4, -2)$; local maximum at $(\pi/4, -8)$. Not defined at $x = \pi/2$; concave down on $(0, \pi/2)$, concave up on $(\pi/2, \pi)$.

18. Graph on $[-\pi/2, \pi/2]$ by $[-20, 20]$. (Period is $-\pi/6 \le x \le \pi/2$). Local minimum at $(0,9)$, local maximum at $(\pi/3, 5)$; concave up on $(-\pi/6, \pi/6)$, concave down on $(\pi/6, \pi/2)$.

19. Inflection points at $(0,0)$ and $(0.268, 0.716)$.   Local minimum at $(-0.341, -0.582)$.

20. Local maximum at $(0.296, 0.148)$; local minimum at $(0,0)$, concave down for $x < 0$ and $x > 0$.

21. y always increasing; concavity changes from up to down at $(-2,0)$.

22. Local minimum at $(3,0)$. Concave down for $x < 3$ and $x > 3$.

23. Graph on $[-\pi, \pi]$ by $[-2,2]$. Minimum at $(0,1)$, maximum at $(\pi/2, -1)$ concave up on $(-\pi/4, \pi/4)$, concave down on $(\pi/4, 3\pi/4)$.

24. Use $[\pi/6, \pi/6 + \pi/3]$ by $[-3,10]$; inflection point at $(\pi/3, 0)$; concave down on $(\pi/6, \pi/3)$.

25. Use $[-5,5]$ by $[0,100]$; always rising and concave up.

26. Graph y on $[-6,6]$ by $[0,10]$; y' on $[-6,6]$ by $[-1,3]$. Always rising and concave up.

27. Graph $y = 3(\ell n(x+1))/\ell n\, 2$ in $[-5,5]$ by $[-10,10]$. Rising for $x > -1$, concave down.

28. Graph on $[-6,6]$ by $[-3,3]$; falling and concave down for $x < 2$.

29. Use $[-5,5]$ by $[0,4]$; concave down where defined, local minima at $(0,0)$ and $(2,0)$.

30. Local maximum at $(-1.155, 1.455)$; local minimum at $(1.155, -1.455)$; inflection points at $(-2,0), (0,0), (2,0)$.

31. Use $[-\pi/2, 3\pi/2]$ by $[-8,8]$; $(0,0)$ and $(\pi,0)$ are inflection points; rising on $(-\pi/2, \pi/2)$, falling on $(\pi/2, 3\pi/2)$, concave up on $(0, \pi/2) \cup (\pi/2, \pi)$.

32. Inflection points at $(-\pi/2, 0), (\pi/2, 0)$. Same graph as #31, but shifted $\pi/2$ units to the left.

33. Use $[-\pi/2, 3\pi/2]$ by $[-3,3]$, $x\, \mathrm{Scl} = \pi/16$;

Local minima at	Local maxima at	Inflection points at
$(-0.968, -1.906)$	$(0.216, 1.216)$	$(-0.413, -0.408)$
$(1.228, -0.223)$	$(1.914, 0.223)$	$(0.673, 0.542)$
$(2.925, -1.216)$	$(4.109, 1.906)$	$(1.571, 0)$
		$(2.469, -0.542)$
		$(3.554, 0.408)$
		$(4.712, 0)$

34.

Local maxima at	Local minima at	Inflection points at
$(3.621, 1.906)$	$(10.724, -1.216)$	$(0, 0)$
$(16.792, 0.223)$	$(20.907, -0.223)$	$(6.949, 0.408)$
$(26.975, 1.216)$	$(34.078, -1.906)$	$(18.850, 0)$
		$(13.463, -0.542)$
		$(24.237, 0.542)$
		$(30.751, -0.408)$

35. Use $[-\pi, \pi]$ by $[-6,6]$; $(-1.298, -4.132)$ is a local minimum, $(-0.858, -3.890)$ inflection point, $(-0.578, -3.718)$ local maximum, $(0.578, 3.718)$ local minimum, $(0.858, 3.890)$ inflection point, $(1.298, 4.132)$ local maximum.

36.

Local maxima at	Local minima at	Inflection points at
$(1.977, 3.186)$	$(2.407, 3.118)$	$(2.220, 3.149)$
$(3.876, -3.118)$	$(4.306, -3.186)$	$(4.063, -3.149)$

37. Minimum at $(0.368, -0.368)$, analytically at $(1/e, -1/e)$.

38. Local minimum at $(0.607, -0.184)$; inflection point at $(0.223, -0.075)$.

39. Local minima at $(\pm 0.60, -0.18) = (\pm\sqrt{(1/e)}, -0.18)$.

40. Local maximum at $(e, 0.368)$; inflection point at $(4.482, 0.335)$.

41. Minimum at $(0, 1/2)$.

42. Local maximum at $(0, 1)$; inflection points at $(-0.675, 0.607)$, $(0.675, 0.607)$.

43. Minimum/maximum at $(\mp 0.849, \mp 0.515)$; inflection points at $(\mp 1.471, \mp 0.328)$ and $(0, 0)$.

44. Local minimum at $(-0.910, -0.335)$; inflection point at $(-1.820, -0.246)$.

45. Maxima at $(\pm 4.493, -4.603)$, $(\pm 10.904, -10.950)$; minima at $(\pm 7.725, 7.790)$. Concavity changes $x = K\pi$, $K = \pm 1, \pm 2, \dots$. Not defined at $x = 0$.

46.

Local maxima at	Local minima at	Inflection points at
$(2.289, 3.945)$	$(-2.289, -3.945)$	$x = 0$
$(-5.087, 24.083)$	$(5.087, -24.083)$	$x = \pm 1.520$
$(8.096, 63.635)$	$(-8.096, -63.635)$	$x = \pm 3.994$
$(-11.173, 122.876)$	$(11.173, -122.876)$	etc.

47. Local maximum at $(3.476, 0.245)$; inflection points at $(-4.652, -0.333)$, $(-2.626, -0.500)$, $(1.090, 0.089)$ and $(5.333, 0.182)$. Not defined at $x = 0$. Concave down $x < -4.652$, $-2.626 < x < -1$ and $1.090 < x < 5.333$; concave up $-4.652 < x < -2.626$, $-1 < x < 1.090$, $5.333 < x$.

48. Graph on $[-5, 5]$ by $[-2, 2]$. (Assume $y(0)$ is defined to be 0). Local maximum at $(-1.743, 0.180)$, inflection point at $(-3.447, 0.104)$; concave up $x < -3.447$ and $x > 2$, concave down $-3.447 < x < 2$.

49. $\min y = (-5)^{3/5} = -2.627$; $\max y = 2.627$.   **50.** $0 \leq y \leq 6.350$

51. $\text{maximum} = 7.460$, $\text{minimum} = -172.64$ **52.** $-35.889 \leq y \leq 42.099$

53. Use $[-3, 3]$ by $[-3, 3]$; inflection point at $(0, 0)$.

54. Use $[-3, 3]$ by $[-3, 3]$; inflection point at $(0, 0)$.

55. Use $[-3, 3]$ by $[-3, 3]$; concavity changes at $x = 0$.

56. Use $[-3, 3]$ by $[-3, 3]$; local maximum at $(0, 1)$.

57. Use $[-3, 3]$ by $[-3, 3]$.

58. 79/4 and 1/4   **59.** 6.25 cm^2 **60.** $\pi/2$ **61.** 5

62. Maximum area occurs when $a^2 = b^2 = 20^2/2$.

63. $\pi/6$ **64.** $\sqrt{1.25}$ **65.** 2

66. Minimum value is $f(\pi) = 0$; $f \geq 0$ and is never negative.

67. No; minimum value is 0.

68. Reflect B in the mirror, obtaining B'. AOB' must be a line.

69. 0.873 miles from point opposite the boat.

70. $r = 10\sqrt{2}/\sqrt{3}$ cm, $h = 20/\sqrt{3}$ cm

71. $A = 8\sin\theta\cos\theta$, 4   **72.** $r/h = \sqrt{2}$ **73.** 29.925

74. b) The asymptotes correspond to triangles with infinitely large bases or heights. $0 \leq x \leq 10$,   c) $h = 15 = 3 \times 5$,   d) A is minimized when $x^2 = 3C^2/4$; the solution follows.

4.6   RELATED RATES OF CHANGE

1. $dA/dt = 2\pi r\, dr/dt$ **2.** $dS/dt = 8\pi r\, dr/dt$

3. $dV/dt = (2/3)\pi rh\, dr/dt$ **4.** $dV/dt = (1/3)\pi r^2 \frac{dh}{dt}$

5. a) $\frac{dP}{dt} = I^2 \frac{dR}{dt} + 2IR\frac{dI}{dt}$ b) $\frac{dP}{dt} = 2IR\frac{dI}{dt}$

6. a) $\frac{1}{s}\left(x\frac{dx}{dt} + y\frac{dy}{dt}\right)$ b) $\frac{dx}{dt} = \frac{-y}{x}\frac{dy}{dt}$.

7. $\frac{ds}{dt} = \left(x\frac{dx}{dt} + y\frac{dy}{dt} + z\frac{dz}{dt}\right)/s$

8. $\frac{dA}{dt} = \frac{1}{2}\left[\frac{da}{dt} \cdot b\sin\theta + a\frac{db}{dt}\sin\theta + (ab\cos\theta)\frac{d\theta}{dt}\right]$

9. π cm^2/min.   **10.** d) $\frac{3}{2}$ ohms/sec

11. a) 14 cm^2/sec, increasing,   b) 0 cm/sec, constant,   c) $-14/13$ cm/sec, decreasing.

12. a) 2 m^3/sec, b) 0, c) 0   **13.** -680 miles/hr; $\frac{-520(x+y)}{\sqrt{x^2+y^2}}$ mph

14. 12 ft/sec, $-119/2$ ft^2/sec **15.** decreasing 0.06366 mm/min

16. 0.0239 in^3/min **17.** a) $1125/32\pi$ cm/min, b) $1500/32\pi$ cm/min

18. a) $\frac{800}{225\pi}$ cm/min, b) $-\frac{400}{15\pi}$ cm/min

19. a) 1.326 cm/min, b) $r = \sqrt{26y - y^2}$, c) -0.553 cm/min

20. $\frac{dV}{dt} = K(4\pi r^2) = 4\pi r^2 \frac{dr}{dt} \Rightarrow \frac{dr}{dt} = K$.

21. 1 ft/min, 40π ft^2/min **22.** 5/2 ft/sec

23. 11 ft/sec **24.** a) $10/9\pi$ in/min, b) $8/5\pi$ in/min

25. 80% per minute **26.** 0.2772 units/min

27. 1 rad/sec **28.** $\frac{2}{5}$ rad/sec

29. a) $\frac{dc}{dt} = 0.3, \frac{dr}{dt} = 0.9, \frac{dp}{dt} = 0.6$, b) $\frac{dc}{dt} = -1.563, \frac{dr}{dt} = 3.5, \frac{dp}{dt} = 5.063$

30. 8 ft/sec, decreasing 3 ft/sec **31.** -1500 ft/sec

32. 20 ft/sec **33.** $\frac{5}{72\pi}$ in/min, $\frac{10}{3}$ in^2/min

34. 80 mph **35.** 7.1 in/min

36. $-344°$/min **37.** 29.5 knots

38. πr units/min, where r is the radius of the clock.

4.7 ANTIDERIVATIVES, INITIAL VALUE PROBLEMS, AND MATHEMATICAL MODELING

1. a) $x^2 + C$, b) $\frac{x^3}{3} + C$ c) $\frac{x^3}{3} - x^2 + x + C$

2. a) $3x^2 + C$, b) $\frac{x^6}{6} + C$, c) $\frac{x^6}{6} - 3x^2 + 3x + C$

3. a) $x^{-3} + C$, b) $-x^{-3}/3 + C$, c) $-x^{-3}/3 + x^2 + 3x + C$

4. a) $-x^{-2} + C$, b) $\frac{-x^{-2}}{4} + \frac{x^3}{3} + C$, c) $\frac{x^{-2}}{2} + \frac{x^2}{2} - x + C$

5. a) $-\frac{1}{x} + C$, b) $-\frac{5}{x} + C$, c) $2x + \frac{5}{x} + C$

6. a) $x^{-2} + C$, b) $\frac{-x^{-2}}{4} + C$, c) $\frac{x^4}{4} + \frac{x^{-2}}{2} + C$

7. a) $x^{3/2} + C$, b) $(8/3)x^{3/2} + C$, c) $(1/3)x^3 - (8/3)x^{3/2} + C$

8. a) $x^{4/3} + C$, b) $\frac{1}{2}x^{2/3} + C$, c) $\frac{3}{4}x^{4/3} + \frac{3}{2}x^{2/3} + C$

9. a) $x^{2/3} + C$, b) $x^{1/3} + C$, c) $x^{-1/3} + C$

10. a) $x^{1/2} + C$, b) $x^{-1/2} + C$, c) $x^{-3/2} + C$

11. a) $(1/3)\cos(3x) + C$, b) $-3\cos x + C$, c) $-3\cos x + (1/3)\cos(3x) + C$

12. a) $\sin(\pi x) + C$, b) $\sin(\frac{\pi x}{2}) + C$, c) $\frac{2}{\pi}\sin(\frac{\pi x}{2}) + C$

13. a) $\tan x + C$, b) $\tan(5x) + C$, c) $(1/5)\tan(5x) + C$

14. a) $-\cot x + C$, b) $-\cot(7x) + C$, c) $-\frac{1}{7}\cot(7x) + C$

15. a) $\sec x + C$, b) $\sec 2x + C$, c) $2\sec 2x + C$

16. a) $-\csc x + C$, b) $-2\csc(4x) + C$, c) $-\frac{1}{4}\csc(4x) + C$

17. $x + (1/2)\cos 2x + C$

18. $3x + 4\sin x + \sin(2x) + C$.

19. a) $-\sqrt{x} + C$, b) $x + C$, c) $\sqrt{x} + C$, d) $-x + C$, e) $x - \sqrt{x} + C$, f) $-3\sqrt{x} - 2x + C$, g) $x^2/2 - \sqrt{x} + C$, h) $-3x + C$

20. a) $e^x + C$ b) $x\sin x + C$ c) $-e^x + C$ d) $-x\sin x + C$ e) $e^x + x\sin x + C$ f) $3e^x - 2x\sin x + C$ g) $\frac{x^2}{2} + e^x + C$ h) $x\sin x - 4x + C$

21. b

22. b

23. $y = x^2 - 7x + 10$

24. $y = 10x - \frac{x^2}{2} - 1$

25. $y = x^3/3 + x + 1$

26. $y = \frac{x^3}{3} + \frac{2}{3}x^{3/2}$

27. $y = 5/x + 2$

28. $y = \frac{x^2}{2} - \frac{1}{x} - \frac{1}{2}$

29. $y = x^3 + x^2 + x - 3$

30. $y = 3x^3 - 2x^2 + 5x + 10$

31. $y = x + \sin x + 4$

32. $y = \sin x - \cos x$

33. $y = -x^3 + x^2 + 4x + 1$

34. $y = x^3 - 4x^2 + 5$.

35. $s = 4.9t^2 + 10$

36. $s = 1 - \cos t$

37. $s = 16t^2 + 20t$

38. $s = 1 - \sin t$

39. $y = 2x^{3/2} - 50$

40. $y = x^3 + 1$; answer is unique.

41. $r = x^3 - 3x^2 + 12x$

42. $c(x) = x^3 - 6x^2 + 15x + 400$

43. 48 m/sec downwards

44. 1200 m/sec

45. -14 m/sec

46. 1162.5 m

47. $y = (C - kt)^2/4$

48. a) $y = (6 - 0.1t)^2/4$;   b) 60 min

49. a) 24 seconds,   c) 45.821, 4.109

50. 24 sec, $1.817 \leq D \leq 48.537$

51. d

52. $y(0) \neq 2$

53. $y = x^2 + C$

54. $y = -x^2 + 2x + C$

55. $y = x - x^3 + C$

56. $y = \frac{x^3}{3} + C$

57. Increasing, inflection point at $(0,1)$ - from concave down to up.

58. Inflection point at $x = 0$; slope becomes infinite as $x \to \pm 1$.

59. minimum at $(0,0)$; $y \to$ constant as $x \to \pm\infty$.

60. Always decreasing, inflection point at $(0,1)$.

61.

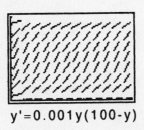
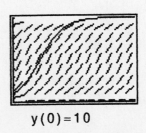

y'=0.001y(100-y)   y(0)=10

PRACTICE EXERCISES, CHAPTER 4

1. $y' = 1/(x+1)^2 > 0$

2. $y' = 2\sin t \cos t - 3 < 0$

3. $y' > 0 \Rightarrow y$ always increasing

4. No   **5.** 12

6. Let $y = x^4 + 2x^2 - 2$. $y(0)y(1) < 0$; $y' > 0$ on $(0,1)$.

7. Local minimum at $x = -1$, inflection points at $x = 0$ and $x = 2$.

8. Local minima at $x = -1$, $x = 2$; local maximum at $x = 0$; inflection points at -0.549 and 1.215.

9. a) T,   b) P 10. day 23

Exercises 11 - 30: See comment at beginning of answers to Exercises, Section 4.5.

11. Use $[-6, 6]$ by $[-4, 4]$; inflection point at $(-1, 0)$.

12. Use $[-4, 10]$ by $[-300, 5]$. Maximum at $(-1, 0)$, minimum at $(7, -256)$, inflection point at $(3, -128)$.

13. Use $[-6, 6]$ by $[-4, 4]$; inflection point at $(2, 0)$.

14. Minimum at $(1, 0)$, no maximum, concave down.

15. Use $[-6, 6]$ by $[-4, 4]$; maximum at $(0.385, 1.215)$, concave down.

16. Use $[-4, 4]$ by $[-4, 30]$; no local extrema, inflection point at $(0, 20)$.

17. Use $[-6, 6]$ by $[-50, 50]$. Since $y' \leq 0$ everywhere, there are no hidden extrema. Always falling. Concavity changes from up to down at inflection point $(1/2, -12.333)$.

18. Use $[-4, 4]$ by $[-4, 25]$. Local maxima at $(0.163, 20.073)$ and $(2.107, 22.056)$, local minimum at $(0.730, 19.870)$, inflection points at $(0.423, 19.978)$ and $(1.577, 21.133)$.

19. Use $[-6, 6]$ by $[-8, 3]$ and $[-0.5, 0.5]$ by $[0.99, 1.01]$ to show the behavior of the graph. Local minima at $(-0.118, 0.9976)$ and $(2.118, -6.456)$, local maximum at $(0, 1)$, inflection points at $(-0.060, 0.9988)$ and $(1.393, -3.414)$.

20. Use $[-2, 2]$ by $[-10, 10]$. There is no hidden behavior. Inflection point (down to up) at $(0, 4)$.

21. Use $[-5, 5]$ by $[-15, 25]$. Local minimum at $(-0.578, 0.972)$, inflection point at $(1.079, 13.601)$, local maximum at $(1.692, 20.517)$.

22. Use $[-6, 4]$ by $[-40, 60]$; then $[-5, -3]$ by $[-40, -30]$ and $[0, 1]$ by $[-0.5, 2.5]$. Local maximum at $(-3.791, -34.193)$, inflection point at $(-3.562, -34.348)$, local minimum at $(-3.303, -34.518)$, inflection point at $(-1.5, -16.55)$, local maximum at $(0.303, 1.418)$, inflection point at $(0.562, 1.248)$, local minimum at $(0.791, 1.093)$.

23. Use $[-5, 5]$ by $[-15, 20]$; inflection point at $(3.710, -3.420)$, local maximum at $(0.215, -2.417)$.

24. Use $[-4, 4]$ by $[-10, 10]$. Local maximum at $(-1.805, -6.483$, local minimum at $(-0.209, 3.525)$.

25. Graph $y = (\ell n|x|)/\ell n\,3$ in $[-1, 4]$ by $[-5, 5]$, not defined at $x = 0$, always concave down.

26. Use $[-4, 4]$ by $[-5, 20]$. No hidden behavior. Local minimum at $(1, 0)$.

27. Use $[1, 5]$ by $[-5, 5]$; defined for $x > 2$, inflection point at $(4.000, 1.204)$; always rising; concave down on $(2, 4.000)$, concave up on $(4.000, \infty)$.

28. Use $[0, 4\pi]$ by $[-2, 2]$ to see two periods. On $[0, 2\pi]$:

Local maxima at	Local minima at	Inflection points at
$(0.176, 1.266)$	$(0.994, -0.513)$	$(0.542, 0.437)$
$(1.571, 0) = (\pi/2, 0)$	$(2.148, -0.513)$	$(1.266, -0.267)$
$(2.965, 1.266)$	$(3.834, -1.806)$	$(1.876, -0.267)$
$(4.712, 2.000)$	$(5.591, -1.806)$	$(2.600, 0.437)$
		$(3.425, -0.329)$
		$(4.281, 0.120)$
		$(5.144, 0.120)$
		$(6.000, -0.329)$

29. Use $[-1, 2]$ by $[-1, 2]$. $(0.500, 0.707)$ is a local maximum; local minima at $(0, 0)$ and $(1, 0)$.

30. Use $[-4, 3]$ by $[-6, 10]$. Inflection point at $(-2, 0)$.

31. $2.1958\ldots$

32. $1.3181\ldots$

33. $0.828\ldots$

34. $0.100, 1.984, -0.977, 0.643$

36. a) $f(0)f(1) < 0$, $f'(x) > 0 \Rightarrow f = 0$ has exactly one solution; b) 0.682

37. Minimum is $f(-6) = -74$; maximum is $f(-4.550) = 16.25$

38. $f(2.840) = 0.730 \leq f(x) \leq f(6.481) = 3.526$

39. $r = 25$, $s = 50$ **40.** 54 square units

41. height = 3 ft, side of base = 6 ft.   **42.** $4 \times 4 \times 2$ ft high.

43. $h = 2$, $r = \sqrt{2}$ **44.** $r = h = 4$

45. $x = 48/\sqrt{7}$ miles, $y = 36/\sqrt{7}$ miles.   **46.** $r = 100/\pi$, $x = 100$

47. 276 Grade A tires, 553 Grade B.

48. a) 1 at $t = 5\pi/6$, $11\pi/6$, etc.   b) they collide at $t = \pi/3$, $4\pi/3, \ldots$

49. $12 \times 6 \times 2$ inches, 144 in^3

50. a) b) $V = 2x(22 - 2x)(17 - 2x)$,   c) $0 < x < 8.5$, $0 < V \leq 1058.37$ e) $x = 3.171$, $V = 1058.37$ f) $x = 0.610$ in. or 6.756 in.

    b) In both cases $V(2.427) = 131.341$ is the maximum volume.

51. Particle starts at $(5, 0)$, moves left until it reaches $(0.94, 0)$ then moves right.

52. The particle moves to the right $0 \leq t < 0.528$, after which time it moves to the left. It passes through the origin at $t = 1.398$.

53. -40 m^2/sec   **54.** 5 m/sec

55. 1 cm/min   **56.** 4 units/sec

57. b) $125/144\pi$ ft/min   **58.** -60 mph

59. -2 rad/sec   **60.** 5 rad/sec

61. All such functions are represented by the formula.

62. The functions differ by a constant.

63. a) C b) $x + C$,   c) $\frac{x^2}{2} + C$ d) $\frac{x^3}{3} + C$ e) $x^{11}/11 + C$ f) $-x^{-1} + C$ g) $-x^{-4}/4 + C$ h) $\frac{2}{7}x^{7/2} + C$ i) $\frac{3}{7}x^{7/3} + C$ j) $\frac{4}{7}x^{7/4} + C$ k) $\frac{2}{3}x^{3/2} + C$ l) $2x^{1/2} + C$ m) $\frac{7}{4}x^{4/7} + C$ n) $\frac{-3}{4}x^{-4/3} + C$

64. a) $-\cos x + C$ b) $\sin x + C$ c) $\sec x + C$ d) $\cot x + C$ e) $\tan x + C$ f) $\csc x + C$

65. $x^3 + (5/2)x^2 - 7x + C$ **66.** $-\frac{1}{x} + \frac{x^2}{2} + x + C$

67. $(2/3)x^{3/2} + 2x^{1/2} + C$

68. $\frac{3}{4}x^{4/3} + \frac{4}{5}x^{5/4} + C$

69. $(3/5)\sin 5x + C$

70. $-16\cos(x/2) + C$

71. $\tan 3x + C$

72. $-2\cot 2x + C$

73. $(1/2)x - \sin x + C$

74. $\frac{1}{2}x^6 + 2\sin 8x + C$

75. $3\sec(x/3) + 5x + C$

76. $x + \csc x + C$

77. $\tan x - x + C$

78. $-\cot x - x + C$

79. $x - (1/2)\sin 2x + C$

80. $\frac{1}{2}\sin 2x + C$

81. $y = 1 + x + x^2/2 + x^3/6$

82. $y = x^4 - 7x^3 + 7x^2 - 7x + 7$

83. $y = x - 1/x - 1$

84. $y = \frac{1}{3}x^3 + 2x - \frac{1}{x} - \frac{1}{3}$

85. $y = \sin x$

86. $y = -\cos x$

87. $y = x$

88. $y = x^3 + 2x - 4$

89. Duck!

90. $v = 2t + 3t^2 + 4;\ 6$

91.

92.

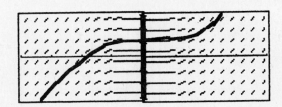

CHAPTER 5

INTEGRATION

5.1   CALCULUS AND AREA

1. a)

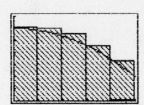 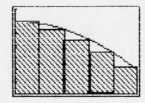 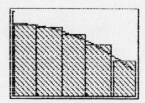

b) $LRAM_5(6 - x^2) = (6 - 0^2)\Delta x + (6 - (0.4)^2)\Delta x + (6 - (0.8)^2)\Delta x + (6 - (1.2)^2)\Delta x + (6 - (1.6)^2)\Delta x = 10.08$(where $\Delta x = 0.4$).

$RRAM_5(6 - x^2) = (6 - 0.4^2)\Delta x + (6 - 0.8)^2)\Delta x + (6 - 1.2^2)\Delta x + (6 - 1.6^2)\Delta x + (6 - 2^2)\Delta x = 8.48$.

$MRAM_5(6 - x^2) = (6 - 0.2^2)\Delta x + (6 - 0.6^2)\Delta x + (6 - 1^2)\Delta x + (6 - 1.4^2)\Delta x + (6 - 1.8^2)\Delta x = 9.36$

2. a)

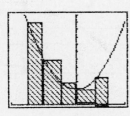  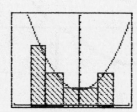

b) $LRAM_5(x^2 + 2) = ((-3)^2 + 2) \cdot 1 + ((-2)^2 + 2) \cdot 1 + ((-1)^2 + 2) \cdot 1 + ((0)^2 + 2) \cdot 1 + ((1)^2 + 2) \cdot 1 = 25$.

$RRAM_5(x^2 + 2) = ((-2)^2 + 2) \cdot 1 + ((-1)^2 + 2) \cdot 1 + ((0)^2 + 2) \cdot 1 + ((1)^2 + 2) \cdot 1 + ((2)^2 + 2) \cdot 1 = 20$.

$MRAM_5(x^2 + 2) = ((-2.5)^2 + 2) \cdot 1 + ((-1.5)^2 + 2) \cdot 1 + ((-0.5)^2 + 2) \cdot 1 + ((0.5)^2 + 2) \cdot 1 + ((1.5)^2 + 2) \cdot 1 = 21.25$.

3. a)

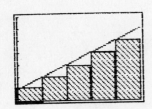 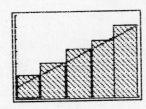 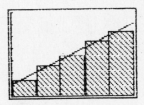

b) $LRAM_5(x+1) = [(0+1)+(1+1)+(2+1)+(3+1)+(4+1)]\Delta x = 15$ (where $\Delta x = 1$).

$RRAM_5(x+1) = [(1+1)+(2+1)+(3+1)+(4+1)+(5+1)]\Delta x = 20$.

$MRAM_5(x+1) = [(0.5+1)+(1.5+1)+(2.5+1)+(3.5+1)+(4.5+1)]\Delta x = 17.5$.

4. a)

 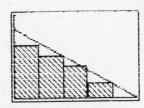 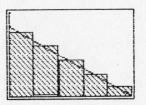

b) $LRAM_5(5-x) = 5\cdot 1 + 4\cdot 1 + 3\cdot 1 + 2\cdot 1 + 1\cdot 1 = 15$.

$RRAM_5(5-x) = 4+3+2+1+0 = 10$.

$MRAM_5(5-x) = 4.5+3.5+2.5+1.5+0.5 = 12.5$.

5. a)

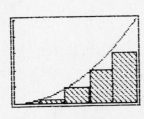 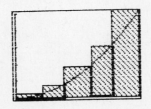 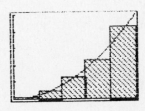

b) $LRAM_5(2x^2) = [2(0)^2+2(1)^2+2(2^2)+2(3^2)+2(4^2)]\Delta x = 60$ (where $\Delta x = 1$).

$RRAM_5(2x^2) = [2(1^2)+2(2^2)+2(3^2)+2(4^2)+2(5^2)]\Delta x = 110$.

$MRAM_5(2x^2) = [2(.5^2)+2(1.5^2)+2(2.5^2)+2(3.5^2)+2(4.5^2)]\Delta x = 82.5$.

6. a)

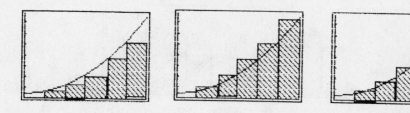

b) $LRAM_5(x^2 + 2) = (1^2 + 2)(1) + (2^2 + 2)(1) + (3^2 + 2)(1) + (4^2 + 2)(1) + (5^2 + 2)(1) = 65$.

$RRAM_5(x^2 + 2) = (2^2 + 2)(1) + (3^2 + 2)(1) + (4^2 + 2)(1) + (5^2 + 2)(1) + (6^2 + 2)(1) = 100$.

$MRAM_5(x^2 + 2) = (1.5^2 + 2)(1) + (2.5^2 + 2)(1) + (3.5^2 + 2)(1) + (4.5^2 + 2)(1) + (5.5^2 + 2)(1) = 81.25$.

7.

n	$LRAM_n f$	$RRAM_n f$	$MRAM_n f$
10	12.645	14.445	13.4775
100	13.41045	13.59045	13.499775
1000	13.4910045	13.5090045	13.49999775

8.

n	$LRAM_n f$	$RRAM_n f$	$MRAM_n f$
10	35	37.5	35.625
100	35.7125	35.9625	35.83125
1000	35.820875	35.845875	35.8333125

9.

n	$LRAM_n f$	$RRAM_n f$	$MRAM_n f$
10	268.125	393.125	325.9375
100	321.28125	333.78125	327.48438..
1000	326.87531..	328.12531..	327.49984..

10.

n	$LRAM_n f$	$RRAM_n f$	$MRAM_n f$
10	40.96	58.56	49.12
100	48.4576	50.2176	49.3312
1000	49.245376	49.421376	49.333312

11.

n	$LRAM_n f$	$RRAM_n f$	$MRAM_n f$
10	1.98352..	1.98352..	2.00825..
100	1.99984..	1.99984	2.00008..
1000	1.99999..	1.99999..	2.00000..

12.

n	$LRAM_n f$	$RRAM_n f$	$MRAM_n f$
10	1.07648..	0.91940..	1.00102..
100	1.00783..	0.99212..	1.00001..
1000	1.00078..	0.99921..	1.00000..

13.

n	$LRAM_n f$	$RRAM_n f$	$MRAM_n f$
10	1.77264..	1.77264..	1.77227..
100	1.77245..	1.77245..	1.77245..
1000	1.77245..	1.77245..	1.77245..

14.

n	$LRAM_n f$	$RRAM_n f$	$MRAM_n f$
10	17.67064..	17.50527..	17.61632
100	17.61493..	17.59839..	17.60694..
1000	17.60768..	17.60602..	17.60685..

15. $17.5, 83\frac{1}{3}, 13.5, 327.5, 2$, respectively.

16. $12.5, 81\frac{2}{3}, 35\frac{5}{6}, 49\frac{1}{3}, 1$, respectively.

19. $\sum_{k=1}^{4} \frac{1}{k} = \frac{1}{1} + \frac{1}{2} + \frac{1}{3} + \frac{1}{4} = \frac{25}{12}$

20. $\sum_{k=1}^{4} \frac{12}{k} = \frac{12}{1} + \frac{12}{2} + \frac{12}{3} + \frac{12}{4} = 12 + 6 + 4 + 3 = 25$

21. $\sum_{k=1}^{3}(k+2) = (1+2) + (2+2) + (3+2) = 12$

22. $\sum_{k=1}^{5}(2k-1) = 1 + 3 + 5 + 7 + 9 = 25$

23. $\sum_{k=0}^{4} \frac{k}{4} = \frac{0}{4} + \frac{1}{4} + \frac{2}{4} + \frac{3}{4} + \frac{4}{4} = \frac{5}{2}$

24. $\sum_{k=-2}^{2} 3k = 3(-2) + 3(-1) + 3(0) + 3(1) + 3(2) = 0$

25. $\sum_{k=1}^{4} \cos k\pi = \cos(1 \cdot \pi) + \cos 2\pi + \cos 3\pi + \cos 4\pi = 0$

26. $\sum_{k=1}^{3} \sin \frac{\pi}{k} = \sin \frac{\pi}{1} + \sin \frac{\pi}{2} + \sin \frac{\pi}{3} = 0 + 1 + \frac{\sqrt{3}}{2} = \frac{2+\sqrt{3}}{2}$

27. $\sum_{k=1}^{4}(-1)^k = (-1)^1 + (-1)^2 + (-1)^3 + (-1)^4 = 0$

28. $\sum_{k=1}^{4}(-1)^{k+1} = (-1)^2 + (-1)^3 + (-1)^4 + (-1)^5 = 0$

29. All   **30.** b   **31.** $\sum_{k=1}^{6} k$

32. $\sum_{k=1}^{4} k^2$ **33.** $\sum_{k=1}^{4} \frac{1}{2^k}$ **34.** $\sum_{k=1}^{5} \frac{1}{k}$

35. $\sum_{k=1}^{5}(-1)^{k+1}\frac{k}{5}$ **36.** $\sum_{k=1}^{5}(-1)^k \frac{k}{5}$ **37.** 55

38. 56   **39.** -91 **40.** 121

41. -20 **42.** 0   **43.** $1,000,000$

44. 0

45. a) -15 b) 1   c) 1   d) -11 e) 16

46. a) 0   b) 250   c) n d) $1-n$

47. $\frac{6\cdot1}{1+1} + \frac{6\cdot2}{2+1} + \frac{6\cdot3}{3+1} + \frac{6\cdot4}{4+1} + \frac{6\cdot5}{5+1}$. $\sum_{k=1}^{100} \frac{6k}{k+1} = 574.816..$

48. $\frac{1-1}{1} + \frac{2-1}{2} + \frac{3-1}{3} + \frac{4-1}{4} + \frac{5-1}{5}$. $\sum_{k=1}^{100} \frac{k-1}{k} = 94.8126..$

49. $1(1-1)(1-2) + 2(2-1)(2-2) + 3(3-1)(3-2) + 4(4-1)(4-2) + 5(5-1)(5-2)$. $\sum_{k=1}^{500} k(k-1)(k-2) = 15,562,437,750$

50. $(1-0)(2-0) + (1-1)(2-1) + (1-3)(2-3) + (1-4)(2-4) + (1-5)(2-5)$. $\sum_{k=0}^{500}(1-k)(2-k) = 41,417,000$

51. 78

54. In $LRAM_n x^2$ each of the rectangles used is an inscribed rectangle and underestimates the area in its interval under the curve $y = x^2$. In $RRAM_n x^2$ each of the rectangles used is a superscribed rectangle and overestimates the area in its interval under the curve $y = x^2$.

56. $LRAM_n f < A_a^b f < RRAM_n f$

57. $RRAM_n f < A_a^b f < LRAM_n f$

62. $RRAM_n(x + 1) = 5\left[\frac{5}{2}\frac{n+1}{n} + 1\right]$. $Lim_{n\to\infty} RRAM_n(x + 1) = \frac{35}{2} = A_0^5(x + 1)$.

63. $RRAM_n(2x^2) = \frac{125}{3}\frac{(n+1)(2n+1)}{n^2} \to \frac{250}{3}$ as $n \to \infty$.

64. $RRAM_n(x^2 + 2) = 25(1 + \frac{1}{n}) + \frac{125}{6}(1 + \frac{1}{n})(2 + \frac{1}{n}) + 15$. $A_1^6(x^2 + 2) = \lim_{n\to\infty} RRAM_n(x^2 + 2) = \frac{245}{3}$.

65. $RRAM_n f = \frac{9}{2}\left(\frac{n+1}{n}\right)\left(\frac{2n+1}{n}\right) - \frac{9}{2}\left(\frac{n+1}{n}\right) + 9 \to \frac{27}{2}$ as $n \to \infty$.

66. $RRAM_n(2x^3 + 3) = 5\left[\frac{125}{2}\left(\frac{n+1}{n}\right)^2 + 3\right]$. $\lim_{n\to\infty} RRAM_n(2x^3 + 3) = 327.5$.

67. $RRAM_n f = 4 + 24\left(\frac{n+1}{n}\right) - \frac{64}{3}\left(\frac{n+1}{n}\right)\left(\frac{2n+1}{n}\right) + 64\left(\frac{n+1}{n}\right)^2 \to \frac{148}{3}$ as $n \to \infty$.

68. $LRAM_n x^2 = \frac{125}{n^3}\frac{(n-1)n[2(n-1)+1]}{6}$.

70. $MRAM_n x^2 = \frac{125}{4n^3}\frac{(2n-1)n(2n+1)}{3}$.

72. $MRAM_n x^3 = \frac{625}{8}\left(2 - \frac{1}{n^2}\right)$

73. $A_0^x(t^3) = \frac{x^4}{4}$

74. If we count the black dots, we get $1 + 3 + 5 + 7 = \sum_{k=1}^{4}(2k - 1)$. If we count the dots in the square we get 4^2 so $\sum_{k=1}^{4}(2k - 1) = 4^2$.

75. The explanation is below the picture.

76. Number of dots in square (n^2)+ number of dots in triangle $(\sum_{k=1}^{n} k)$ = number of dots in trapezoid $(\sum_{k=n+1}^{2n} k)$.

5.2 DEFINITE INTEGRALS

1. a)   b)   c)

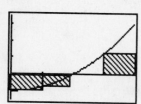 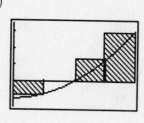 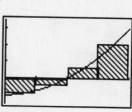

2. a)   b)   c)

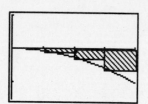 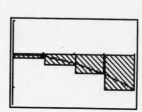 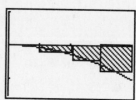

3. a)   b)   c)

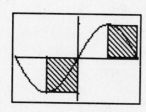 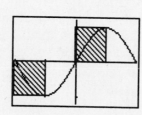 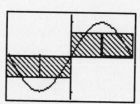

4. a)   b)   c)

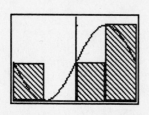 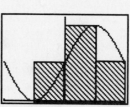 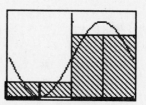

5. 0.8   **6.** 1.1   **7.** $\int_0^2 x^2 dx$ **8.** $\int_{-1}^0 2x^3 dx$ **9.** $\int_{-7}^5 (x^2 - 3x)dx$ **10.** $\int_1^4 \frac{1}{x}dx$

11. $\int_2^3 \frac{1}{1-x}dx$ **12.** $\int_0^1 \sqrt{4-x^2}dx$ **13.** $\int_0^4 \cos x\, dx$ **14.** $\int_{-\pi}^\pi \sin^3 x\, dx$

15. $A = -\int_0^2 (x^2 - 4)dx = 5.333$ **16.** $A = \int_0^3 (9 - x^2)dx = 18$

17. $A = \int_0^5 \sqrt{25 - x^2}dx = 19.635$ **18.** $A = \int_{-3}^3 2\sqrt{9 - x^2}dx = 28.274$

19. $A = \int_0^{\pi/4} \tan x\, dx = 0.347$ **20.** $A = -\int_{\pi/2}^{3\pi/2} \cos x\, dx = 2.$

21.

	$LRAM_nf$	$RRAM_nf$	$MRAM_nf$
$n = 100$	0.44290145	0.44293477	0.44291878
$n = 1000$	0.44291688	0.44292022	0.44291856
NINT(f)		0.442918559	

22.

	$LRAM_nf$	$RRAM_nf$	$MRAM_nf$
$n = 100$	0.61053958	0.67201053	0.64257251
$n = 1000$	0.63905608	0.64520317	0.64214246
NINT(f)		0.64213818	

23.

	$LRAM_nf$	$RRAM_nf$	$MRAM_nf$
$n = 100$	0.75272914	0.67210056	0.71218935
$n = 1000$	0.71629745	0.70823459	0.71226377
NINT(f)		0.71226452	

24.

	$LRAM_nf$	$RRAM_nf$	$MRAM_nf$
$n = 100$	0.94392766	0.91964098	0.93175713
$n = 1000$	0.93298071	0.93055204	0.93176610
NINT(f)		0.93176619	

25.

	$LRAM_nf$	$RRAM_nf$	$MRAM_nf$
$n = 100$	2.0282123	2.0575260	2.0427050
$n = 1000$	2.0412951	2.0442265	2.0427592
NINT(f)		2.0427597	

26.

	$LRAM_nf$	$RRAM_nf$	$MRAM_nf$
$n = 100$	0.91122692	0.86122692	0.88622693
$n = 1000$	0.88872692	0.88372692	0.88622692
NINT (f)		0.88622692	

27. $\text{NINT}((2 - x - 5x^2, x, -1, 3) = -42.666$.

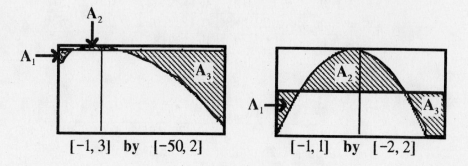

$$[-1, 3] \ \ \textbf{by} \ \ [-50, 2] \qquad\qquad [-1, 1] \ \ \textbf{by} \ \ [-2, 2]$$

The definite integral has the value $A_2 - A_1 - A_3$. Since A_1 and A_3 are below the x-axis, they each contribute a negative value to the integral.

28. $\text{NINT}(x^2 e^{-x^2}, x, 0, 3) = 0.443$. Graph $y = x^2 e^{-x^2}$ in $[0, 3]$ by $[0, 0.5]$. The integral gives the area of the region between the curve and the x-axis for $0 \leq x \leq 3$.

29. $\text{NINT}(\sin(x^2), x, 0, 2\pi) = 0.642$. Graph $y = \sin(x^2)$ in $[0, 2\pi]$ by $[-1, 1]$. The integral is the sum of the signed areas (positive if above the x-axis, negative if below the x-axis) between the x-axis and the curve.

30. $\text{NINT}\left(\frac{\sin x}{x}, x, 1, 10\right) = 0.712$. Graph $y = \frac{\sin x}{x}$ in $[0, 10]$ by $[-1, 1]$. The value of the integral is the sum of the signed areas between the x-axis and the curve.

31. $\int_{-1}^{1} \sqrt{1 - x^2}\, dx = \frac{\pi}{2}$. $\text{NINT}(\sqrt{1 - x^2}, x, -1, 1) = 1.571$.

32. This is the area of the quarter of the circle lying in the first quadrant. $\pi r^2 / 4 = \pi$. $\text{NINT}(\sqrt{4 - x^2}, x, 0, 2) = 3.142$.

33. $\int_{-1}^{1}(1 - |x|)\, dx = 1 = \text{NINT}(1 - |x|, x, -1, 1)$.

34. This region may be regarded as the rectangle with vertices $(-1, 0)$, $(1, 0)$, $(-1, 1)$, $(1, 1)$ surmounted by a semicircle of radius 1. Hence its area is $2 \cdot 1 + \pi(1^2)/2 = 2 + \pi/2$. $\text{NINT}(1 + \sqrt{1 - x^2}, x, -1, 1) = 3.571$.

35. For $[0, 5]$, $\text{MRAM}_n f = \frac{625}{8}\left(2 - \frac{1}{n^2}\right) \to \frac{625}{4}$ as $n \to \infty$. For $[0, a]$, $\text{MRAM}_n f = \frac{a^4}{8}\left(2 - \frac{1}{n^2}\right) \to \frac{a^4}{4}$ as $n \to \infty$.

36. 6

37. Graph $y_1 = 1 + 0\sqrt{x}$ and $y_2 = -1 + 0\sqrt{-x}$ in $[-2, 3]$ by $[-2, 2]$. $x = 0$ is the only discontinuity. Integral $= 1$.

38. In dot format graph $y = 2\,\text{int}(abs(x - 3))$ in $[-6, 5]$ by $[-2, 19]$. The discontinuities occur at $x = n$ for every integer n. Integral $= 74$.

39. Graph $y = \frac{x^2-1}{x+1}$ in $[-3, 4]$ by $[-5, 4]$. $x = -1$ is the only discontinuity. Integral $= -3.5$.

40. Graph $y = \frac{9-x^2}{x-3}$ in $[-5, 6]$ by $[-10, 3]$. $x = 3$ is the only discontinuity. $I = -38.5$.

41. a) $g(x) = \frac{\sin x}{x}$, $x \neq 0$, $g(0) = 1$ b) 1.848   c) 3.697

42. a) $g(x) = \frac{1-\cos x}{x^2}$, $x \neq 0$, $g(0) = \frac{1}{2}$.   b) 1.185   c) 0

45. Conjecture: $\text{NINT}(y_i(x), 0, 2) = \text{NINT}(y_i(x), 0, 1) + \text{NINT}(y_i(x), 1, 2)$.

47. $a = c = -1$, $b = 1$

49. $S_n = \text{RRAM}_n(x^2)$ on $[0, 1]$ and $\lim_{n \to \infty} S_n = 0.333$.

50. $S_n = \text{RRAM}_n(8x^2)$ on $[0, 1]$. $\lim_{n \to \infty} S_n = 2.667$.

51. $S_n = \text{RRAM}(1 + x)$ on $[0, 1]$. $\lim_{n \to \infty} S_n = 1.5$.

52. $S_n = \text{RRAM}_n(\frac{1}{1+x})$ on $[0, 1]$. $\lim_{n \to \infty} S_n = 0.693$.

53. $S_n = \text{RRAM}_n((2 + x)^2)$ on $[0, 1]$. $\lim_{n \to \infty} S_n = 6.333$.

5.3 ANTIDERIVATIVES AND DEFINITE INTEGRALS

1. $\frac{8}{3}$ **2.** 3   **3.** $\frac{16}{3}$ **4.** $\frac{3}{2}$ **5.** $\frac{8}{3}$ **6.** $\frac{4}{3}$

7. $\frac{27}{4}$ **8.** $\frac{32}{15}$ **9.** 1   **10.** 1   **11.** 1   **12.** 1

13. $\frac{2}{\pi}$ **14.** $2 + \pi$ **15.** $1 + \sqrt{3}$ **16.** 1   **17.** $\frac{b^{n+1}}{n+1}$

19. a) 0   b) -8 c) -12 d) 10   e) -2 f) 16

20. a) 2   b) 9   c) -2 d) 1   e) -6 f) 1

21. a) 5 b) -5 c) -3 **22.** a) 3 b) -7 c) 4

23. $\frac{-13}{3}$ **24.** 4 **25.** $\frac{2}{\sqrt{3}}$ **26.** $\frac{1}{2}$ **27.** $-0.475...$ **28.** $0.0929...$

29. $\frac{1}{2} \leqq \int_0^1 \frac{1}{1+x^2}dx \leqq 1$

30. $\frac{13}{20} \leqq \int_0^1 \frac{1}{1+x^2}dx \leq \frac{9}{10}$

31. $c = \frac{1}{\sqrt[3]{4}}$. Graph $y_1 = x^3 + 1$ and $y_2 = f(c) = \frac{5}{4}$ in $[0,1]$ by $[-1,2]$.

32. $c = \sqrt{3}$. Graph $y_1 = 9 - x^2$, $y_2 = 9 - c^2 = 6$ in $[0,3]$ by $[-1,9]$.

33. $c = \sqrt{\frac{4}{\pi} - 1}$. Graph $y_1 = \frac{1}{x^2+1}$, $y_2 = f(c) = \frac{\pi}{4}$ in $[0,1]$ by $[-0.5,1]$.

34. $c = \pm\sqrt{1 - 9/\pi^2}$. Graph $y_1 = 1/\sqrt{1 - x^2}$, $y_2 = f(c) = \frac{\pi}{3}$ on $[-\frac{1}{2}, \frac{1}{2}]$ by $[-\frac{1}{2}, \frac{3}{2}]$.

35. $\frac{15}{4}$ **36.** $\frac{710}{11}$

37. This is an immediate consequence of the Mean Value Theorem for Definite Integrals.

5.4 THE FUNDAMENTAL THEOREM OF CALCULUS

1. 3 **2.** $\frac{7}{3}$ **3.** 1 **4.** $10\sqrt{5}$

5. $\frac{5}{2}$ **6.** 1 **7.** 2 **8.** π

9. $2\sqrt{3}$ **10.** $2\sqrt{3}$ **11.** 0 **12.** 4

13. $\frac{8}{3}$ **14.** 3 **15.** $\frac{5}{2}$ **16.** 12

17. $\frac{1}{2}$ **18.** 8 **19.** $-\frac{5}{2}$ **20.** $-\frac{55}{6}$

21. The integral does not exist. **22.** The integral does not exist.

23. $2.551..$ **24.** $2.082..$ **25.** $\frac{5}{6}$

26. 3 **27.** π **28.** $\sqrt{3} - \frac{\pi}{3}$

29. $F(x) = \frac{x^2}{2} - 2x$. The two graphs appear to be the same in $[-10, 10]$ by $[-10, 10]$. $F(0.5) = -0.875$ and we get the same value after zooming in. $F(1) = -1.5$ compared to -1.516 as one approximation. $F(1.5) = -1.875$ compared to -1.879 as one approximation. $F(2) = -2$ compared to -2. $F(5) = 2.5$ compared to 2.53 as one approximation.

30. $F(x) = \frac{x^4}{4} + x$. The two graphs are indistinguishable in $[-2, 2]$ by $[-0.75, 6]$. The values of $F(x)$ and $\text{NINT}(t^3+1, t, 0, x)$ agree when accurately calculated.

31. $F(x) = \frac{x^3}{3} - \frac{3}{2}x^2 + 6x$. The two graphs are indistinguishable in the viewing rectangle $[-15, 15]$ by $[-1,000, 1,000]$. The values of $F(x)$ and $\text{NINT}(f(t), t, 0, x)$ agree when accurately calculated.

32. $F(x) = 3[1 - \cos x]$. The two graphs are indistinguishable in $[-2\pi, 2\pi]$ by $[0, 6]$. The values of $F(x)$ and $\text{NINT}(f(t), t, 0, x)$ agree when accurately calculated.

33. Graph $y = \text{NINT}(t^2 \sin t, t, 0, x)$ in the viewing window $[-3, 3]$ by $[0, 9]$.

34. Graph $y = \text{NINT}(\sqrt{1 + t^2}, t, 0, x)$ in the viewing window $[0, 5]$ by $[0, 20]$.

35. Graph $y = \text{NINT}(5e^{-0.3t^2}, t, 0, x)$ in the viewing window $[0, 5]$ by $[0, 10]$.

36. Graph $y = \text{NINT}(t \sin(t^3), t, 0, x)$ in $[0, \pi]$ by $[-1, 1]$.

37. The two graphs are identical.

38. Graph $y = \text{NDER}(\text{NINT}(t \sin t, t, 0, x), x, x)$ and $y = x \sin x$ in $[0, 2\pi]$ by $[-2\pi, 2\pi]$ and see that the graphs are identical. This visually supports $D_x \int_0^x t \sin t \, dt = x \sin x$.

39. $K = -\frac{3}{2}$ 40. $K = -1.189...$

41. $x = 0.699$ is the solution to $\int_0^x e^{-t^2} dt = 0.6$.

42. $x = 2.598, 3.758$

43. $\sqrt{1 + x^2}$ 44. $\frac{1}{x}, \ x > 0$ 45. $\frac{\sin x}{2\sqrt{x}}$

46. $2\cos(2x)$ 47. d)   48. c)

49. b)   50. a)   51. $x = a$

52. $f(x) = 2x - 2$ 53. $f(4) = 1$ 54. $L(x) = 2 + 10x$

56. a) $\frac{125}{6}$. b) $\frac{25}{4}$

57. a) \$9 b) \$10 **58.** \$4500

59. $I_{av} = 300$. Average daily holding cost $= 6$ dollars per day.

60. Average daily inventory is 200 cases. Average daily holding cost is \$1.00.

61. a) Compare your drawing with the result of graphing $y = (\cos x)/x$ in $[-15, 15]$ by $[-1, 1]$. The $x-$ and $y-$axes are asymptotes. b) Graph $y = \text{NINT}((\cos t)/t, t, 1, x)$ in $[0, 15]$ by $[-1, 1]$. c) Because $f(0)$ is undefined. d) For $x > 0$, $g(x)$ and $h(x)$ have the same derivative $f(x)$ and so they differ by an additive constant. This is confirmed if one graph can be obtained from the other by a vertical shift. Along with the function in b), graph $y = \text{NINT}((\cos t)/t, t, 0.5, x)$ in $[0.01, 3]$ by $[-3, 3]$ to see that this is the case. Alternatively, $\int_{0.5}^{x} f(t)dt = \int_{0.5}^{1} f(t)dt + \int_{1}^{x} f(t)dt \approx 0.5 + \int_{1}^{x} f(t)dt$.

62. The graph of y can be obtained from the graph of $f(x)$ by stretching the graph of $f(x)$ horizontally by a factor of 2. This is supported by graphing $f(x) \approx \text{NINT}$ $(\frac{\sin 2t}{t}, t, 0.1, x)$ and $y \approx \text{NINT}(\frac{\sin t}{t}, t, 0.1, x)$ in $[0.1, 2]$ by $[0, 2]$.

63. a) $[-1, 1]$ b) $F'(x) = 2x\sqrt{1 - x^4}$ c) Zeros of $F'(x) : x = 0, \pm 1$. F' increasing on $[-\frac{1}{\sqrt[4]{3}}, \frac{1}{\sqrt[4]{3}}]$, decreasing on $[-1, -\frac{1}{\sqrt[4]{3}}]$ and $[\frac{1}{\sqrt[4]{3}}, 1]$. Local extrema of F' at $\pm 1, \pm\frac{1}{\sqrt[4]{3}}$. d) The zeros of $F'(x)$ tell us where the graph has a horizontal tangent and possible local extremes. The graph of F is concave up where F' is increasing and concave down where F' is decreasing. The local extrema of F' at $x = \pm\frac{1}{\sqrt[4]{3}}$ correspond to inflection points of F. Graph $\text{NINT}(\sqrt{1 - t^2}, t, 1, x^2)$ in $[-1, 1]$ by $[-2, 1]$.

64. The graph can be obtained from the graph of Exercise 63 by shifting it up $\frac{\pi}{4}$. The data on the derivatives is the same.

65. a) $(-\frac{1}{2}, \frac{1}{2})$. Later work will show that F has a continuous extension to a function with domain $[-\frac{1}{2}, \frac{1}{2}]$. b) $\frac{2}{\sqrt{1 - 4x^2}}$ c) F' is decreasing on $(-\frac{1}{2}, 0]$, increasing on $[0, \frac{1}{2})$ and has a local minimum at $x = 0$, the only local extreme on $(-\frac{1}{2}, \frac{1}{2})$. d) c) tells us that the graph of F is concave down on $(-\frac{1}{2}, 0)$, concave up on $(0, \frac{1}{2})$ and that F has an inflection point at $x = 0$. In parametric mode (to save time) graph $x = t$, $y = \text{NINT}(\frac{1}{\sqrt{1 - s^2}}, s, 1, 2t)$, $-0.499 \leq t \leq 0.499$, t step $= 0.05$ in $[-0.499, 0.499]$ by $[-\pi, 0]$.

66. The graph can be obtained from that of Exercise 65 by a horizontal shrinking by a factor $\frac{2}{3}$.

67. $F'(x) = 3x^2\cos(2x^3) - 2x\cos(2x^2)$. This is supported by graphing, in parametric mode, $x_1 = t$, $y_1 = \text{NDER}(\text{NINT}(\cos(2s), s, t^2, t^3), t, t)$ and $x_2 = t$, $y_2 = 3t^2\cos(2t^3) - 2t\cos(2t^2)$, $-1.5 \leq t \leq 1.5$, t Step $= 0.05$, in $[-1.5, 1.5]$ by $[-12, 12]$.

68. $F'(x) = -\sin x \cos x(\sin x + \cos x)$. This is supported by graphing, in parametric mode, $x_1 = t$, $y_1 = \text{NDER}(\text{NINT}(s^2, s, \sin t, \cos t), t, t)$ and $x_2 = t$, $y_2 = -\sin t \cos t(\sin t + \cos t)$, $0 \leq t \leq 2\pi$, t Step $= 0.05$ in $[0, 2\pi]$ by $[-1, 1]$.

5.5   INDEFINITE INTEGRALS

1. $\int x^3 dx = \frac{x^4}{4} + C$. $(\frac{x^4}{4} + C)' = x^3$

2. $7x + C$

3. $\frac{x^2}{2} + x + C$

4. $6x - 3x^2 + C$

5. $2x^{3/2} + C$

6. $-\frac{4}{x} + C$

7. $\frac{3}{2}x^{2/3} + C$

8. $x + 2x^{-2} + C$

9. $\frac{5}{3}x^3 + x^2 + C$

10. $\frac{x^3}{6} + \frac{x^4}{12} + C$

11. $\frac{1}{2}x^4 - \frac{5}{2}x^2 + 7x + C$. We graph the integrand and $\text{NDER}(\frac{1}{2}x^4 - \frac{5}{2}x^2 + 7x, x)$ in $[-3, 3]$ by $[-50, 50]$ and see that two graphs are identical.

12. $x - \frac{x^3}{3} - \frac{x^6}{2} + C$

13. $2\sin x + C$

14. $-5\cos\theta + C$

15. $-3\cos\frac{x}{3} + C$

16. $\frac{3}{5}\sin 5x + C$

17. $-3\cot x + C$

18. $\frac{\tan x}{3} + C$

19. $-\frac{1}{2}\csc x + C$

20. $\frac{2}{5}\sec x + C$

21. $4\sec x - 2\tan x + C$

22. $\frac{1}{2}(-\cot x + \csc x) + C$

23. $-\frac{1}{2}\cos 2x + \cot x + C$

24. $\sin 2x + \cos 3x + C$

25. $2y - \sin 2y + C$

26. $\frac{1}{14}(x + \frac{\sin 2x}{2}) + C$

27. $-\frac{1}{4}\cos 2x + C$

28. $\frac{t}{2} - \frac{\sin 2t}{4} + C$

29. $\tan\theta + C$

30. $-\frac{\cot x}{2} + C$

31. $g(x) = \frac{1-\cos x}{x^2}$, $-10 \leq x \leq 10$, $x \neq 0$, $g(0) = \frac{1}{2}$. Graph $y = \int_0^x f(t)dt = \text{NINT}(f(t), t, 0, x)$ in $[-10, 10]$ by $[-2, 2]$. For quicker results, use parametric mode, $x = t$, $y = \text{NINT}((1-\cos s)/s^2, s, 0, t)$, t step $= 0.3$, $-10 \leq t \leq 10$, in the above window.

32. $g(x) = f(x)$, $x \neq 0$, $g(0) = 1$. Graph $\text{NINT}((1 + t^{-1})^t, t, 0, x)$ in $[0, 5]$ by $[0, 12]$.

37. Only c) is right. **38.** Only c) is right. **39.** $y = 2x^{3/2} - 50$

40. $y = \sqrt{x} - 2$

41. $y = \int_0^x 2^t dt + 2 = \frac{1}{\ln 2} \cdot 2^x - \frac{1}{\ln 2} + 2$. Graph $y = 2 + \text{NINT}(2^t, t, 0, x)$ in $[-7.5, 9.5]$ by $[0, 10]$.

42. Graph $y = 0.5 + \int_0^x \frac{(1-\cos t)}{t} dt$ in $[-20, 20]$ by $[-1, 5]$. Analytic means are unavailable.

43. $y = 2x$ **44.** $y = 2x + \frac{1}{x} - 2$ **45.** $y = \frac{x^3}{16}$

46. $y = 5 - 4x^2 + x^3$ **47.** 16 ft/sec^2

48. a) $v = 10t^{3/2} - 6t^{1/2}$ b) $s = 4(t^{5/2} - t^{3/2})$

49. 1.24 sec

54. $\lim_{t \to 0+} f(t)$ is: A) ∞ B) ∞ C) π D) ∞

55. A) $\frac{\sqrt{\pi^2 + 4}}{\sqrt{g}}$ C) $\frac{\pi}{\sqrt{g}}$

56.

		$h = 0.1$	0.01	0.001
B	$T =$	$2.15/\sqrt{g}$	$2.92/\sqrt{g}$	$3.16/\sqrt{g}$
D	$T =$	$1.95/\sqrt{g}$	$2.53/\sqrt{g}$	$2.81/\sqrt{g}$

5.6 INTEGRATION BY SUBSTITUTION - RUNNING THE CHAIN RULE BACKWARD

1. $-\frac{1}{3}\cos 3x + C$ **2.** $-\frac{1}{4}\cos(2x^2) + C$ **3.** $\frac{1}{2}\sec 2x + C$

4. $\frac{2}{3}(1 - \cos\frac{t}{2})^3 + C$ **5.** $(7x - 2)^4 + C$ **6.** $\frac{(x^4-1)^3}{3} + C$

7. $-6\sqrt{1 - r^3} + C$ **8.** $(y^4 + 4y^2 + 1)^3 + C$

9. a) $-\frac{\cot^2 2\theta}{4} + C$ b) $-\frac{\csc^2 2\theta}{4} + C$ **10.** $\frac{2}{5}\sqrt{5x} + C$ in both a) and b)

11. $\frac{3}{16}$ **12.** $\frac{38}{15}$ **13.** $\frac{1}{2}$ **14.** $\frac{7}{24}$ **15.** 0 **16.** $\frac{1}{6}$ **17.** $\frac{2}{3}$ **18.** 2

19. $\frac{1}{1-x} + C$ **20.** $2\sqrt{2y^2 + 1} + C$ **21.** $\tan(x + 2) + C$

22. $4\tan(\frac{x}{4}) + C$ **23.** $3(r^2 - 1)^{4/3} + C$ **24.** $-\frac{1}{20}(7 - x^5)^4 + C$

25. $\sec(\theta + \frac{\pi}{2}) + C$ 26. $\frac{2}{3}(\tan x)^{3/2} + C$ 27. $2(1 + x^4)^{3/4} + C$

28. $\frac{(s^3 + 2s^2 - 5s + 6)^3}{3} + C$ 29. a) $\frac{14}{3}$ b) $\frac{2}{3}$ 30. a) $\frac{1}{3}$ b) 0

31. a) $\frac{1}{2}$ b) $-\frac{1}{2}$ 32. a) $\frac{15}{16}$ b) 0

33. a) $\frac{1}{2}(\sqrt{10} - 3)$ b) $\frac{1}{2}(3 - \sqrt{10})$ 34. a) 0 b) $\frac{1}{4}$ 35. a) $\frac{45}{8}$ b) $-\frac{45}{8}$

36. a) 2 b) 2   37. a) $\frac{1}{6}$ b) $\frac{1}{2}$ 38. a) 4 b) 0

39. a) 0 b) 0   40. a) $-\frac{1}{12}$ b) $\frac{1}{12}$ 41. $2\sqrt{3}$

42. $\frac{116}{15}$ 43. 0 44. $\frac{2}{3}$ 45. 8 46. $\frac{1}{5}$ 47. $\frac{38}{3}$ 48. $-\frac{25}{6}$ 49. $\frac{16}{3}$ 50. 2

51. $s = (3t^2 - 1)^4 - 1$ 52. $y = 3[(x^2 + 8)^{2/3} - 4]$

53. $s = -6\cos(t + \pi) - 6$ 54. $s = 100t + \sin(2t - \frac{\pi}{2}) + 1$

55. 1   56. $\frac{1}{3}[1 + \sin^2(x - 1)]^{3/2} + C$

57. All integrations are correct. The graph of any one of the antiderivatives can be obtained from the graph of any other antiderivative by a vertical shift verifying that they differ by an additive constant.

5.7 NUMERICAL INTEGRATION: TRAPEZOIDAL RULE & SIMPSON'S METHOD

1. a) 2 b) 2 c) 2   2. a) $\frac{11}{4}$ b) $\frac{8}{3}$ c) $\frac{8}{3}$ 3. a) 4.25 b) 4 c) 4

4. a) 0.50899 b) 0.50042 c) 0.5

5. a) 5.146... b) 5.252... c) $\frac{16}{3} = 5.333...$

6. a) $\frac{\pi}{4}(1 + \sqrt{2}) = 1.89612$ b) $\frac{\pi}{6}[1 + 2\sqrt{2}] = 2.00456$ c) 2

7. $\int_{-1}^{3} e^{-x^2}\, dx$

n	TRAP	SIMP	LRAM	RRAM	MRAM
10	1.62316	1.63322	1.69671	1.54961	1.63799
100	1.63293	1.63303150	1.64029	1.62558	1.63308
1000	1.6330305	1.63303148	1.63377	1.63229	1.63303

NINT yields 1.63303148105.

8. $\int_2^5 \sqrt{x^2 - 2}\, dx$

n	TRAP	SIMP	LRAM	RRAM	MRAM
10	9.519	9.52128	9.01	10.026	9.5227
100	9.52133	9.52135547	9.47	9.57	9.521369
1000	9.5213552	9.52135548278	9.516	9.526	9.5213556

NINT yields 9.52135548276.

9. $\int_{-5}^5 x \sin x\, dx$

n	TRAP	SIMP	LRAM	RRAM	MRAM
10	-4.682	-4.73	-4.68	-4.68	-4.79
100	-4.7537	-4.754469	-4.7537	-4.7537	-4.7549
1000	-4.75446	-4.7544704038	-4.75446	-4.75446	-4.754474

NINT yields -4.75447040396.

10. $\int_{-2}^2 \sin x^2\, dx$

n	TRAP	SIMP	LRAM	RRAM	MRAM
10	1.535	1.63	1.535	1.535	1.649
100	1.6088	1.6095547	1.60886	1.60886	1.6099
1000	1.609546	1.60955297886	1.609546	1.609546	1.609556

NINT yields 1.60955297869.

11. $\int_{3\pi/4}^{4.5} \frac{\tan x}{x}\, dx$

n	TRAP	SIMP	LRAM	RRAM	MRAM
10	0.257	0.246	0.101	0.413	0.238
100	0.244	0.243771	0.228	0.260	0.244
1000	0.2437718	0.2437703542	0.242	0.245	0.2437696

NINT yields 0.243770354155.

12. $\int_1^{2\pi} \frac{2\sin x}{x}\, dx$

n	TRAP	SIMP	LRAM	RRAM	MRAM
10	0.966	0.94386	1.41	0.52	0.933
100	0.94435	0.94413698	0.989	0.8999	0.94403
1000	0.944139	0.944137011524	0.9486	0.9397	0.9441359

NINT yields 0.944137011531.

13. $|E_T| \leqq \frac{1}{600} = 0.0016666\ldots$ **14.** $|E_S| \leqq 0.00001333\ldots$

15. a) $n = 1$ b) $n = 2$ **16.** a) $n = 116$ b) $n = 2$

17. a) $n = 283$ b) $n = 2$ **18.** a) $n = 71$ b) $n = 10$

19. a) $n = 76$ b) $n = 12$ **20.** a) $n = 161$ b) $n = 12$

21. 3.1379,   3.14029   **22.** 1.08942941322,   1.08942941322

23. 1.3669,   1.3688   **24.** 0.828116396058,   0.828116333053

25. a) $0.057\ldots$ and $0.0472\ldots$ b) Let $y_1 = \sin x/x$, $y_2 = \text{der2}(y_1, 2, 2)$, $y_3 = \left(\frac{1.5\pi}{12}\right)\left(\frac{1.5\pi}{10}\right)^2 abs y_2$, $y_4 = \text{NDER}(\text{NDER}(y_2, x, x), x, x)$, $y_5 = \frac{1.5\pi}{180}\left(\frac{1.5\pi}{10}\right)^4 abs y_4$. We graph y_3 in $[\frac{\pi}{2}, 2\pi]$ by $[0, 0.03]$ and y_5 in $[\frac{\pi}{2}, 2\pi]$ by $[0, 3 \times 10^{-4}]$. Max $y_3 = 2.168\ldots \times 10^{-2}$, max $y_5 = 2.26\ldots \times 10^{-4}$ c) $\max E_T(x) = 5.42\ldots \times 10^{-3}$, $\max E_S(x) = 1.41\ldots \times 10^{-5}$ d) $\max E_T(x) = 8.67 \times 10^{-4}$, $\max E_S(x) = 3.62\ldots \times 10^{-7}$ e) We cannot find the exact value, but we can approximate the integral as closely as we like by increasing n. With $n = 50$, Simpson's Rule gives the value $0.0473894\ldots$. By d) the error is at most 3.62×10^{-7}.

26. Refer to the method of Exercise 25. a) $0.64\ldots$, $0.73\ldots$ b) $\max E_T = 0.77095\ldots$, $\max E_S = 0.0948\ldots$ c) $\max E_T = 0.1927\ldots$, $\max E_S = 0.0059\ldots$ d) $\max E_T = 0.0308\ldots$, $\max E_S = 1.5\ldots \times 10^{-4}$ e) $\frac{1}{2}[\cos 1 - \cos \pi^2]$ (exact value) $\approx 0.721493833901\ldots$

27. Refer to the method of Exercise 25. a) $3.6664\ldots$ and $3.65348218\ldots$ b) $\max E_T = 0.2466\ldots$, $\max E_S = 2.55\ldots \times 10^{-4}$ c) $\max E_T = 6.16\ldots \times 10^{-2}$, $\max E_S = 1.59\ldots \times 10^{-5}$ d) $\max E_T = 9.86\ldots \times 10^{-3}$, $\max E_S = 4.08\ldots \times 10^{-7}$ e) Simpson's Rule with $n = 50$ yields $3.6534844\ldots$ with error at most $4.08\ldots \times 10^{-7}$.

28. Our calculator finds $\max |y_1 - y_2| = 0.004$ in $-1 \leqq x \leqq 1$. If E_S turns out to be very small, say 10^{-7}, it makes little difference whether y_1 or y_2 is used to compute E_S.

29. $\text{LRAM}_{50} f = 3.2591$, $\text{RRAM}_{50} f = 3.3205$ and $T_{50} f = 3.2898$. Yes, $2T_{50} f = \text{LRAM}_{50} f + \text{RRAM}_{50} f$.

30. $T_{50} f = 3.6825$, $\text{MRAM}_{25} f = 3.6816$ and $S_{50} f = 3.6822$. Yes, $(\text{MRAM}_{25} f + 2T_{50} f)/3 = S_{50} f$

33. 1013   **34.** 10.63 ft   **35.** $466.66\ldots$ in^2

36. a) 541.5   b) $0.62\ldots L/\mathrm{min}$

37. Using the odd-numbered hours, we get 56.86 kwh per customer.

38. Using all 24 data, $T = 51.605$ kwh.

39. In parametric mode graph $x(t)$, $y(t)$, $0 \leq t \leq 1$, t step $= 0.05$ in $[0, \pi]$ by $[0, 2]$. Domain $= [0, \pi]$, range $= [0, 2]$.

40. 1.728.   (We used the fact that the first trapezoid, for example, has base approximately 0.0783.)

41. $A \approx 1.596507\ldots$

42. $x = \cos^{-1}(y - 1) - \sqrt{2y - y^2}$. Graph $y = g(x) = \cos^{-1}(x - 1) - \sqrt{2x - x^2}$ in $[0, 2]$ by $[0, \pi]$.

43. $g(x) = \cos^{-1}(x - 1) - \sqrt{2x - x^2}$. $\mathrm{NINT}(g(x), x, 0, 2) = 1.57079603391$.

44. With 100 trapezoids $T = 1.57105469968$.

PRACTICE EXERCISES, CHAPTER 5

1. a)

b) $20, 15, 17.5$

2. a)

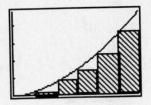 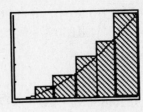 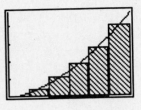

b) $80, 125, 101.25$

3.

	n=10	n=100	n=1000
$LRAM_n$	22.695	23.86545	23.9865045
$RRAM_n$	25.395	24.13545	24.0135045
$MRAM_5$	23.9775	23.999775	23.99999775

4. $f(x) = x^3 - 2x + 2.$

	n=10	n=100	n=1000
$LRAM_n$	3.64	3.9604	3.996004
$RRAM_n$	4.44	4.0404	4.004004
$MRAM_n$	3.98	3.9998	3.999998

5.

	n=10	n=100	n=1000
$LRAM_n$	3.9670	3.99967	3.9999967
$RRAM_n$	3.9670	3.99967	3.9999967
$MRAM_n$	4.0165	4.00016	4.0000016

6.

	n=10	n=100	n=1000
$LRAM_n$	0.886319	0.8862269	0.886226925
$RRAM_n$	0.886319	0.8862269	0.886226925
$MRAM_n$	0.886135	0.8862269	0.886226925

7. a) 75   b) -10 **8.** a) 90   b) 112

9. a) 0   b) 60   **10.** a) 7   b) 5   c) 8   d) $\frac{11}{30}$

11. a) $\sum_{k=0}^{3} 2^k$ b) $\sum_{k=0}^{4} \frac{1}{3^k}$ c) $\sum_{k=1}^{5} (-1)^{k+1} k$ d) $\sum_{k=1}^{3} \frac{5}{2^k}$

12. $\int_1^2 \frac{1}{x} dx$ **13.** $\int_0^1 e^x dx$

14. $RRAM_n f = \frac{32}{3}(1 + \frac{1}{n})(2 + \frac{1}{n}) + 16(1 + \frac{1}{n}) + 12.$ $\lim_{n \to \infty} RRAM_n f = \frac{148}{3}$

15. $RRAM_n f = \frac{625}{2}(1 + \frac{1}{n}) + \frac{75}{2}(1 + \frac{1}{n}).$ $\lim_{n \to \infty} RRAM_n f = 350$

16. a) True   b) True   c) False   **17.** a) π b) $-\pi$ c) -3π

18. $\pi - 2$ **19.** $\pi - 2$ **20.** $\frac{32}{3}$ **21.** 10   **22.** 4

23. 16   **24.** 3   **25.** 2   **26.** 2   **27.** 1

28. 13, $NINT(3\sqrt{(4x + 1)}, x, 0, 2) = 12.999\ldots$

29. $\frac{2}{5}$ **30.** 0   **31.** $\sqrt{3}$ **32.** 2   **33.** $6\sqrt{3} - 2\pi$

34. $3\sqrt{3} - \pi = 2.054559\ldots$ **35.** 8   **36.** 2   **37.** -1

38. 0; $NINT((\sin x \tan x)^{-1}, x, \frac{\pi}{4}, \frac{3\pi}{4}) = 1.9 \times 10^{-13}$ **39.** 2

40. 0   **41.** $0.6931\ldots$ **42.** $2.1972\ldots$ **43.** $0.2938\ldots$ **44.** 0

45. $\frac{17}{3}$, $NINT((x - 2/x)(x + 2/x), x, 2, 3) = 5.6666\ldots$

46. 7   **47.** 8   **48.** $\frac{147}{8}$ **49.** -2 **50.** 1

55. Graph $NINT((\sin(3t))/t, t, 1, x)$ in $[0.01, 8]$ by $[-2, 0.004]$. There is no explicit elementary formula for this integral.

56. Graph $NINT(0.25e^{-(0.5t^2)}, t, 0, x)$ in $[-10, 10]$ by $[-1, 1]$. There is no explicit elementary formula for this integral.

57. $-3.091, 1.631$ **58.** $\int_1^x \frac{1}{2}e^{-t^2} dt = 0.05$ has solution $x = 1.421$.

59. No solution

60. $(0, \infty)$ is the domain. We may graph $y = NINT(\cos t/t, t, 1, , x)$ in $[0.01, 20]$ by $[-1, 0.5]$.

61. a) and c)

62. Both integrations are correct. $\frac{\sec^2 x}{2} = \frac{1+\tan^2 x}{2} = \frac{\tan^2 x}{2} + \frac{1}{2}$ shows that the two results differ by a constant.

63. $f(x) = \cos x$, $0 \leqq x \leqq 1$ **64.** All are true except d) and f)

65. $F(1) - F(0)$ **67.** 10m   **68.** a) $y = \cos x + x^2 + 2x + 2$ b) $y = \frac{2x^2}{1+x^2}$

69. 21.511ft/sec^2 **70.** b)   **71.** a) $(V^2)_{av} = \frac{(V_{max})^2}{2}$ b) 339.411volts

72. $25°$ **74.** a) 2   b) $\frac{2a}{3}$ **75.** $n = 16$, $h = \frac{1}{8}$

76. 26 subdivisions using the Trapezoidal Rule

77. T and S both agree with π up to the limits of calculator accuracy.   **78.** 8

79. By Simpson's Rule the approximate area of the lot is 6059ft^2. The job cannot be done for $11,000.

CHAPTER 6

APPLICATIONS OF DEFINITE INTEGRALS

6.1 AREAS BETWEEN CURVES

1. $\frac{125}{6}$ 2. $\frac{343}{24}$ 3. $\frac{125}{6}$ 4. $\frac{5}{6}$ 5. $\frac{\pi}{2}$

6. $2\sqrt{2}$ 7. $\frac{32}{3}$ 8. $\frac{4}{3}$ 9. $\frac{32}{3}$ 10. $\frac{32}{3}$

11. $\frac{1}{6}$ 12. $\frac{4}{3}$ 13. 26.15341

14. $0.739 + 0.511 = 1.250$ 15. $\frac{9}{2}$ 16. 36 17. 0.22016

18. 8.661 19. $\frac{1}{6}$ 20. 4 21. 15.68376 22. 4.25108

23. $\frac{1}{12}$ 24. $\frac{104}{15}$ 25. 1 26. $\frac{128}{15}$ 27. $\sqrt{2} - 1$

28. $\frac{32}{3}$ 29. $c = 2^{4/3}$ 30. $\frac{3}{4}$

31. a) and b) $A(t) = \frac{2}{3}t^3 (1 - \frac{1}{\sqrt{2}})$,   c) $0.195\ldots$

32. a) and b) $A(t) = \frac{t^3}{3}$,   c) $\frac{1}{6}$

33. 4 34. e^{-x^2} never intersects the x-axis.

6.2 VOLUMES OF SOLIDS OF REVOLUTION - DISKS AND WASHERS

1. $8\pi/3$ 2. $32\pi/5$ 3. 36π 4. $\pi/30$ 5. $128\pi/7$

6. $3\pi/2$ 7. π 8. 2π 9. $32\pi/3$ 10. 8π

11. 2π 12. $16\pi/15$ 13. 4π 14. 2π 15. $4\pi \ln 4$

16. 2π 17. $2\pi/3$ 18. π 19. $128\pi/5$ 20. $48\pi/5$

21. $117\pi/5$ 22. $108\pi/5$ 23. $\pi^2 - 2\pi$ 24. $4\pi(3 - \ln 4)$ 25. $4\pi/3$

26. 27π 27. 8π 28. $2\pi/15$ 29. $500\pi/3$ 30. 36π

31. $\pi^2 - 2\pi$ 32. $\pi(8 \ln 2 - 3)$ 33. $\pi/3$

34. a) $11\pi/3$, b) $\pi(4\ln 4 - 3)$ **35.** a) 8π, b) $32\pi/5$, c) $8\pi/3$, d) $224\pi/15$

36. a) $2\pi/3$, b) $8\pi/3$ **37.** a) $16\pi/15$, b) $56\pi/15$, c) $64\pi/15$

38. $\pi r^2 h$ **39.** $\frac{\pi r^2 h}{3}$ **40.** $c = 2/\pi$, minimum value is 0.935

41. a) $x = -2$, $x = 0.59375\ldots$ b) 76.8153067 **42.** $c = 1.53, V = 5.610$

43. $1053\pi \approx 3.3L$ **44.** $36\pi/5$, 192.27gm

6.3 CYLINDRICAL SHELLS – AN ALTERNATIVE TO WASHERS

1. 8π **2.** $128\pi/5$ **3.** $3\pi/2$ **4.** $7\pi/15$

5. 3π **6.** $4\pi\ln 2$ **7.** $4\pi/3$ **8.** $4\pi/3$

9. $16\pi/3$ **10.** $16\pi(3\sqrt{2}+5)/15$ **11.** $8\pi/3$ **12.** $\pi/6$

13. $14\pi/3$ **14.** $2\pi(2+(\ln 2)^2 - (\ln 4)^2) \approx 3.510$ **15.** $6\pi/5$

16. $8\pi/3$ **17.** a) $\frac{5\pi}{3}$, b) $4\pi/3$ **18.** a) $4\pi/15$, b) $8\pi/105$

19. a) $11\pi/15$, b) $97\pi/105$, c) $121\pi/210$, d) $23\pi/30$

20. a) 16π, b) $32\pi/3$, c) $64\pi/3$, d) 48π **21.** a) $512\pi/21$, b) $832\pi/21$

22. a) $24\pi/5$, **23.** a) $\pi/6$, b) $\pi/6$

24. a) 8π, b) $32\pi/5$, c) $224\pi/15$, d) $8\pi/3$

25. a) 20.367π, b) $2\pi(11.610)$ **26.** a) 20.367π, b) $2\pi(11.25)$

27. 94.782 **28.** 45.627 **29.** b) $\pi/4$, c) 5.033

30. a) Not always true b) Always true c) Not always true

6.4   LENGTHS OF CURVES IN THE PLANE

1. 12   2. $\frac{8}{27}(10^{3/2} - 1)$ 3. $\frac{14}{3}$ 4. $\frac{8}{27}[(1 + 9 \cdot 4^{-1/3})^{3/2} - 1] = 4.807$

5. $\frac{53}{6}$ 6. $\frac{32}{3}$ 7. $\frac{123}{32}$ 8. $\frac{13}{4}$ 9. $\frac{3}{2}$

10. $8 + \frac{1}{8}\ln 3$ 11. 3.1385   12. 7.640   13. $e^3 - e^{-3}$ 14. 9.138

15. 6   16. 1   17. $y = x^{1/2}$, $0 \le x \le 4$

18. $y = e^x$ 19. $y = \ln x + 3$

20. The left-hand side is twice the area of a semi-circle of radius 1; the right-hand integral is its arc length. Both integrals have the value π.

21. $\int_0^{1/2} \frac{1+x^2}{1-x^2} dx = 0.5986\ldots$ 22. $\int_0^{\pi/3} \sec x\, dx = 1.316957\ldots$

23. 21.068 inches   24. \$38,422   25. $9.033\ldots$ million miles

26. About $(-19.9, 8.41)$ 27. $100.89\ldots$ 28. 15.5

6.5   AREAS OF SURFACES OF REVOLUTION

1. $4\pi\sqrt{5}$ 2. $8\sqrt{5}\pi$ 3. $3\pi\sqrt{5}$ 4. $4\pi\sqrt{5}$

5. $98\pi/81$ 6. $(\sqrt{8} - 1)\pi/9$ 7. $28\pi/3$ 8. 4π

9. $49\pi/3$ 10. 84.140   11. $2\pi(2\sqrt{2} - 1)/3$ 12. $\pi\left(\frac{15}{16} + \ln 2\right)$

13. $253\pi/20$ 14. $\frac{99\pi}{2}$ 15. $\frac{\pi}{27}[(\frac{5}{4})^3 - 1]$ 16. 4π

17. 4.591π 18. $12\pi/5$ 19. 452.390 L of each color

20. $S_{AB} = 2\pi rh$ which is independent of a 21. 11,900 tiles   22. $2.648\ldots$

6.6   WORK

1. 400 ft $\cdot$ lb   2. 240 ft $\cdot$ lb   3. 925 $N \cdot m$ 4. 10.625 ft $\cdot$ lb

5. $64,800$ ft $\cdot$ lb   6. 1944 ft $\cdot$ lb   7. 1.2 $N \cdot m$ 8. 1125 $N \cdot m$

9. a) $104\frac{1}{6}$ ft $\cdot$ lb,   b) 312.5 ft $\cdot$ lb   10. 300 lb,   1.5625 ft $\cdot$ lb

11. $245,436.926$ ft $\cdot$ lb   **12.** $282,252.465$ ft $\cdot$ lb   **13.** $7,238,229.473$ ft $\cdot$ lb

14. a) $34,582.652$ ft $\cdot$ lb,   b) $53,482.473$ ft $\cdot$ lb

15. a) $1,500,000$ ft $\cdot$ lb,   b) 100 minutes

16. a) $2,250,000$ ft $\cdot$ lb,   b) 2 hrs 47 minutes,   c) 1 hr, 9 min.

17. $21,446,605.85$ $N \cdot m$ **18.** $96,129.463$ ft $\cdot$ lb

19. Through the valve (84823 ft $\cdot$ lb vs. 98960 ft $\cdot$ lb)

20. 91.324 in $\cdot$ oz   **21.** $967,610.537$ ft $\cdot$ lb; cost is $4838.05, yes.

22. 30 hours 51 minutes   **23.** 5.1441×10^{10} $N \cdot m$

24. a) $1.15 \times 10^{-28} N \cdot m$ b) $7.67 \times 10^{-29} N \cdot m$

6.7   FLUID PRESSURES AND FLUID FORCES

1. 2812.5 lb   **2.** full: $114,511,052$ lb, half: $28,627,763$ lb

3. 375 lb. No.   **4.** 111.1 lb   **5.** 1166.67 lb

6. 114.583 lb   **7.** 41.67 lb

8. Sides (total): 840.278 lb; ends (total): 420.139 lb

9. $F = 1309$ lb/in^3 **10.** 4.204 lb   **11.** 1161 lb

12. a) 93.333 lb; b) 3 ft   **13.** 1034.16 ft^3 **14.** a) 333.33 lb, b) 8.987 ft

15. A plate, $h \times w$ with top d below the surface experiences a force of $\omega w\left[\frac{h^2+2dh}{2}\right] = \frac{\omega d + \omega(d+h)}{2}\, hw$.

6.8 CENTERS OF MASS

1. 4 ft

2. At the midpoint of the line joining the center of each rod $(L/4, L/4)$.

3. $M_0 = 8$, $\bar{x} = 1$ 　　**4.** $M_0 = 7.5$, $\bar{x} = \frac{5}{3}$ 　　**5.** $M_0 = \frac{68}{3}$, $\bar{x} = \frac{17}{7}$

6. $M_0 = 22.5$, $\bar{x} = 2.5$ 　　**7.** $(0, 2/3)$ 　　**8.** $(0, 2.4)$

9. $(16/105, 8/15)$ 　　**10.** $(1, -\frac{3}{5})$ 　　**11.** $(3/5, 1)$

12. $(0, 10)$ 　　**13.** $(0, \pi/8)$ 　　**14.** $(0, 0.567)$

15. $(1, -2/5)$ 　　**16.** a) $(\frac{4}{\pi}, \frac{4}{\pi})$　b) $(0, \frac{4}{\pi})$ 　**17.** $(\frac{2}{4-\pi}, \frac{2}{4-\pi})$

18. $(\ln 4, 0)$ 　　**19.** $(0, 1)$ 　　**20.** $(\frac{1}{3}, \frac{1}{3})$ 　　**21.** $(\frac{a}{3}, \frac{a}{3})$

22. $(\frac{a}{3}, \frac{b}{3})$ 　　**23.** $(14/9, (\ln 4)/3)$ 　　**24.** $(\frac{3}{5}, \frac{1}{2})$

25. $V = 32\pi$; $S = 32\sqrt{2}\,\pi$ 　　**26.** 72π 　　**27.** $4\pi^2$

28. Centroid of region is at $(\frac{r}{3}, \frac{h}{3})$; $V = \frac{1}{3}\pi r^2 h$; centroid of arc is at $(\frac{r}{2}, \frac{h}{2})$; $S = \pi r \sqrt{r^2 + h^2}$

29. $(0, 2a/\pi)$ 　　**30.** $2\pi a^2(\pi - 2)$ 　　**31.** $(0, 4a/3\pi)$

32. $\pi a^3 \frac{(4+3\pi)}{3}$ 　　**33.** $\frac{\pi a^3}{6}(4 + 3\pi)\sqrt{2}$ 　　**34.** $\sqrt{2}\,\pi a^2(\pi + 2)$

6.9 THE BASIC IDEA. OTHER MODELING APPLICATIONS

1. 16 　　**2.** 8/3 　　**3.** 16/3 　　**4.** $16\pi/15$ 　　**5.** $\pi \ln 2$ 　　**6.** 8π

7. 8/3 　　**8.** $2\sqrt{3}$ 　　**9.** $4\pi r^3/3$ 　　**10.** $\frac{\pi r^2 h}{3}$ 　　**11.** $s^2 h$, $s^2 h$

13. b) 20 m 　　c) 0 m 　　**14.** b) $\frac{4}{\pi}$ m 　　c) 0 m

15. b) 6 m 　　c) 2 m 　　**16.** b) 8 m 　　c) 0 m

17. a) 245 m 　b) 0 m 　　**18.** a) 40 m 　c) 0 m

19. b) 6 m 　　c) 4 m 　　**20.** b) 11 m 　c) 9 m

21. a) $d = 2$, $s = 2$ 　b) $d = 4$, $s = 0$ 　c) $d = 4$, $s = 4$ 　d) $d = 2$, $s = 2$

22. shift $= \frac{52}{3}$ in, distance $= \frac{268}{3}$ in. 　　**23.** approximately 1.73π instead of 2π

24. $\int_0^h 2\pi r \, dx = 2\pi r h$

PRACTICE EXERCISES, CHAPTER 6

1. 1   **2.** $\frac{7}{2} - 2\sqrt{2}$ **3.** 9/2   **4.** 1/6   **5.** 18

6. 243/8   **7.** 9/8   **8.** 16/3   **9.** $\frac{\pi^2}{32} + \frac{\sqrt{2}}{2} - 1$ **10.** $\pi - 2$

11. 4   **12.** $6\sqrt{3}$ **13.** $(8\sqrt{2} - 7)/6$ **14.** 13/6   **15.** 3

16. $4\ln 4$ **17.** a) 2π b) π

18. $243\pi/5$ b) $81\pi/2$ **19.** a) 8π b) $1088\pi/15$ c) $512\pi/15$

20. a) $32\pi/3$ b) $128\pi/15$ c) $64\pi/5$ d) $32\pi/3$

21. $\pi(\sqrt{3} - \pi/3)$ **22.** $\pi(9\pi/2 - 8)$ **23.** $\pi\ln 16$ **24.** $\pi(2 - \ln 3)$

25. $28\pi/3$ **26.** 276 in^3 **27.** $2\sqrt{3}$ **28.** 7.634

29. 92/9   **30.** 43/12   **31.** $\frac{2\pi}{3}[26^{3/2} - 2^{3/2}] \approx 86.5\pi$

32. 0.114π **33.** 3π **34.** 21.995   **35** $3\pi/2$

36. $13\pi/3$ **37.** $4560N \cdot m$ **38.** 22.8×10^6 ft $\cdot$ lb

39. 10 ft $\cdot$ lb, 30 ft $\cdot$ lb   **40.** 4 cm, 8 N $\cdot$ cm

41. $6400\pi\omega/3$ ft $\cdot$ lb, where $\omega = 62.5$

42. $53125\omega\pi/192$ ft $\cdot$ lb, where $\omega = 62.5$

43. 333.3 lb   **44.** 118.63 lb   **45.** 2200 lb

46. bottom, 6.638lb; end, 5.773 lb; side, 9.484 lb

47. $(0, 8/5)$ **48.** $(0, 6/5)$ **49.** $(3/2, 12/5)$ **50.** $(8/5, 1)$ **51.** $(0, 8/15)$

52. $(0, 4/3)$ **53.** $(7, \frac{1}{3}\ln 2)$ **54.** $(15/\ln 16, 3/(4\ln 16))$ **55.** $9\pi/280$

56. $8\sqrt{3}/15$ **57.** π^2 **58.** 14.4   **59.** 18

60. Generate the cone by revolving $y = x/4$, $0 \le x \le 12$, about the x-axis. Area of a cross-section is $\pi x^2/16$ for both solids, and the altitude of each solid is 12.

61. b) 5 ft   c) 3 ft   **62.** b) 64/3 ft   c) 0 ft

63. b) 15 ft   c) -5 ft   **64.** b) 3 ft   c) 1 ft

CHAPTER 7

THE CALCULUS OF TRANSCENDENTAL FUNCTIONS

7.1 THE NATURAL LOGARITHM FUNCTION

1. $2(\ln 2 - \ln 3)$
2. $2\ln 2 + \ln 3$
3. $-\ln 2$
4. $-\ln 3$

5. $2\ln 3 - \ln 2$
6. $\frac{2}{3}\ln 3$
7. $\ln 3 + \frac{1}{2}\ln 2$
8. $\frac{1}{2}[3\ln 3 - \ln 2]$

9. $\frac{2}{x}$. The result is supported by graphing $2/x$ and $\text{NDER}(\ln(x^2), x, x)$ in $[-5, 5]$ by $[-5, 5]$.

10. $\frac{2\ln x}{x}$
11. $-\frac{1}{x}$
12. $-\frac{1}{x}$
13. $\frac{1}{x+2}$

14. $\frac{1}{x+1}$
15. $\frac{\sin x}{2-\cos x}$
16. $\frac{2x}{x^2+1}$
17. $\frac{1}{x\ln x}$.

18. $\ln x$
19. $\frac{2x+1}{2\sqrt{x(x+1)}}$
20. $\frac{1}{2\sqrt{x}\ (x+1)^{3/2}}$
21. $\frac{\sin x + 2(x+3)\cos x}{2\sqrt{x+3}}$

22. $\frac{\tan x}{\sqrt{2x+1}}\left[\frac{\sec^2 x}{\tan x} - \frac{1}{2x+1}\right]$
23. $3x^2 + 6x + 2$
24. $\frac{-1}{x(x+1)(x+2)}\left[\frac{1}{x} + \frac{1}{x+1} + \frac{1}{x+2}\right]$

25. $\frac{x+5}{x\cos x}\left[\tan x - \frac{5}{x(x+5)}\right]$
26. $\frac{x\sin x}{\sqrt{\sec x}}\left[\frac{1}{x} + \cot x - \frac{1}{2}\tan x\right]$

27. $\frac{x\sqrt{x^2+1}}{(x+1)^{2/3}}\left[\frac{1}{x} + \frac{x}{x^2+1} - \frac{2}{3(x+1)}\right]$
28. $5\sqrt{\frac{(x+1)^{10}}{(2x+1)^5}}\left[\frac{1}{x+1} - \frac{1}{2x+1}\right]$

29. $\frac{2(x^2+x-1)}{3x(x-2)(x^2+1)}\sqrt[3]{\frac{x(x-2)}{x^2+1}}$
30. $\frac{1}{3}\sqrt[3]{\frac{x(x+1)(x-2)}{(x^2+1)(2x+3)}}\left[\frac{1}{x} + \frac{1}{x+1} + \frac{1}{x-2} - \frac{2x}{x^2+1} - \frac{2}{2x+3}\right]$

31. $\ln 2 - \ln 3$
32. $\ln\frac{2}{3}$
33. $\ln 2 - \ln 5$
34. $\frac{1}{2}\ln 3$

35. $-\ln 2$
36. $-\ln 4$
37. $2\ln(0.8)$
38. $-\ln 5$

39. $\ln 4$
40. $\ln\frac{25}{9}$
41. $\ln 3$
42. $-\ln 3$

43. $(\ln 2)^2$
44. $\frac{5}{2}[(\ln 4)^2 - (\ln 3)^2]$
45. $\ln 2$
46. $-\frac{1}{2}\ln 2$

47. $3\ln 3$
48. $\ln 2$
49. $\ln x^2 + C$
50. $\frac{1}{3}\ln|3x+1| + C$

51. $\frac{1}{2}\ln(x^2+4) + C$
52. $-\frac{1}{2}\ln|1+2\cos x| + C$
53. $-3\ln|\cos\frac{x}{3}| + C$

54. $\frac{1}{2}\ln|\sin 2x| + C$
55. $-\infty$
56. ∞
57. $-\infty$

58. ∞
59. $\ln 2$
60. $\pi\ln 2$

62. a) $[-3, 1) \cup (1, \infty)$ b) Graph y in $[-3, 4]$ by $[-3, 15]$. c) $(-3, 1) \cup (1, \infty)$

63. a) Graph $y_1 = \sqrt{x + 3} \ \sin x$ in $[-4, 20]$ by $[-5, 5]$. b) In the same viewing rectangle graph $y_2 = \text{NDER}(y_1, x)$ and $y_3 = \frac{dy}{dx}$ (found in Exercise 21). The fact that y_2 and y_3 coincide supports that y_3 is valid where $y < 0$.

64. a) Graph $y_1 = x(x+1)(x+2)$ in $[-5, 3]$ by $[-5, 5]$. Proceed now as in Exercise 63.

65. Graph $y_1 = \frac{x+5}{x \cos x}$ in $[-20, 20]$ by $[-20, 20]$. Proceed now as in Exercise 63.

66. Graph $y_1 = \frac{x\sqrt{x^2+1}}{(x+1)^{2/3}} = x\sqrt{x^2 + 1}/((x + 1)^2)^{1/3}$ in $[-7.6, 5.7]$ by $[-16, 9.7]$. Proceed now as in Exercise 63.

67. Graph $y_1 = (x(x - 2)/(x^2 + 1))^{1/3}$ in $[-20, 20]$ by $[-1.1, 1.2]$. Proceed now as in Exercise 63.

68. $\frac{dy}{dx} = \frac{df}{dx} g + f \frac{dg}{dx}$

69. $\frac{dy}{dx} = \frac{\frac{df}{dx} g - f \frac{dg}{dx}}{g^2}$

70. a) Graph $y = f(x) = \text{NINT}(\tan t, t, 0, x)$ in $[-\frac{\pi}{2}, \frac{\pi}{2}]$ by $[-3, 3]$. (Use $tol = 1$.) Conjecture: $\lim_{x \to (-\pi/2)+} f(x) = \lim_{x \to (\pi/2)-} f(x) = \infty$. b) Near $x = 2$ there is rather wild oscillating behavior due to the discontinuity of the integrand at $x = \frac{\pi}{2}$. c) Except for the vertical asymptote at $x = \frac{\pi}{2}$ the graph of the antiderivative $- \ln |\cos x|$ is smooth. The graphs are the same on $(-\frac{\pi}{2}, \frac{\pi}{2})$.

71. a) Graph $y = f(x) = \text{NINT}(\cot t, t, \pi/2, x)$ in $[0, \pi]$ by $[-5, 5]$. (Use $tol = 1$.) Conjecture: $\lim_{x \to 0+} f(x) = \lim_{x \to \pi-} f(x) = -\infty$. b) Near $x = 4$ there is rather wild oscillating behavior due to the discontinuity of the integrand at $x = \pi$. c) Except for the vertical asymptote at $x = \pi$ the graph of the antiderivative $\ln |\sin x|$ is smooth. The two graphs are identical on $(0, \pi)$.

72. a) Graph y_1 and y_2 in $[-5, 5]$ by $[-3, 5]$ for several values of a. The graph of y_1 can be obtained from the graph of y_2 by a vertical shift. b) There is no value of a for which $y_1 = y_2$.

7.2   THE EXPONENTIAL FUNCTION

1. 7

2. $\frac{1}{7}$

3. 2

4. 8

5. $3e^2$

6. $\frac{1}{9}$

7. $\ln 2$

8. $-\frac{\ln 4}{5}$

9. $\frac{ln2}{10}$

10. $\ln 0.01$

11. $\frac{\ln 2}{\ln \frac{3}{2}}$

12. $k = \frac{\ln 2}{\ln 2 - \ln 3}$

13. 0 **14.** $-\frac{\ln 2}{k}$ **15.** $-10 \ln 3$ **16.** $-300 \ln 10$

17. $t = 0$ is the only solution   **18.** -1.328 **19.** $y = e^{2t+4}$

20. e^{-t+5} **21.** $y = 40 + e^{5t}$ **22.** $\frac{1-e^t}{2}$ **23.** $y = e^{(2x^2+1-5)}$

24. $\frac{\ln(e^{x^2-3}+1)}{\ln 2}$ **25.** $2e^x$ **26.** $2e^{2x}$ **27.** $-e^{-x}$

28. $-5e^{-5x}$ **29.** $\frac{2}{3}e^{2x/3}$ **30.** $-\frac{1}{4}e^{-x/4}$ **31.** $(xe^2 - e^x)' = e^2 - e^x$

32. $x^2 e^x + xe^x - e^x$ **33.** $\frac{e^{\sqrt{x}}}{2\sqrt{x}}$ **34.** $2xe^{x^2}$

35. 2 **36.** 2 **37.** 1 **38.** $e^2 - 1$

39. 8 **40.** $\frac{1}{2}$ **41.** $\frac{1}{2}(e^2 + 2e - 3)$ **42.** 1

43. $\ln(3/2)$ **44.** $4 \ln 3$ **45.** 0 **46.** $\frac{\ln 5}{8}$

47. $e^2 - e$ **48.** $\ln 2$ **49.** $2\sin(e^x) + C$ **50.** $-3\cos(e^x) + C$

51. $\ln(1 + e^x) + C$ **52.** $\ln|e^x - 1| + C$

53. $-2\ln|\cos(\sqrt{x})| + C$ **54.** $\sqrt{2}\ln|\sin(\sqrt{2x})| + C$

55. a) $f^{-1}(x) = \frac{x-3}{2}$ b) We may graph $y = 2x + 3$ and $y = \frac{x-3}{2}$ together in $[-10, 10]$ by $[-10, 10]$.

56. a) $f^{-1}(x) = \frac{5-x}{4}$ b) Graph f and f^{-1} in $[-7.4, 10.1]$ by $[-2.9, 7.4]$.

57. a) $f^{-1}(x) = f(x) = \frac{1-2x}{x+2}$ b) The graph of $f(x)$ is symmetric about the line $y = x$ confirming that f is self-inverse.

58. a) $f^{-1}(x) = \frac{3x-5}{x-1}$ b) Graph f and f^{-1} in $[-6.5, 9.4]$ by $[-6.1, 7.7]$.

59. $\frac{1}{4}$ **60.** $\frac{1}{6}$ **62.** 0 **63.** ∞

64. $\ln 2$ **65.** $\ln 2$ **66.** $x = 0.84162123357$

67. $\{0.679\ldots, 1.3086\ldots\}$ **68.** $1 + x$ **69.** $1 + 5x$

70. $\frac{1}{2e}$ **71.** e and e^{-1} **72.** $y = e^{\sin x} - 1$ **73.** $y = 2 + x + \ln|x|$

74. $4\ln(3/2) + 1$ meters   **78.** $4^{24} \approx 2.81 \times 10^{14}$ **79.** 1250

80. a) 8.00 years   b) 32.02 years

81. a) The amount in the account after t years is $A(t) = A_0 e^t$. b) 1.0986 years (rounded) c) e times the original amount

82. 4.50% **83.** 4.875...% **84.** 262,090,086

85. a) 14 years, 10 years b) 14%, 3.5% **86.** About December, 2015

87. August, 2015

88. In May of 1995, 1997, 1999 the purchasing power of the dollar will be, respectively, 0.65, 0.61, 0.58.

89. About 3.9% **90.** 32 days **91.** $\frac{100 \ln 2}{r}$ years **92.** In 16.09 years

93. a) $p(x) = 20.09 e^{1-0.01x}$ b) (rounded) \$49.41, \$22.20 d) Graph $y = 20.09 x e^{1-0.01x}$ in $[0, 200]$ by $[0, 2100]$

94. a) 13.52, 8.11, 6.34 years, respectively b) 23.3, 14, 10.9 years, respectively

95. a) $0.04 \ln 10$ b) 109.65 (rounded) c) We will always get the same result in b) and c).

96. a) $p(t) = 100 e^{t + 1.3t^2/2}$ b) $p(1) = 520.70$, $p(2) = 9948.43$. The respective percentage increases in the associated CPI are 420.70% and 9848.43%.

97. a) 8 b) 1000 c) 8.07 months, impossible

d) 7.082 months, 173.919 rabbits/month

98. a) 1 b) 200 c) 6.4 days d) After 5.252 days, 49.971 students/day

99. a) $D_x F^{-1}(x) \approx 6$.

7.3 OTHER EXPONENTIAL AND LOGARITHMIC FUNCTIONS

1. $\pi x^{\pi-1}$ **2.** $(1 + \sqrt{2})x^{\sqrt{2}}$ **3.** $-\sqrt{2}\, x^{-\sqrt{2}-1}$ **4.** $(1-e)x^{-e}$

5. $8^x \ln 8$ **6.** $-9^{-x} \ln 9$ **7.** $-\csc x \cot x (3^{\csc x}) \ln 3$

8. $-(\csc^2 x)3^{\cot x} \ln 3$ **9.** $2(\frac{\ln x}{x})x^{\ln x}$ **10.** 0

11. $(x+1)^x [\frac{x}{x+1} + \ln(x+1)]$ **12.** $(x+2)^{x+2}[1 + \ln(x+2)]$

13. $x^{\sin x}[\frac{\sin x}{x} + (\cos x)\ln x]$ **14.** $(\sin x)^{\tan x}[1 + (\sec^2 x)\ln \sin x]$

15. $\frac{1}{x\ln 2}$ **16.** $\frac{1}{2x\ln 5}$, $x > 0$ **17.** $\frac{3}{(\ln 2)(3x+1)}$ **18.** $\frac{1}{2(\ln 10)(x+1)}$

19. $-\frac{1}{x\ln 2}$, $x > 0$ **20.** $-\frac{\ln 2}{x(\ln x)^2}$ **21.** $\frac{1}{x}$ **22.** $\frac{1}{1+x\ln 3}$

23. $\frac{1}{\ln 10}$ **24.** $\ln 10$ **25.** $\frac{3}{\sqrt{3}+1} = \frac{3}{2}(\sqrt{3}-1)$.

26. $\frac{1}{\sqrt{2}+1}$ **27.** $\frac{4}{\ln 5}$ **28.** $\frac{1}{\ln 2}$ **29.** $\frac{1}{\ln 4}$

30. $\frac{3}{\ln 2}$ **31.** $\frac{3}{2}$ **32.** $\frac{24}{\ln 5}$ **33.** $\frac{1}{\ln 2}$

34. $\frac{1}{\ln 2}$ **35.** $\frac{\ln 10}{2}$ **36.** $\ln 4$ **37.** $\frac{3}{2}\ln 2$

38. $2\ln 10$ **39.** $\ln 10$ **40.** $\ln 2$ **41.** $\frac{2^{\sin x}}{\ln 2} + C$

42. $\frac{2(3^{\sqrt{x}})}{\ln 3} + C$ **43.** $\frac{(\ln(x-2))^2}{2\ln 3} + C$ **44.** $-\frac{(\ln(2x-1))^2}{4\ln 5} + C$

45. No local extrema or inflection points. The graph is falling and concave up on $(0,\infty)$. Check your graph by graphing y in $[0,10]$ by $[0,3]$.

46. The domain is $(0,\infty)$. y steadily rises and is concave up. Graph $y = x^{\sqrt{7}}$ in $[0,10]$ by $[0,20]$.

47. Graph $y = x^{\sqrt{x}}$ in $[-1,3]$ by $[-2,8]$. y is deceasing on $(0,e^{-2}]$, has a relative minimum at $x = e^{-2}$, and is increasing on $[e^{-2},\infty)$. The graph of y is concave up for all $x > 0$.

48. The graph falls on $(0,1]$ to the point $(1,1)$, a local minimum, and then rises on $[1,\infty)$. The graph is always concave up. Graph y in $[0,10]$ by $[0,20]$.

49. Period 2π. Graph y in $[-\frac{\pi}{2},\frac{3\pi}{2}]$ by $[0,4]$. Rel. min. at $(0,2)$, rel. max. at $(\pi,\frac{1}{2})$. Let $v = 1.90392136$. Inflection points at $(v, 0.12)$ and $(2\pi - v, 0.12)$. Rising on $[0,\frac{\pi}{2})$ and $(\frac{\pi}{2},\pi]$, falling on $(-\frac{\pi}{2},0]$ and $[\pi,\frac{3\pi}{2})$. Concave up on $(-\frac{\pi}{2},\frac{\pi}{2})$, $(\frac{\pi}{2},v)$ and $(2\pi - v,\frac{3\pi}{2})$. It is concave down on $(v,2\pi - v)$.

50. Graph one period of y in $[-\frac{\pi}{2},\frac{\pi}{2}]$ by $[0,10]$. y is always rising, concave up on $(-\frac{\pi}{2},-1.188]$ and $[-0.383,\frac{\pi}{2})$, concave down on $[-1.188,-0.383]$. $x = \frac{\pi}{2}$ is a vertical asymptote.

51. Period 2π. Graph y in $[0,2\pi]$ by $[-3,0]$. Rel. max at $(\frac{\pi}{2},0)$. No inflection point. Rising on $(0,\frac{\pi}{2}]$, falling on $[\frac{\pi}{2},\pi)$. Concave down on $(0,\frac{\pi}{2}) \cup (\frac{\pi}{2},\pi)$.

52. Graph $y = (2/\ln 5)\ln(x+1)$ in $[-1,5]$ by $[-2,4]$. y is rising and concave down on $(-1,\infty)$.

53. 6.052   **54.** 2.496   **55.** 3.591   **56.** 14.5085

57. 12   **58.** The solution set is $\{1,2\}$.

59. The solution set is $\{(-0.77, 0.58), (2, 4), (4, 16)\}$.

60. The solution set is $\{(-0.827, 0.149), (1.371, 23.512), (10, 10^{10})\}$

61. a) ∞ b) $-\infty$ **62.** a) $-\infty$ b) ∞ **63.** a) ∞ b) 0   **64.** a) 0 b) ∞

65. a) The ratio and its limit are both $\ln 10$. b) The ratio and its limit are both $\frac{\ln 3}{\ln 2}$.

66. a) The ratio and its limit are both $\frac{1}{2}$.   b) The ratio and its limit are both $\frac{\ln 2}{\ln 10}$.

67. Check your result by graphing $y = x^{\sin x}$ in $[0, 40]$ by $[0, 40]$.

68. Graph y in $[0, 6\pi]$ by $[0, 20]$.

69. In each case we have $x^{\beta} < x^{\sqrt{3}} < x^{\alpha}$ for $0 < x < 1$ and $x^{\alpha} < x^{\sqrt{3}} < x^{\beta}$ for $x > 1$ where $0 < \alpha < \sqrt{3} < \beta$. The closer α and β are, the more we must zoom in to distinguish the curves. For $x > 0$, $(1, 1)$ is the only point of intersection.

70. a) $(\ln 2)\frac{2^{\ln x}}{x}$ b) $\ln 2$ c) $\frac{2}{x}$ d) $\frac{2 \ln x}{x}$

73. 3.63×10^{-8} and 4.27×10^{-8} **74.** 7.32   **75.** 10

7.4 THE LAW OF EXPONENTIAL CHANGE REVISITED

1. a) $k = \frac{\ln 0.99}{1000}$ b) 10,483 years   c) about 82%

2. a) $p = p_0 e^{kh}$ where $p_0 = 1013$ and $k = \frac{1}{20} \ln \frac{90}{1013} = -0.121043091696$ b) 2.383 millibars   c) 0.977 km.

3. 54.88 grams   **4.** 585.350 kg   **5.** 0.59 day   **6.** About 605 days

7. We use $m = 66 + 7 = 73$.   a) 168.46 m   b) 41.1 sec

8. a) 7780 m   b) About 1899 sec or about 31.65 minutes

9. a) 17.53 min. longer   b) About 13.26 min.

10. $-30°$ F   **11.** $-3°$ C

12. 53.449° C, 23.794° C, 232.469 minutes = 3.874 hours from now

13. 92.10 sec   **15.** About 6658.30 years

16. a) 12,571 B.C.   b) 12,101 B.C.   c) 13,070 B.C. d) To graph the age of the bone as a function of the percentage of C-14 remaining, graph $y = abs((5700/\ln 2)\ln(\frac{x}{100}))$ in $[16, 18]$ by $[14101, 15070]$.

17. 41.22 years

18. Assuming the room temperature is 70° F and that the liquid originally has temperature 180°, $T = 70 + 110e^{-kt}$. k may be found using your data.

19. b) Never   **20.** The solution is $y = y_0 e^{kt}$ in all cases.

21. 13.768 years from now

7.5   INDETERMINATE FORMS AND L'HÔPITAL'S RULE

1. $\frac{1}{4}$ **2.** 4   **3.** $\frac{3}{11}$ **4.** $\frac{1}{2}$

5. 0   **6.** 5   **7.** $\frac{3}{2}$ **8.** 2

9. -2 **10.** $\ln(1/2)$ **11.** $\frac{5}{7}$ **12.** $-\frac{1}{2}$

13. $\frac{1}{4}$ **14.** 1   **15.** 0   **16.** $-\frac{2}{3}$

17. $-\frac{5}{3}$ **18.** 3   **19.** 0   **20.** ∞

21. e **22.** 0   **23.** e^2 **24.** e

25. 1   **26.** 1

27. If we define $y = 0$ when $x = 0$, then y is continuous on $[0, \infty)$.

28. No   **29.** No. $y \to \infty$ as $x \to 0^+$.   **30.** Yes, define $y(0) = 0$.

31. a) The function $F(x)$ defined by $F(x) = f(x)$, $x > 0$ and $F(0) = 1$ is continuous on $[0, \infty)$.

33. b) is correct.   a) is incorrect because L'Hôpital's rule does not apply to the limit form $\frac{0}{6}$; it is not an indeterminate form.

36. Both limits are 1.

37. Graph f in $[-10, 10]$ by $[0, 20]$. The graph resembles the one in Fig. 7.30.

38. Graph f in $[-20, 20]$ by $[0, 100]$.   **39.** $f(x) = e$ for $x > 0$, $x \neq 1$

40. Graph f in $[-2, 3]$ by $[-10, 50]$.

41. $\lim_{x \to 0} f(x) = \ln 3$. Graph in $[-2\pi, 2\pi]$ by $[-1, 2]$. The function is continuous except at $x = 0$ where it has a removable discontinuity.

42. $\lim_{x \to 0} f(x) = 0$. f is continuous on the interval except at $x = 0$ where it has a removable discontinuity.

43. a) 1   b) $\frac{\pi}{2}$ c) π **45.** b) 106.184   c) $1,060,000$ d) 1061836.55

7.6   THE RATES AT WHICH FUNCTIONS GROW

1. Function grows a) slower than b) slower than c) slower than d) faster than e) slower than f) slower than g) slower than h) slower than i) at the same rate as j) at the same rate as e^x as $x \to \infty$.

2. The function grows a) slower than b) slower than c) slower than d) slower than e) at the same rate as f) faster than g) slower than h) at the same rate as e^x.

3. The function grows a) at the same rate as b) faster than c) faster than d) slower than e) at the same rate as f) at the same rate as g) slower than h) slower than i) slower than j) faster than x^2 as $x \to \infty$.

4. The function grows a) at the same rate as b) at the same rate as c) at the same rate as d) slower than e) slower than f) slower than g) faster than h) at the same rate as i) slower than j) slower than $\ln x$ as $x \to \infty$.

5. $e^{x/2}, e^x, (\ln x)^x, x^x$ **6.** $(\ln 2)^x, x^2, 2^x, e^x$

11. Only c), d), e), f), h) are true.   **12.** Only c) and h) are false.

15. b) $x = e^{e^u}$ where $u = 16.6265089014$

21. g is an end behavior model for f.   **22.** g is an end behavior model for f.

23. g is an end behavior model for f.   **24.** g is an end behavior model for f.

25. g is only a left end behavior model for f.

26. g is a right end behavior model for f.

27. g is an end behavior model for f. **28.** g is a right end behavior model for f.

29. g is an end behavior model for f. **30.** g is a right end behavior model for f.

35. $n > 1$

36. If $p(x)$ and $q(x)$ have leading coefficients p_n and q_n, respectively, then $\lim_{|x|\to\infty} \frac{p(x)}{q(x)} = \frac{p_n}{q_n}$.

37. The first algorithm. **38.** One million steps; 20 steps.

7.7 THE INVERSE TRIGONOMETRIC FUNCTIONS

1. a) $\frac{\pi}{4}$ b) $\frac{\pi}{3}$ c) $\frac{\pi}{6}$ **2.** a) $-\frac{\pi}{4}$ b) $-\frac{\pi}{3}$ c) $-\frac{\pi}{6}$

3. a) $-\frac{\pi}{6}$ b) $-\frac{\pi}{4}$ c) $-\frac{\pi}{3}$ **4.** a) $\frac{\pi}{6}$ b) $\frac{\pi}{4}$ c) $\frac{\pi}{3}$

5. a) $\frac{\pi}{3}$ b) $\frac{\pi}{4}$ c) $\frac{\pi}{6}$ **6.** a) $\frac{2\pi}{3}$ b) $\frac{3\pi}{4}$ c) $\frac{5\pi}{6}$

7. a) $\frac{3\pi}{4}$ b) $\frac{5\pi}{6}$ c) $\frac{2\pi}{3}$ **8.** a) $\frac{\pi}{4}$ b) $\frac{\pi}{6}$ c) $\frac{\pi}{3}$

9. a) $\frac{\pi}{4}$ b) $\frac{\pi}{3}$ c) $\frac{\pi}{6}$ **10.** a) $-\frac{\pi}{4}$ b) $-\frac{\pi}{3}$ c) $-\frac{\pi}{6}$

11. a) $\frac{3\pi}{4}$ b) $\frac{5\pi}{6}$ c) $\frac{2\pi}{3}$ **12.** a) $\frac{\pi}{4}$ b) $\frac{\pi}{6}$ c) $\frac{\pi}{3}$

13. $\cos\alpha = \frac{\sqrt{3}}{2}$, $\tan\alpha = \frac{1}{\sqrt{3}}$, $\sec\alpha = \frac{2}{\sqrt{3}}$, $\csc\alpha = 2$

14. $\sin\alpha = \frac{\sqrt{3}}{2}$, $\tan\alpha = -\sqrt{3}$, $\sec\alpha = -2$, $\csc\alpha = \frac{2}{\sqrt{3}}$

15. $\sin\alpha = \frac{4}{5}$, $\cos\alpha = \frac{3}{5}$, $\sec\alpha = \frac{5}{3}$, $\csc\alpha = \frac{5}{4}$ and $\cot\alpha = \frac{3}{4}$.

16. $\sin\alpha = \frac{2}{\sqrt{5}}$, $\cos\alpha = -\frac{1}{\sqrt{5}}$, $\tan\alpha = -2$, $\csc\alpha = \frac{\sqrt{5}}{2}$ and $\cot\alpha = -\frac{1}{2}$.

17. $\frac{\sqrt{2}}{2}$ **18.** 2 **19.** $-\frac{1}{\sqrt{3}}$ **20.** $-\frac{\sqrt{3}}{3}$ **21.** $\frac{2}{\sqrt{3}} + \frac{1}{2}$

22. $-\frac{1}{2}$ **23.** 1 **24.** 0 **25.** $-\sqrt{2}$ **26.** -2

27. $\frac{\pi}{6}$ **28.** $\frac{3\pi}{4}$ **29.** $\frac{\sqrt{x^2+4}}{2}$ **30.** $\sqrt{4x^2+1}$

31. $\tan(\sec^{-1} 3y) = \begin{cases} -\sqrt{9y^2-1} & \text{if } 3y \leq -1 \\ \sqrt{9y^2-1} & \text{if } 3y \geq 1 \end{cases}$

32. $\tan[\sec^{-1} \frac{y}{5}] = \begin{cases} -\sqrt{y^2 - 25}/5 & \text{if } y \leq -5 \\ \sqrt{y^2 - 25}/5 & \text{if } y \geq 5 \end{cases}$

33. $\sqrt{1 - x^2}$ **34.** $\frac{\sqrt{1-x^2}}{x}$ **35.** $\frac{\sqrt{x^2-2x}}{|x-1|}$ **36.** $\frac{x}{\sqrt{2x^2+1}}$ **37.** $\sqrt{9 - 4y^2}/3$

38. $\sqrt{25 - y^2}/5$ **39.** $\frac{\sqrt{x^2-16}}{|x|}$ **40.** $\frac{2}{\sqrt{x^2+4}}$ **41.** $\frac{\pi}{2}$ **42.** π

43. $\frac{\pi}{2}$ **44.** $-\frac{\pi}{2}$ **45.** $\frac{\pi}{2}$ **46.** $\frac{\pi}{2}$ **47.** 0

48. 0   **50.** $\pi[\frac{4\pi}{3} - \sqrt{3}]$ **51.** 0.955 radian or 54.736°   **52.** 42.218°

53. 0.464, 0.841 and 0.730 in radian measure

54. In the diagram three angles are indicated with arrows. The lowest is $\tan^{-1} 1$, the next highest is $\tan^{-1} 2$ and the third is $\tan^{-1} 3$. Their sum is clearly π.

60. Graph $y = x$, $-1 \leq x \leq 1$. Domain = range = $[-1, 1]$.

61. Graph $y = \sin^{-1}(1/2x) = \sin^{-1}((2x)^{-1})$ in $[-3.5, 3.5]$ by $[-\frac{\pi}{2}, \frac{\pi}{2}]$

62. Graph $y = 3\tan^{-1} x$ in $[-10, 10]$ by $[-1.5\pi, 1.5\pi]$.

63. Graph $y = 2\cos^{-1}(1/3x) = 2\cos^{-1}((3x)^{-1})$ in $[-3, 3]$ by $[0, 2\pi]$.

64. Graph $y = \cot^{-1}(x + 2) = \frac{\pi}{2} - \tan^{-1}(x + 2)$ in $[-10, 10]$ by $[0, \pi]$.

65. Graph $y = 3 + \cos^{-1}(x - 2)$ in $[1, 3]$ by $[3, 3 + \pi]$.

66. Graph $y = -2 + \sin^{-1}(x - 3)$ in $[-1, 5]$ by $[-4, 1]$.

7.8 DERIVATIVES OF INVERSE TRIGONOMETRIC FUNCTIONS; RELATED INTEGRALS

1. $-\frac{2x}{\sqrt{1-x^4}}$. To confirm graphically we graph this last result and NDER(y, x) in $[-1, 1]$ by $[-5, 5]$ and see that the two graphs match.

2. $\frac{1}{|x|\sqrt{x^2-1}}$ **3.** $\frac{15}{1+9x^2}$ **4.** $-\frac{1}{2\sqrt{x}(1+x)}$ **5.** $\frac{1}{\sqrt{4-x^2}}$

6. $-\frac{1}{\sqrt{1-(1-x)^2}} = -\frac{1}{\sqrt{2x-x^2}}$ **7.** $\frac{1}{|x|\sqrt{25x^2-1}}$ **8.** $\frac{1}{9+x^2}$

9. $\frac{-2x}{(x^2+1)\sqrt{x^4+2x^2}}$ **10.** $-\frac{2}{\sqrt{1-4x^2}}$ **11.** $y = \pi/2$, $y' = 0$ **12.** $\frac{1}{\sqrt{1-x^2}}$

13. $-\frac{1}{2x\sqrt{x-1}}$ **14.** $2\sqrt{1 - x^2}$ **15.** $\frac{x|x|-1}{|x|\sqrt{x^2-1}}$

16. $y' = 0$, $x \neq 0$. (Remark: $y = \pi$, $x < 0$ and $y = 0$, $x > 0$.)

17. $2\tan^{-1} x$ **18.** $\frac{2x(1-x)}{x^2+1}$ **19.** $\frac{\pi}{6}$ **20.** $\frac{\pi}{2}$ **21.** $\frac{\pi}{12}$

22. $-\frac{\pi}{12}$ **23.** π **24.** π **25.** $\frac{\pi}{12}$ **26.** $\frac{\pi}{12}$

27. $\frac{\pi}{6}$ **28.** $\frac{\pi}{8}$ **29.** $\frac{\pi}{3}$ **30.** $\frac{\pi}{6}$ **31.** $\sin^{-1}\frac{x}{3} + C$

32. $\frac{1}{2}\sin^{-1}(2x) + C$ **33.** $\frac{1}{\sqrt{17}}\tan^{-1}\frac{x}{\sqrt{17}} + C$

34. $\frac{1}{3\sqrt{3}}\tan^{-1}\frac{x}{\sqrt{3}} + C$.   **35.** $\frac{1}{\sqrt{2}}\sec^{-1}(\frac{5}{\sqrt{2}}|x|) + C$.   **36.** $\frac{1}{2}\sec^{-1}(\frac{\sqrt{5}}{2}|x|) + C$.

37. $\frac{1}{2}\sin^{-1}(y^2) + C$.   **38.** $\sin^{-1}(\tan y) + C$.   **39.** $\frac{\pi}{12}$

40. $\frac{\pi}{2}$ **41.** $2\ln(4/3)$ **42.** $\frac{\pi}{12}$ **43.** $\frac{\pi}{12}$ **44.** π

45. 1 **46.** ∞ **47.** 1 **48.** ∞ **49.** $\frac{\pi^2}{2}$

50. $\frac{\pi}{3}$ **51.** $3\sqrt{5}\text{ft} \approx 6.71\text{ft}$ **52.** $((\ln 4)/\pi, 0)$ **53.** $x = 1$, $\theta = \frac{\pi}{2}$

54. The linearizations are, respectively, x, $\frac{\pi}{2} - x$, x, $\frac{\pi}{2} - x$.

55. $y = \sec^{-1} x + \frac{2\pi}{3}$ **56.** $1 + \sin^{-1} x$ **57.** $y = \cos^{-1} x - \frac{\pi}{4}$

58. $\frac{\pi}{2} - \tan^{-1} x$

60. 3.14159265358 (agrees with π up to the last decimal place)

61. Both answers can be correct because they differ by a constant: $\sin^{-1} x = \frac{\pi}{2} - \cos^{-1} x$.

62. b) $C = -\frac{\pi}{2}$

70. Graph $y = \tan^{-1}\sqrt{x+1}$ in $[-1, 10]$ by $[0, \frac{\pi}{2}]$.

71. Graph $y = \sec^{-1}(3x) = \cos^{-1}(\frac{1}{3x})$ in $[-5, 5]$ by $[0, \pi]$. Other windows can show that $y = 0$ when $x = \frac{1}{3}$ and $y = \pi$ when $x = -\frac{1}{3}$.

72. $y = \csc^{-1}\sqrt{x} + \sec^{-1}\sqrt{x} = \frac{\pi}{2}$, $x \geq 1$. Graph $y = \sin^{-1}(1/\sqrt{x}) + \cos^{-1}(1/\sqrt{x})$ in $[-1, 10]$ by $[-1, 8]$.

73. Graph $y = \cot^{-1}\sqrt{x^2 - 1} = \frac{\pi}{2} - \tan^{-1}\sqrt{x^2 - 1}$ in $[-10, 10]$ by $[-1, 2]$.

7.9   HYPERBOLIC FUNCTIONS

1. -0.693 or $-\ln 2$ **2.** 0.693 **3.** ± 1.317 **4.** 0.549

5. ± 0.896 **6.** -0.549 **7.** $x + \frac{1}{x}$, $x > 0$

8. $\frac{1}{2}(x^2 - \frac{1}{x^2})$, $x > 0$. Use $[0, 5]$ by $[-5, 12]$.

9. e^{5x} **10.** e^{4x} **11.** e^{-3x} **12.** 0

15. Graph $y = \sinh 3x$ in $[-3, 3]$ by $[-3, 3]$. This graph may be obtained from the graph of $y = \sinh x$ by horizontally shrinking it by a factor of $\frac{1}{3}$.

16. Graph in $[-3.5, 3]$ by $[-10, 10]$.

17. Graph $y = 2 \tanh \frac{x}{2}$ in $[-4, 4]$ by $[-2, 2]$. The graph can be obtained from the graph of $y = \tanh x$ by stretching vertically and horizontally by a factor of 2.

18. Graph $y = x - \tanh x$ in $[-2.5, 2.5]$ by $[-2.5, 2.5]$.

19. Graph in $[-10, 10]$ by $[-10, 0]$. Graph rises on $(-\infty, 0]$, falls on $[0, \infty)$ and is concave down for all x.

20. Graph $y = \ln(\text{csch } x)$ in $[0, 3]$ by $[-10, 10]$. Since $\lim_{x \to 0+} \text{csch } x = \infty$ and $\lim_{x \to \infty} \text{csch } x = 0$, $\lim_{x \to 0+} y = \infty$ and $\lim_{x \to \infty} y = -\infty$.

21. Graph $y = \sinh^{-1}(2x)$ in $[-5, 5]$ by $[-5, 5]$. The graph may be obtained from the graph of $y = \sinh^{-1} x$ by shrinking horizontally by a factor of $\frac{1}{2}$.

22. Graph $y = 2 \cosh^{-1} \sqrt{x}$ in $[-1, 5]$ by $[-1, 5]$.

23. Graph in $[-1, 1]$ by $[-4, 0.5]$. The domain is $(-1, 1)$. $\lim_{x \to 1+} = -\infty$ and $\lim_{x \to 1-} y = 0$. y is rising on $(-1, 0.564]$ and falling on $[0.564, 1)$. The curve is concave down on $(-1, 1)$.

24. Graph $y = (1 - x^2) \coth^{-1} x = (1 - x^2) \tanh^{-1}(\frac{1}{x})$ in $[-10, 10]$ by $[-10, 10]$.

25. Graph y in $[0, 1]$ by $[0, 1]$. y has domain $(0, 1)$. It is rising for $0 < x \le x_0$ and falling for $x_0 \le x \le 1$ where $x_0 = 0.552$. The curve is concave down on $(0, 1)$.

26. Graph $y = x^2 \text{csch}^{-1} x^2 = x^2 \sinh^{-1}(\frac{1}{x^2})$ in $[-10, 10]$ by $[-1, 2]$.

27. $-\text{csch } x$ **28.** $x \sinh x$ **29.** $\text{csch}(2x)$ **30.** $\text{sech } x$

31. All three have derivative $\sinh(2x)$.

32. $y = 2x$, $x > 0$. $y' = 2$ for all $x > 0$.   **33.** $|\sec x|$ **34.** $\sec x$, $0 < x < \frac{\pi}{2}$

35. $\sec x$ **36.** $-\csc x$, $-\frac{\pi}{2} < x < \frac{\pi}{2}$, $x \neq 0$ **37.** $-\csc x$

38. $-\csc x$ **39.** $\frac{2\sinh 5}{5}$ **40.** $\sinh 1$ **41.** 0

42. 0 **43.** e **44.** $\frac{1}{e}$ **45.** $\frac{3}{4}$

46. $\ln \frac{5}{4}$ **47.** $\frac{4}{5}$ **48.** $(\ln 2) - \frac{3}{5}$ **49.** $2\sinh 2$

50. $\frac{5}{12}$ **51.** $\frac{\cosh 2x}{2} + C$ **52.** $\frac{4}{3}\sinh(3x - \ln 2) + C$

53. $\frac{e^{3t}}{3} + e^t + C$ **54.** $2(2t + e^{-2t}) + C$ **55.** $7\ln(\cosh \frac{x}{7}) + C$

56. $\frac{1}{\sqrt{2}}\ln|\sinh \sqrt{2}\, x| + C$ **57.** $-2\,\mathrm{sech}\,\sqrt{t} + C$

58. $-\mathrm{csch}\,(\ln t) + C$ **61.** a) $\sinh^{-1}(1)$ b) $\ln(1 + \sqrt{2})$

62. a) $\mathrm{sech}^{-1}(3/5) - \mathrm{sech}^{-1}(4/5)$ b) $\ln(3/2)$

63. a) $\cosh^{-1}\left(\frac{5}{3}\right) - \cosh^{-1}\left(\frac{5}{4}\right)$ b) $\ln \frac{3}{2}$

64. a) $\tanh^{-1}\left(\frac{1}{2}\right)$ b) $\frac{1}{2}\ln 3$ **65.** a) $\coth^{-1} 2 - \coth^{-1}\left(\frac{5}{4}\right)$ b) $-\frac{\ln 3}{2}$

66. a) $\sinh^{-1}\sqrt{3}$ b) $\ln(\sqrt{3} + 2)$

67. a) $\frac{1}{2}\left[\sinh^{-1} 2 - \sinh^{-1}(1)\right]$ b) $\frac{1}{2}\ln \frac{2+\sqrt{5}}{1+\sqrt{2}}$

68. 0 **69.** 3.916 **70.** 723.8204 **71.** 7.589

72. $\mathrm{NINT}(\frac{\sinh^{-1} x}{x}, x, -2, 2.000001) = 3.5069\ldots$

73. Graph $y = \mathrm{NINT}(\frac{\sinh t}{t}, t, 1, x)$ in $[-4, 4]$ by $[-10, 10]$.

74. Graph $y = \int_0^x \cosh(t^2)dt = \mathrm{NINT}(\cosh(t^2), t, 0, x)$ in $[-3, 3]$ by $[-10, 10]$. We used Tol $= 1$.

75. Graph $\mathrm{NINT}((\cosh t - 1)/t, t, 1, x)$ in $[-5, 5]$ by $[-1, 10]$.

76. Graph $y = \int_1^x \frac{\sinh^{-1} t}{t}\, dt = \mathrm{NINT}((\sinh^{-1} t)/t, t, 1, x)$ in $[-2, 2]$ by $[-3, 3]$.

77. 2π **78.** π **79.** $(0, 0.477)$

80. $\pi\left[(2\ln\frac{199}{100}) - \frac{99}{100}\right]$ **82.** The equation becomes $f(x) = f(x)$ in both cases.

83. b) $\sqrt{\frac{mg}{k}}$ c) 178.885 ft/sec   **85.** 99   **86.** 990

87. $\pi\left(\frac{63}{8} + 2\ln 8\right)$ **89.** c) $A(0) = 0$ so $A(u) = \frac{1}{2}u + C = \frac{1}{2}u$ and $u = 2A(u)$.

PRACTICE EXERCISES, CHAPTER 7

1. $\frac{dy}{dx} = \frac{1}{2x}$. Support by graphing NDER($\ln\sqrt{x}, x$) in $[0,2]$ by $[0,10]$.

2. $\frac{dy}{dx} = 1$. Confirm by graphing NDER($\ln(e^x/2), x$).   **3.** $\frac{dy}{dx} = \frac{2x}{x^2+2}$

4. $\frac{dy}{dx} = \frac{e^x}{1+e^x}$. We may confirm this graphically by graphing $\frac{e^x}{1+e^x} + 2$ and NDER($\ln(1 + e^x), x$) and seeing that the first curve may be obtained from the second by vertically shifting the latter curve 2 units upward.

5. $\frac{dy}{dx} = -\frac{1}{e^x}$ **6.** $\frac{dy}{dx} = e^{-x}(1 - x)$ **7.** $\frac{dy}{dx} = e$

8. $\frac{dy}{dx} = \ln x$. This can be confirmed by graphing $\ln x + 2$ and NDER(NINT($\ln t, t, 1, x$), x) in $[1, 10]$ by $[-5, 5]$ and observing that one graph can be obtained from the other by a vertical shift.

9. $-\tan x$ **10.** $\cot x$ **11.** $-\frac{1}{\sqrt{1-x^2}\cos^{-1}x}$ **12.** $\frac{1}{\sqrt{1-x^2}\sin^{-1}x}$

13. $\frac{2}{(\ln 2)x}$ **14.** $\frac{1}{(\ln 5)(x-7)}$ **15.** $-(\ln 8)8^{-x}$ **16.** $9^x\ln 9$

17. $\frac{-1}{2\sqrt{x(1-x)}}$ **18.** 2   **19.** $\frac{2}{x\sqrt{x^2-1}}$, $x > 0$

20. $2\left[x\cot^{-1}(2x) - \frac{1+x^2}{1+4x^2}\right]$ **21.** $\frac{1}{x} + \frac{\sec^{-1}\sqrt{x}}{\sqrt{x-1}}$ **22.** $y' = -1$, $0 < x < \frac{\pi}{2}$

23. a) $2x$ b) $1 + \ln 2$ c) -1 **24.** a) 4   b) $\frac{1}{4}$ c) $\ln x$

25. $y = e^x - 1$ **26.** $y = 4 + e^{-4t}$ **27.** $y = \ln 2x$

28. $y = 10\ln 2$ **29.** $\frac{2(x^2+1)}{\sqrt{\cos 2x}}\left(\frac{2x}{x^2+1} + \tan 2x\right)$

30. $y' = \frac{1}{10}\left[\frac{3}{3x+4} - \frac{2}{2x-4}\right]\sqrt[10]{\frac{3x+4}{2x-4}}$

31. $5\left(\frac{(x+5)(x-1)}{(x-2)(x+3)}\right)^5\left[\frac{1}{x+5} + \frac{1}{x-1} - \frac{1}{x-2} - \frac{1}{x+3}\right]$ **32.** $2\left(\frac{\ln x}{x}\right)x^{\ln x}$, $x > 1$

33. $e^{\tan^{-1} x}(2x+1)$

34. $y' = \frac{2x2^x}{\sqrt{x^2+1}} \left[\frac{1}{x} + \ln 2 - \frac{x}{x^2+1} \right]$

35. $\coth^2 x$

36. $x \cosh x$

37. $-x \operatorname{csch}^2 x$

38. $x \operatorname{sech}^2 x$

39. $\operatorname{sech} x$

40. $\operatorname{sech} x$

41. $1 + \frac{x \sinh^{-1} x}{\sqrt{1+x^2}}$

42. $1 + \frac{x \cosh^{-1} x}{\sqrt{x^2-1}}$

43. $\frac{1}{x^2-1}$

44. $\sec x$

45. $2 \sec 2x$

46. $\sec x,\ 0 < x < \frac{\pi}{2}$

47. Graph y in $[-30, 30]$ by $[0, 5]$.

48. Graph $y = e^{\cot^{-1} x} = e^{\pi/2 - \tan^{-1} x}$ in $[-50, 30]$ by $[-5, 24]$.

49. Graph in $[0, 4]$ by $[0, 5]$. Minimum at $(0.544, 0.578)$.

50. Graph y in the viewing window $[-2, 2]$ by $[-5, 1]$.

51. $-\frac{\ln 7}{3}$

52. $\frac{2}{3}$

53. 1

54. 4

55. $e - 1$

56. $e^2 - e$

57. $\ln 8$

58. $\frac{\ln 2}{\pi}$

59. $\ln(9/25)$

60. $\frac{2\pi}{3}$

61. $\ln(1 + \sqrt{2})$

62. $\ln 3$

63. $\frac{(\ln 8)^2}{2 \ln 4} = \frac{9}{8} \ln 4 = \frac{9}{4} \ln 2$

64. 4

65. $\frac{1}{\ln 3}$

66. $\frac{1}{\ln 2}$

67. π

68. $\frac{\pi}{4}$

69. $\frac{\pi}{2}$

70. $\frac{\pi}{3}$

71. $\frac{\pi}{6}$

72. $\frac{\pi}{12}$

73. $3 + \ln 4$

74. $\ln \frac{9}{8}$

75. $8\sqrt{2}$

76. 3

77. $5(\operatorname{csch}^2 2 - \operatorname{csch}^2 4)$

78. $\frac{17}{81}$

79. $e^{\tan x} + C$

80. $-e^{\cot x} + C$

81. $-\ln|\cos(\ln v)| + C$

82. $\ln(|\ln v|) + C$

83. $\frac{3^{x^2}}{2 \ln 3} + C$

84. $\frac{2^{\tan x}}{\ln 2} + C$

85. $\sec^{-1}|2y| + C$

86. $6 \sec^{-1}(|y|/4) + C$

87. a) $\sinh^{-1} 1$ b) $\ln(1 + \sqrt{2})$

88. a) $\cosh^{-1} 17 - \cosh^{-1} 2$ b) $\ln \frac{17 + 12\sqrt{2}}{2 + \sqrt{3}}$

89. a) $2 \left[(\tanh^{-1}(\frac{1}{2}))^2 - (\tanh^{-1}(\frac{1}{5}))^2 \right]$ b) $\frac{1}{2}(\ln 2) \ln \frac{9}{2}$

90. a) $\operatorname{csch}^{-1} \frac{1}{2} - \operatorname{csch}^{-1} \frac{1}{\sqrt{2}}$ b) $\ln \frac{2 + \sqrt{5}}{\sqrt{2} + \sqrt{3}}$

91. a) $(\text{sech}^{-1}\frac{3}{5})^2 - (\text{sech}^{-1}\frac{4}{5})^2$ b) $(\ln\frac{3}{2})\ln 6$

92. a) $e^{\coth^{-1}\sqrt{3}} - e^{\coth^{-1}\sqrt{8}}$ b) $\sqrt{\frac{\sqrt{3}+1}{\sqrt{3}-1}} - \sqrt{\frac{\sqrt{8}+1}{\sqrt{8}-1}}$

93. $\frac{6\ln 6 - 5}{\ln 5}$　　　**94.** 1.5266　　　**95.** 2.714　　　**96.** 7.08085

97. Graph $\int_1^x \frac{\tanh t}{t}dt = \text{NINT}\left(\frac{\tanh t}{t}, t, 1, x\right)$ in $[-10, 10]$ by $[-5, 3]$.

98. Graph $y = \int_1^x t\coth t\, dt = \text{NINT}(t(\tanh t)^{-1}, t, 1, x)$ in the "squared" window $[-17, 17]$ by $[-10, 10]$.

99. $\frac{1}{3}$　　　**100.** 1　　　**101.** $\ln\frac{5}{3}$

103. Areas: $\frac{1}{\ln 2}$ and $\frac{1}{\ln 4}$. Ratio: 2

104. a) 0.698970004336   b) 1.58496250072   c) 0.356207187108

105. 18935 years

106. a) 0.262   b) 3.816 years   c) By Exercise 14 of 7.4, $t = 3/k = 11.448$ years

107. About 5.3%　　　**108.** 59.795 ft　　　**109.** About 7.19 years

110. a) 3.11%   b) 255.414 using the exact value of k

111. a) About 8%   b) About 771.8 using the 8% of a)

112. a) 2   b) 150   c) 5.9 days   d) After 4.3 days, 37.5 students/day

114. a) 14 years   b) 10 years　　　**115.** 91.943 minutes

116. a) $y = c - (c - y_0)e^{-(kA/V)t}$ assuming $c > y$ b) c

117. The limit is ∞ as $t \to 0^-$ and $-\infty$ as $t \to 0^+$.

118. The limit does not exist.　　**119.** 2　　**120.** $\frac{1}{2}$

121. Define $f(0) = \ln 2$　　　**122.** Graph $y = x\ln x$ in $[0, 2]$ by $[-2, 3]$.

123. 1　　　**124.** 1　　　**125.** e^3　　**126.** e^3

127. In all three cases the functions grow at the same rate as $x \to \infty$ because $\lim_{x\to\infty} \frac{f(x)}{g(x)} = L$, L finite and not 0.

128. a) All three grow at the same rate.   b) $x^{\log_2 x}$ grows faster than $x^{\ln x}$.
   c) $(1/2)^x$ grows faster than $(1/3)^x$.

129. a) True b) False c) True   **130.** a) True b) True c) False

131. g is a right end behavior model for f.

132. g is an end behavior model for f.

133. g is an end behavior model for f.

134. g is an end behavior model for f.

135. g is a right end behavior model for f.

136. g is a left end behavior model for f.

137. $f(x) = \frac{\pi}{2}$ for $x > 0$ and $f(x) = -\frac{\pi}{2}$ for $x < 0$.

139. $100 - 20\sqrt{17} \approx 17.538$ m   **140.** b) $61°$

141. $y = \text{sech}^{-1}|x| - \sqrt{1 - x^2} = \cosh^{-1}\left(\frac{1}{|x|}\right) - \sqrt{1 - x^2}$

CHAPTER 8
TECHNIQUES OF INTEGRATION

8.1 FORMULAS FOR ELEMENTARY INTEGRALS

1. $2(8x^2 + 1)^{1/2} + C$
2. $2\sqrt{1 + 3\sin x}$
3. $\int_2^{10} \frac{1}{u} du \approx 1.60944$

4. $\ln 4$
5. $-\ln(\cos^2 x^2) + C$
6. $-\frac{1}{7}\ln|\sin(3 - 7x)| + C$

7. $3\int_{-\pi/3}^{\pi/3} \sec u \, du \approx 7.902$
8. $\frac{1}{2}\ln|\sec(x^2 - 5) + \tan(x^2 - 5)| + C$

9. 0.881
10. $\ln|\csc(\frac{1}{x}) + \cot(\frac{1}{x})| + C$

11. $-\ln|\csc(e^x + 1) + \cot(e^x + 1)| + C$
12. $\ln|\sin(3 + \ln x)| + C$

13. $\int_0^{\ln 2} e^u du = 1$
14. $1 - \frac{1}{e}$
15. $\int_0^1 3^u du \approx 1.82048$

16. $\frac{1}{\ln 2}[2^{\ln 2} - 1]$
17. $12\int_1^{\sqrt{3}} \frac{du}{1 + u^2} \approx 3.14159 \ (\pi)$
18. π
19. $\pi/18$

20. $\frac{\pi}{6}$
21. $6\int_{2/\sqrt{3}}^2 du/(u\sqrt{u^2 - 1}) \approx 3.14159 \ (\pi)$
22. $-\pi/36$

23. $u = x - 2; \ \sin^{-1}(x - 2) + C$
24. $\sin^{-1}(x - 1) + C$

25. $u = x - 1; \ 6.28319 \ (2\pi)$
26. π

27. $u = x + 1; \ \sec^{-1}|x + 1| + C$
28. $\sec^{-1}|x - 2| + C$

29. $4 - \pi/2$
30. $5 + 4\pi$
31. 0

32. 1
33. $\pi/3 - 1/2$
34. $1 + \ln 2.5$

35. $\sqrt{2}$
36. $\pi/4 - \ln 2$
37. $\int_0^{\pi/3} \sec x \, dx \approx 1.31696$

38. $\ln(\sqrt{2} + 1)$
39. $\bar{x} = 0, \ \bar{y} = \frac{1}{2\ln(1 + \sqrt{2})}$
40. $2(\sqrt{2} - \ln(1 + \sqrt{2}))$

41. 8.30169 cm
42. 10.8896 cm
43. $u = \sin x; \ 2$

44. $9/4$
45. $\ln(1/3)$
46. $\frac{1}{8}\ln 17$

47. $u = \pi x; \ \frac{1}{\pi}\ln(1 + \sqrt{2})$
48. $\frac{1}{\pi}\ln(3 + 2\sqrt{2})$
49. $u = \tan x; \ e^{\sqrt{3}} - 1$

50. 2
51. $u = \sqrt{x}; \ 2/\ln 2$
52. $99/\ln 100$

53. $u = 3x;\ \pi$ **54.** $\pi/12$ **55.** $u = 2x;\ \pi/6$

56. $\pi/6$ **57.** $u = 2x;\ \pi/12$ **58.** $(\sqrt{3} - 1)/2$

59. $C = -\pi/4$ **60.** $C = 0$

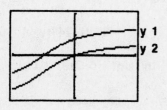

8.2   INTEGRATION BY PARTS

1. $-x \cos x + \sin x + C$ **2.** $\frac{x}{2} \sin 2x + \frac{\cos 2x}{4} + C$

3. $-x^2 \cos x + 2x \sin x + 2 \cos x + C$ **4.** $x^2 \sin x + 2x \cos x - 2 \sin x + C$

5. $\frac{x^2}{2} \ln x - \frac{1}{4}x^2 + C$ **6.** $\frac{x^4}{4}(\ln x - \frac{1}{4}) + C$

7. $x \tan^{-1} x - \frac{1}{2} \ln(1 + x^2) + C$ **8.** $x \sin^{-1} x + (1 - x^2)^{1/2} + C$

9. $x \tan x + \ln|\cos x| + C$ **10.** $2x \tan 2x - \ln|\sec 2x| + C$

11. $x^3 e^x - 3x^2 e^x + 6x e^x - 6e^x + C$ **12.** $-e^{-x}(x^4 + 4x^3 + 12x^2 + 24x + 24) + C$

13. $(x^2 - 7x + 7)e^x + C$ **14.** $(x^2 - x + 2)e^x + C$

15. $(x^5 - 5x^4 + 20x^3 - 60x^2 + 120x - 120)e^x + C$ **16.** $(x^2 - \frac{x}{2} + \frac{1}{8})\frac{e^{4x}}{4} + C$

17. $(\pi^2 - 4)/8$ **18.** $\frac{3}{16}(4 - \pi^2)$ **19.** $2\pi/3 - \sqrt{3}/2$

20. $\frac{4\pi}{3} - \sqrt{3}$ **21.** 11.614 **22.** -8.435

23. -18.186 **24.** 125.0276

25. a) π,   b) 3π (area is positive)   **26.** $\pi(\pi - 2)$

27. $2\pi(1 - 2/e)$ **28.** a) $\frac{\pi^2}{2}(\frac{\pi^2}{3} - \frac{1}{2})$,   b) 8π

29. $\pi^2 + \pi - 4$ **30.** $\frac{1}{2}(x^2 + 1)\tan^{-1} x - \frac{1}{2}x + C$

31. Exact answer is $3[(\ln 3)^4 - 4(\ln 3)^3 + 12(\ln 3)^2 - 24\ln 3 + 16]$

32. b) $\frac{\pi}{6} + \frac{8\sqrt{3}}{27}$

33. a) 1   b) $\ln \frac{27}{4} - 1$, $(a) + (b) + 2\ln(2) = 3\ln 3$ d) let $u = y = e^x$, $v = x$

34.

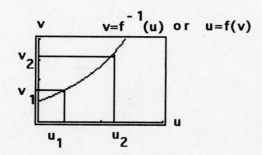

8.3   INTEGRALS INVOLVING TRIGONOMETRIC FUNCTIONS

1. $-\cos x + 2\frac{\cos^3 x}{3} - \frac{\cos^5 x}{5} + C$

2. $-2\cos\frac{x}{2} + \frac{4\cos^3\left(\frac{x}{2}\right)}{3} - \frac{2\cos^5\left(\frac{x}{2}\right)}{5} + C$

3. $-\frac{\sin^3 x}{3} + \sin x + C$

4. $\sin(3x) - \frac{2\sin^3(3x)}{3} + \frac{\sin^5(3x)}{5} + C$

5. $-\cos y + \frac{3\cos^3 y}{3} - \frac{3\cos^5 y}{5} + \frac{\cos^7 y}{7} + C$

6. $7[\sin t - \sin^3 t + \frac{3\sin^5 t}{5} - \frac{\sin^7 t}{7}] + C$

7. $\frac{8}{4}[\frac{3}{2}x - \sin 2x + \frac{1}{8}\sin 4x] + C$

8. $3x + \frac{1}{\pi}\sin 4\pi x + \frac{1}{8\pi}\sin 8\pi x + C$

9. $2[x - \frac{\sin 4x}{4}] + C$

10. $\frac{1}{2}(y - \frac{\sin 4y}{4}) - \frac{1}{2}\frac{\sin^3 2y}{3} + C$

11. $35[\frac{\sin^5 x}{5} - \frac{\sin^7 x}{7}] + C$

12. $-\frac{1}{2}\frac{\cos^3 2x}{3} + C$

13. $-4\frac{\cos^4 2\theta}{4} + C$

14. $\frac{1}{2}[\frac{\sin^3 2\theta}{3} - \frac{\sin^5 2\theta}{5}] + C$

15. 4   **16.** $2\sqrt{2}$ **17.** 2   **18.** 2   **19.** $\ln(3 + 2\sqrt{2})$

20. $\ln 2$ **21.** $\sqrt{2}$ **22.** 8/3   **23.** $2\sqrt{3} - \ln(2 - \sqrt{3})$

24. -0.9065 **25.** 4/3   **26.** 4/3   **27.** 4/3   **28.** 8

29. $2 - \ln 4$ **30.** $3\pi - 8$ **31.** $4/3 - \ln\sqrt{3}$ **32.** $2\pi - 16/3$

33. $-6/5$ **34.** $-2/5$ **35.** π **36.** $1/2$ **37.** 0 **38.** 0

39. (a), (b), (c), (e), (g) and (i) are zero. (d), (f) and (h) are not zero.

40. Only g is non-zero.   **41.** (d) 2,   (f) 4/3,   (h) 4/3

42. f) 0;   g) 2/3

44. Integrate by parts, $u = \csc x$, then use an identity.

45. a)   b)

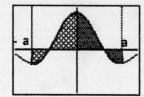

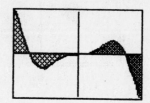

46. $\int_{-a}^{0} f(x)\,dx = -\int_{a}^{0} f(-t)\,dt$, etc. where $t = -x$

47. even, 2, 1   **48.** odd, 0, $\pi - 2$ **49.** odd, 0, 0.5

50. odd, 0, $\sqrt{2} - 1$ **51.** even, 2.404, 1.202   **52.** even, 1.7627, 0.88137

8.4 TRIGONOMETRIC SUBSTITUTION

1. $\pi/4$ **2.** $\pi/16$ **3.** $\pi/6$ **4.** $\pi/4$

5. $\ln|x + \sqrt{x^2 - 4}| + C$ **6.** $\ln|3x + \sqrt{9x^2 - 1}| + C$

7. $\pm[\frac{25}{2}\sin^{-1}(\frac{x}{5}) + \frac{x}{2}\sqrt{25 - x^2}] + C$ **8.** $\pm[\frac{1}{6}\sin^{-1}(3x) + \frac{x}{2}\sqrt{1 - 9x^2}] + C$

9. $\pm 4[\frac{x}{\sqrt{1-x^2}} - \sin^{-1}x] + C$ **10.** $\pm\frac{x}{4\sqrt{4-x^2}} + C$

11. $\pi/3$ **12.** $\ln(\sqrt{2} + 1)$ **13.** $-\sqrt{2x - x^2} + C$

14. $-\sqrt{5 + 4x - x^2} + C$ **15.** $\ln|x - 1 + \sqrt{x^2 - 2x}| + C$

16. $\ln|x + 1 + \sqrt{x^2 + 2x}| + C$ **17.** $\pi/8$ **18.** $25\pi/4$

19. $\pi/3$ **20.** π **21.** $\ln(\sqrt{2}+1)$ **22.** $(2-\sqrt{2})/3$

23. π **24.** $\sqrt{3}+\pi/6-\pi/2$ **25.** $\pi/8$ **26.** $\pi/12$

27. 2 **28.** $3-2\sqrt{2}$ **29.** $0.6435011\ldots$ **30.** 576.102

31. $4\left[\frac{x}{\sqrt{1-x^2}}-\sin^{-1}x\right]+C$ **32.** $1/\sqrt{3}$ **33.** $3\pi/4$ **34.** $\pi/4$

35. $x=3\sin\theta$ would mean $\sin\theta=4/3$ at the left hand endpoint. Use $x=3\sec\theta$.

36. The domain of the integrand is $0<x<2$; the domain of $\sin^{-1}(x-1)$ is $0\le x\le 2$.

8.5 RATIONAL FUNCTIONS AND PARTIAL FRACTIONS

1. $\frac{2}{x-3}+\frac{3}{x-2}$ **2.** $\frac{2}{x-1}+\frac{3}{x-2}$ **3.** $\frac{1}{x+1}+\frac{3}{(x+1)^2}$ **4.** $\frac{2}{x-1}+\frac{4}{(x-1)^2}$

5. $-\frac{2}{x}-\frac{1}{x^2}+\frac{2}{x-1}$ **6.** $\frac{1/5}{(x-3)}+\frac{-1/5}{x+2}$ **7.** $1+\frac{17}{x-3}+\frac{-12}{x-2}$ **8.** $x+\frac{-4x+1}{x^2+4}$

9. $\frac{1}{2}\ln 3$ **10.** $\frac{1}{2}\ln\left(\frac{3}{2}\right)$ **11.** $\frac{1}{2}\ln 15$

12. $7\ln 2-3\ln 3\approx 1.556$ **13.** $\frac{1}{6}\ln\left|\frac{(t+2)(t-1)^2}{t^3}\right|+C$

14. $-\frac{3}{8}\ln|2t|+\frac{5}{16}\ln|t-2|+\frac{1}{16}\ln|t+2|+C$ **15.** $4-\ln 3$

16. $\ln 2+\pi/4-2/3$ **17.** $5[\sqrt{3}-\pi/3]$

18. 8.5419

19. $-\frac{1}{4}\ln|x-1|-\frac{1}{4}\frac{1}{(x-1)}+\frac{1}{4}\ln|x+1|-\frac{1}{4}\frac{1}{(x+1)}+C$

20. $\frac{1}{4}\ln|x-1|+\frac{3}{4}\ln|x+1|+\frac{1}{2(x+1)}+C$

21. $\frac{1}{7}\ln\left|(x+6)^2(x-1)^5\right|+C$ **22.** $\ln\left|\frac{(x-4)^9}{(x-3)^7}\right|+C$

23. $2\tan^{-1}(x-1)+C$ **24.** $3\tan^{-1}(x-2)+C$

25. $\ln\left|\frac{x^2+x+1}{x-1}\right|+C$ **26.** $3\ln|x+1|-\ln|x^2-x+1|+C$

27. $2x+\frac{1}{2}\ln(x^2+4)+C$ **28.** $x-\frac{3}{2}\ln(x^2+1)$

29. $1-\ln 2$ **30.** $1-\pi/4$ **31.** $7+\ln 8$

32. $-4 + \ln 9$　　　　　　**33.** $3\pi \ln 25$　　　　　　**34.** $\ln 3 - \frac{1}{2}$

35. a) $x(t) = 1000e^{4t}/(499 + e^{4t})$　　b) 1.55 days

36. a) i) $x = a^2kt/(akt + 1)$,　　ii) $x = ab(e^{(b-a)kt} - 1)/(be^{(b-a)kt} - a)$　　b) Use $[0,2]$ by $[0,15]$

37. 1　　　　　　　　　**38.** $\frac{\pi}{2}(\sqrt{3} - 1)$　　　　　**39.** $2/(1 - \tan(x/2)) + C$

40. $\frac{2}{\sqrt{3}} \tan^{-1}\left[\frac{\tan(\frac{x}{2})}{\sqrt{3}}\right] + C$　　**41.** $-\cot(x/2) - x + C$　**42.** $\ln|1 + \tan(\frac{x}{2})| + C$

43. $\frac{1}{\sqrt{2}} \ln\left|\frac{\tan(x/2)+1-\sqrt{2}}{\tan(x/2)+1+\sqrt{2}}\right| + C$　**44.** $\frac{1}{2}(\ln\sqrt{3} - 1)$

8.6　IMPROPER INTEGRALS

1. $\frac{\pi}{4}$　　　　**2.** 2　　　　**3.** 6　　　　**4.** 1000　　　**5.** 4

6. $\frac{\pi}{2}$　　　　**7.** 1000　　**8.** diverges　**9.** $\ln 4$　　**10.** π

11. diverges　**12.** converges　**13.** converges　**14.** diverges　**15.** converges

16. converges　**17.** diverges　**18.** diverges　**19.** converges　**20.** diverges

21. diverges　**22.** diverges　**23.** diverges　**24.** converges　**25.** converges

26. converges　**27.** converges　**28.** converges　**29.** diverges　**30.** diverges

31. diverges　**32.** diverges　**33.** converges　**34.** diverges　**35.** diverges

36. converges　**37.** converges　**38.** converges　**39.** converges　**40.** converges

41. converges　**42.** converges　**43.** converges　**44.** converges　**45.** b) 7.5

46. diverges　**47.** 0.8862　　**48.** π

51. converges if $p < 1$, diverges if $p \geq 1$

52. converges for $p > 1$, diverges if $p \leq 1$.

53. 1　　　　**54.** $(1, \frac{1}{4})$　　**55.** 2π　　**56.** $\frac{\pi}{2}$　　　**57.** $\ln 2$

58. both $= \pi$　**59.** diverges　　**60.** converges　**61.** converges　**62.** diverges

64. Using the triangle formed by $y = 1 \pm \frac{2}{3}x$ gives an approximate value of 1.5.

8.7 DIFFERENTIAL EQUATIONS

9. a) $x = 1000(11e^{0.10t} - 10)$ b) 23.026 years   **10.** 10 minutes

11. $y = 95 - 65e^{0.017x}$ **12.** $x = 20 - 14e^{0.013t}$ **13.** $y = \frac{1050e^{0.4375x}}{32 + 3e^{0.4375x}}$

14. $x = 500e^{2.5t}/(24 + e^{2.5t})$ **15.** $y = \frac{1}{2}\ln(2x + 1)$ **16.** $y = \frac{1}{2}(e^{2x} - x^2 + 1)$

17. $y = \arctan x + 1$ **18.** $y = \sin(x + \frac{\pi}{2})$ **19.** $y = xe^x - e^x + 1$

20. The solution satisfies $\frac{y^2}{2}\ln y - \frac{y^2}{4} = x - \frac{1}{4}$ **21.** $y = \sin x$

22. $y = \cos x$ **24** a) $y = e^x \sin x$ b) $y = e^x \cos x - e^x \sin x$

25. $y(1) \approx y_5 = 2.48832; y(1) = e^1 = 2.71828\ldots$

26. $y_k = y_0(1 + \frac{1}{n})^k; \ y(1) \approx y_n; \ e$ **27.** $2.7027\ldots$ **28.** 2.7182511366

29. $y = 1/(1 - x)$ is the solution to $y' = y^2, \ y(0) = 1$ **30.** $y = \tan x$

31. The computed values of y (4) are:
Euler, 2.1142857142... Improved
Euler and R-K, 2.142857142...

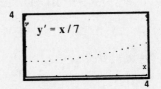

32. The computed values of $y(4)$ are:
Euler,   0.80491664235;
Improved Euler, 0.83868770875;
Runge-Kutta,   0.838119526483

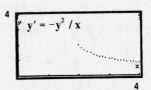

33. The computed values of $y(2)$ are:
Euler,   2.07334340632;
Improved Euler, 2.21157126441;
Runge-Kutta,   2.20283462521

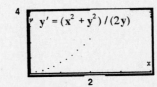

34. The computed values of $y(2)$ are:
Euler,   2.13448296411;
Improved Euler, 2.20482251496;
Runge-Kutta,   2.20273270952

35. a) 0.310268270416   b) 0.310268299767

36. a) 0.160602806363   b) 0.160602794907; $2 - 5/e = 0.16060279414$

37. Differentiate $y = \tan(a^2 - x^2)$.

38.

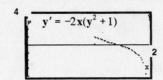

39. $\sqrt{\pi/4 + 1} \approx 1.336$ **40.** Differentiate $y = \frac{1}{1+x^2}$

41.

	x	y(R-K)	y(true)	Difference
$y' = x - y$				
$y(0) = 1$	3	2.09981094687	$\cdots$	2.37×10^{-4}
$y' = x - y$				
$y(0) = -2$	3	1.95009452656	$\cdots$	-1.18×10^{-4}

The errors are much greater because the step size is five times as large.

42. a) $y = 150e^{0.225t}/(24 + e^{0.225t})$

e) 17.2 weeks, 21.3 weeks

f) 40 weeks

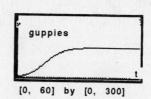

[0, 60] by [0, 300]

43. a) $y = \frac{3500e^{0.1t}}{111+14e^{0.1t}}$

e) 16.65 years, 34.57 years

f) 92 years

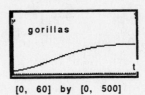

[0, 60] by [0, 500]

44. $a^2\frac{\pi}{2}$

45. $a = \sqrt{\frac{2}{\pi}}$

46. a) $y'_1(x) = -2/\pi$, $y'_2(x) = -\frac{1}{\pi\sqrt{t}}$, $y'_3(x) = -\frac{\sin \pi t}{1 - \cos \pi t}$, $y'_4(x) = \frac{4(t-1)}{\pi}$, $y'_5(x) = \frac{-2}{\pi}\frac{(1-t)}{\sqrt{2t-t^2}}$; all < 0 for $0 < t < 1$.

b)

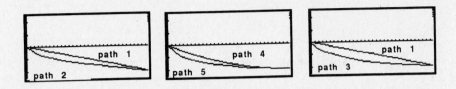

c) 1) $T = \frac{1}{\sqrt{g}}\int_0^1 \sqrt{\frac{\pi^2+4}{-2(-2t)}}\, dt$, improper

2) $T = \frac{1}{\sqrt{g}}\int_0^1 \sqrt{\frac{\pi^2+\frac{1}{t}}{4\sqrt{t}}}\, dt$, improper

3) $T = \frac{1}{\sqrt{g}}\int_0^1 \sqrt{\frac{(\pi-\pi\cos\pi t)^2+(\pi\sin\pi t)^2}{2(1-\cos\pi t)}}\, dt$, improper

4) $T = \frac{1}{\sqrt{g}}\int_0^1 \sqrt{\frac{\pi^2+16(t-1)^2}{-4((t-1)^2-1)}}\, dt$, improper

5) $T = \frac{1}{\sqrt{g}}\int_0^1 \sqrt{\frac{\pi^2+\frac{(2-2t)^2}{2t-t^2}}{4\sqrt{2t-t^2}}}\, dt$, improper

d) $\frac{\sqrt{\pi^2+4}}{\sqrt{g}}$

e) Using a lower limit of 0.0000001, the values of T are: a) $3.7230/\sqrt{g}$, 2) $3.1368/\sqrt{g}$, 3) $3.1415923/\sqrt{g}$, 4) $3.27519/\sqrt{g}$ 5) $3.1110/\sqrt{g}$.

f) T becomes $\frac{\pi}{\sqrt{g}}\int_0^1 1\, dt$

8.8   COMPUTER ALGEBRA SYSTEMS

1. (Using *Mathematica*)

```
In[2]:= Integrate[Exp[-x^2],{x,0,Infinity}]

            Sqrt[Pi]
Out[2]=  --------
               2
```

2.

```
In[3]:= Integrate[x ArcCos[x],x]

                    2          2
         -(x Sqrt[1 - x ])    x  ArcCos[x]   ArcSin[x]
Out[3]=  -----------------  +  ------------ + ---------
                 4                  2             4
```

3.

```
In[5]:= Integrate[1/(x Sqrt[x-3]),{x,6,9}]

           -Pi        2 ArcTan[Sqrt[2]]
Out[5]=  ---------  +  ------------------
         2 Sqrt[3]         Sqrt[3]
```

4.

```
In[6]:= Integrate[x ArcTan[2x],{x,0,1/2}]

         -2 + Pi
Out[6]=  -------
           16
```

5.

```
In[7]:= Integrate[1/(9-x^2)^2,x]

            -x           Log[-3 + x]   Log[3 + x]
Out[7]=  ------------  -  -----------  + ----------
                 2           108           108
         18 (-9 + x )
```

6.

```
In[8]:= Integrate[(Sqrt[4 x+9])/x^2,{x,4,10}]

                          5                7
                4 ArcTanh[-]      4 ArcTanh[-]
          11              3                3
Out[8]=  -- +  ------------    -  ------------
         20         3                  3
```

7.

```
In[9]:= Integrate[1/(x^2 Sqrt[7+x^2]),{x,3,11}]

          4    8 Sqrt[2]
Out[9]=  -- -  ---------
          21     77
```

8.

```
In[10]:= Integrate[1/(x^2 Sqrt[7-x^2]),x]

                      2
          -Sqrt[7 - x ]
Out[10] = -------------
               7 x
```

9.

```
In[11]:= Integrate[(Sqrt[x^2-2])/x,{x,-2,-Sqrt[2]}]

           Pi        4 + Pi
Out[11]=  ------- -  ---------
          Sqrt[2]    2 Sqrt[2]
```

10.

```
In[12]:= Integrate[1/(5+4Sin[2x]),{x,-Pi/12,Pi/4}]

          Pi
Out[12]=  --
          18
```

11.

```
In[13]:= Integrate[1/(4+5Sin[2x]),x]

          -Log[2 Cos[x] + Sin[x]]       Log[Cos[x] + 2 Sin[x]]
Out[13]=  -----------------------   +   ----------------------
                    6                             6
```

12.

```
In[14]:= Integrate[x/Sqrt[x-2],{x,3,6}]

          26
Out[14]= --
          3
```

13.

```
In[15]:= Integrate[x Sqrt[2x-3],x]

                            2
                   3   x   2 x
Out[15]= Sqrt[-3 + 2 x] (-(-) - - + ----)
                   5   5    5
```

14.

```
In[16]:= Integrate[(Sqrt[3x-4])/x,x]

                                      Sqrt[-4 + 3 x]
Out[16]= 2 Sqrt[-4 + 3 x] - 4 ArcTan[--------------]
                                            2
```

15.

```
In[17]:= Integrate[x^10 Exp[-x],{x,0,Infinity}]

Out[17]= 3628800
```

16.

```
In[1]:= Integrate[x^2 ArcTan[x],{x,0,1}]

          -2 + Pi + 2 Log[2]
Out[1]=  ------------------------
                  12
```

17.

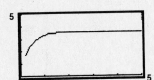

18.

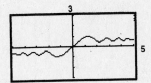

19.

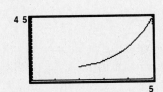

20.

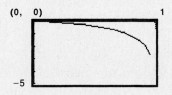

21.

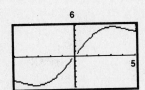

22.

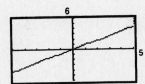

23.

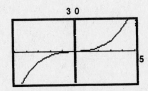

24.

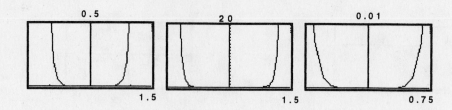

25. $x = 0.7705$ **26.** $x = 1.1714$ **27.** $x = 0.4970$ **28.** $x = \pm 0.971$

29. f always increasing, concave up on $(0,1)$; inflection point at 1, $f \to$ constant as $x \to \infty$.

30. f is increasing, concave down on $(0, 0.840)$, then decreasing, concave down until $x = 2.166$, an inflection point; f has a local minimum at $x = 3.933$; on $(3.933, 5)$ it increases more and more sharply; for $x \geq 5$ the function is undefined.

31. $\bar{x} = 1.33333333143, \bar{y} = 0.34657359028$ **32.** 24.34

35. $\frac{1}{a^2}\left[\ln|ax + b| + \frac{b}{ax+b}\right] + C$

PRACTICE EXERCISES, CHAPTER 8

1. $2[\sqrt{2} - 1]$ **2.** $\frac{1}{2}\ln 2$ **3.** 0 **4.** $e^{\sec x} + C$ **5.** $\pi^2/32$

6. $\ln(1.5)$ **7.** $(\ln 3)/4$ **8.** $\ln(2 + \sqrt{3})$ **9.** $\frac{1}{2}\ln(x^2 + 1) + 4\tan^{-1} x + C$

10. $-(1 - x^2)^{1/2} + 2\sin^{-1} x + C$ **11.** $\frac{x^3}{3}\ln x - \frac{x^3}{9} + C$ **12.** $\ln(4) - 1$

13. $-x^5 \cos x + 5x^4 \sin x + 20x^3 \cos x - 60x^2 \sin x - 120x \cos x + 120 \sin x + C$

14. $\frac{-2\tan^{-1} x}{x} + 2\ln|x| - \ln(1 + x^2) + C$ **15.** $e^x[\cos 2x + 2\sin 2x]/5 + C$

16. $\frac{-e^{-x}}{2}(\sin x + \cos x) + C$ **17.** $-\cos y + \frac{\cos^3 y}{3} + C$

18. $\frac{-\cos^3 y}{3} + \frac{\cos^5 y}{5} + C$ **19.** $\frac{\sin^5 x \cos x}{6} - \frac{\sin^3 x \cos x}{24} + \frac{x}{16} - \frac{\sin 2x}{32} + C$

20. $\frac{\sin^4 x}{4} - \frac{\sin^6 x}{6} + C$ **21.** 2 **22.** $\ln(3 + 2\sqrt{2})$ **23.** $\frac{3}{2} - \ln 2$

24. 16 **25.** $3/80$ **26.** $7/3$ **27.** $-\sqrt{1 - x^2}/x + C$

28. $\frac{\sin^{-1}x}{2} - \frac{x\sqrt{1-x^2}}{2} + C$ **29.** 5   **30.** $\ln\left(\frac{2+\sqrt{3}}{3}\right)$ **31.** $\pi/8$

32. $\pi/6$ **33.** $\pi/3$ **34.** $\pi/2$ **35.** $16 + (\ln 400)/3$ **36.** $1 + \ln\left(\frac{4}{3}\right)$

37. $\ln|x-1| - \frac{1}{x-1} + C$ **38.** $\ln|x| + \frac{2}{x} - \frac{2}{x^2} - \ln|x+2| + C$ **39.** $\ln\left[\frac{|x|}{\sqrt{x^2+4}}\right] + C$

40. $\frac{1}{16}\ln\left(\frac{3}{5}\right)$ **41.** $\ln 3$ **42.** 1   **43.** 1   **44.** $\ln(4) - 1$

45. $32\pi/35$ **46.** $(2\sqrt{3} + \ln(2 + \sqrt{3}))/4$ **47.** $s = 22.254$ **48.** $(2/\pi, 0)$

49. 2π **50.** $\pi[\frac{8}{3}(\ln 2)^2 - \frac{16}{9}\ln 2 + \frac{16}{27}]$ **51.** Diverges   **52.** Converges

53. Diverges   **54.** Converges   **55.** $y(2) = -1.377$ **56.** $y(2) = 1.393$

57. $y(6) = -7.349$ **58.** $y(5) = 0.144$ **59.** $y(3) = -2.691$

60. $y(1) = 0.675$ **61.** $y(3) = 0.907$ **62.** $y(6) = 9.508$

63. $y = 28e^{-0.15x} + 22$ **64.** $x = 55 - 5e^{0.03t}$ **65.** $P = 500e^t/(24 + e^t)$

66. $P = 200/(1 + 3e^{-1.1t})$ **67.** $x = ax_0/(x_0 + (a - x_0)e^{-akt})$

CHAPTER 9

INFINITE SERIES

9.1 LIMITS OF SEQUENCES OF NUMBERS

1. $a_1 = 0$, $a_2 = -1/4$, $a_3 = -2/9$, $a_3 = -3/16$

2. $1, \frac{1}{2}, \frac{1}{6}, \frac{1}{24}$

3. $a_1 = 1$, $a_2 = -1/3$, $a_3 = 1/5$, $a_4 = -1/7$

4. $1, 3, 1, 3$

5. $1, \frac{3}{2}, \frac{7}{4}, \frac{15}{8}, \frac{31}{16}, \frac{63}{32}, \frac{127}{64}, \frac{255}{128}, \frac{511}{256}, \frac{1023}{512}$

6. $1, \frac{1}{2}, \frac{1}{6}, \frac{1}{24}, \ldots, x_{10} = \frac{1}{10!}$

7. $2, 1, \frac{1}{2}, \frac{1}{4}, \ldots, x_{10} = \frac{1}{2^8}$

8. $-2, -1, -\frac{2}{3}, -\frac{2}{4}, -\frac{2}{5}, \ldots, x_{10} = -\frac{2}{10}$

9. $x_1 = 1$, $x_2 = 1$, $x_3 = 2$, $x_4 = 3$, $x_5 = 5$, $x_6 = 8$, $x_7 = 13$, $x_8 = 21$, $x_9 = 34$, $x_{10} = 55$

10. $1, 1, 2, 4, 8, \ldots, x_{10} = 2^{10-2} = 256$

11. Converges to 2

12. Diverges

13. Converges to 5

14. Converges to 10

15. Diverges

16. Diverges

17. Converges to -1

18. Converges to $-\frac{2}{3}$

19. Diverges

20. Converges to 0

21. Converges to -5

22. Diverges

23. Converges to 1

24. Diverges

25. Converges to 1/2

26. Converges to 6

27. 0

28. 0

29. 0

30. 0

31. $\sqrt{2}$

32. 1

33. $\pi/2$

34. 0

35. Converges to 0

36. Diverges

37. Converges to 0

38. Converges to 1

39. Converges to 1

40. 1

41. e^7

42. $1/e$

43. Diverges

44. Diverges

45. Converges to 1

46. Converges to 1

47. Converges to 1

48. Converges to 1

49. Diverges

50. 4   **51.** Converges to 0   **52.** 0

53. Converges to 0   **54.** 0   **55.** Converges to $1/e$

56. Diverges   **57.** Diverges   **58.** 0

59. $N = 693$ **60.** $N = 9124$

61. $N = 66$ **62.** $N = 15$

63.

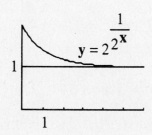

$$y = 2^{2^{\frac{1}{x}}}$$

64.

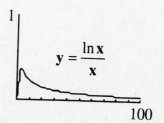

$$y = \frac{\ln x}{x}$$

67. $a_1 = 1 \rightarrow 0.877,\ a_1 = 2 \rightarrow 0.877,\ a_1 = 0 \rightarrow 0$

68. $a_1 = 1 \rightarrow 0.824,\ a_1 = -1,\ a_1 = -2 \rightarrow -0.824$

71. $\pm 1.895494\ldots$ **72.** $\pm 1.165561\ldots$

9.2   INFINITE SERIES

1. $s_n = 2(1 - (1/3)^n)/(1 - 1/3), 3$

2. $s_n = \frac{9}{100}[1 - 1/100^n]/(1 - 1/100);\ \frac{1}{11}$

3. $s_n = (1 - (-1/2)^n)/(1 - (-1/2)), 2/3$

4. $s_n = (1 - (-2)^n)/3$; series diverges

5. $s_n = 1/2 - 1/(n+2), 1/2$ **6.** $s_n = 5(1 - 1/(n+1)), 5$

7. $s_5 = 1.3320\ldots,\ s_n \rightarrow 4/3$ **8.** $1/12$

9. $s_5 = 2.33105\ldots,\ s_n \rightarrow 7/3$ **10.** 4   **11.** $s_n \rightarrow 11.5$

12. $17/2$ **13.** $s_n \rightarrow 17/6$ **14.** $10/3$

15. $a_n = 1/(4n - 3) - 1/(4n + 1),\ s_n \rightarrow 1$

16. $1/4$

17. $s_n \to 1/9$　　**18.** 1

19. Converges to $2 + \sqrt{2}$

20. Diverges　　**21.** Converges to 1

22. Diverges

23. Diverges, $a_n \not\to 0$

24. Converges to $5/6$

25. Converges to $e^2/(e^2 - 1)$

26. Diverges

27. Diverges, $a_n \not\to 0$

28. Converges to $2/9$

29. Converges to $3/2$

30. Diverges

31. Diverges, $a_n \not\to 0$

32. $\frac{x}{x-1}$

33. $a = 1,\ r = -x$

34. $a = 1,\ r = -x^2$

35. a) 18 terms needed,　b) 30 terms needed

36. 100

37. 28 m　　**38.** 12.5842 sec

39. $\frac{234}{999} = \frac{26}{111}$

40. $\frac{123{,}999}{99{,}900}$

41. $a_n = $ a) $\frac{1}{(n+4)(n+5)}$, b) $\frac{1}{(n+2)(n+3)}$, c) $\frac{1}{(n-3)(n-2)}$

42. a) $\sum_{n=-1}^{\infty} \frac{5}{(n+2)(n+3)}$, b) $\sum_{n=3}^{\infty} \frac{5}{(n-2)(n-1)}$, c) $\sum_{n=20}^{\infty} \frac{5}{(n-19)(n-18)}$

45. Appears to converge to 2

46. Appears to converge to 52,500

47. Diverges

48. Converges to e

49. $71,428.58

50. $20,000

51. a) $6,900.38,　b) $7,134.63

52. a) $21,188.03,　b) $28,538.51

53. 8 m^2

54. $\pi/2$

55. $a_n = n,\ b_n = -n$

56. $a_n = 1/2^n,\ b_n = 1/3^n$

57. $\sum 1/3^n = 3/2,\ \sum 1/2^n = 2,\ \sum \left(\frac{2}{3}\right)^n = 3 \neq 3/4$

58. $\lim_{n\to\infty}\left(\frac{1}{a_n}\right) \neq 0$

9.3 SERIES WITHOUT NEGATIVE TERMS: COMPARISON AND INTEGRAL TESTS

1. Converges to 1/9; geometric series

2. Converges to $-\frac{1}{7}$

3. Diverges, $a_n \not\to 0$

4. Diverges by comparison with $\sum \frac{1}{n}$

5. Converges by the comparison with $\frac{1}{2^n}$; sum ≈ 0.637

6. Converges by comparison test; $s_{666} = 1.968$

7. Diverges by comparison test

8. Diverges, $a_n \not\to 0$

9. Converges by the integral test

10. Converges to 2, geometric series

11. Diverges by limit comparison test

12. Diverges by limit comparison test

13. Diverges by limit comparison test

14. Diverges, $a_n \not\to 0$

15. Diverges, $a_n \not\to 0$

16. Converges by comparison with $\sum (\frac{1}{3})^n$

17. Diverges by comparison with $\sum \frac{1}{n}$

18. Converges by the integral test

19. Converges by comparison with $\sum \frac{1}{n^{3/2}}$

20. Diverges by comparison with $\sum \frac{1}{n}$

21. Converges

22. Diverges, geometric series with $r > 1$

23. Converges by comparison with $\sum \frac{1}{3^{n-1}}$

24. Converges by limit comparison test

25. 12

27. Between 40.5 and 41.6

28. $\sum \frac{1}{nx} = \frac{1}{x} \sum \frac{1}{n}$ which diverges

29. Compare $\sum (a_n/n)$ with $\sum a_n$

31. $\{-s_n\}$ is nondecreasing and either bounded above or not

9.4   SERIES WITH NONNEGATIVE TERMS: RATIO AND ROOT TESTS

1. Converges, by the ratio test, sum ≈ 12.   2. Diverges, by the ratio test.

3. Converges, by the ratio test, to approximately 376.179.

4. Converges, by the ratio test.   5. Diverges, by the ratio test.

6. Converges, geometric series; -0.4.   7. Diverges; $a_n \not\to 0$.

8. Converges, by the comparison test, stabilizes at 7.55555555556.

9. Diverges, $a_n \not\to 0$.   10. Diverges, $a_n \not\to 0$.   11. Diverges

12. Converges by comparison with $\sum 1/n^2$; $s_{2000} = 0.198125\ldots$.

13. Diverges, by comparison test.   14. Converges, by the ratio test; 1.786.

15. Converges, by the ratio test; $17.0279727\ldots$.

16. Converges, by the ratio test; $6.0065\ldots$.

17. Converges, by the ratio test; 4.0625.

18. Converges, by the ratio test; $0.17520119\ldots$.

19. Converges by the ratio test; -6.

20. Converges by the ratio test; $1.87985\ldots$.

21. Converges, by the root test; $8.25271035\ldots$.

22. Diverges, by the comparison test.

23. Converges by comparison with $\sum 1/n^2$; 0.5.

24. Converges by the ratio test; $0.18459307\ldots$.

25. Diverges by the ratio test.

26. Converges by the comparison test; $1.26105\ldots$.

27. Converges, by the ratio test; $10.61830\ldots$.

28. Diverges by the ratio test.   29. Diverges, $a_n = 3/n$.

30. Converges by the ratio test; 14.778 . . . .

31. Converges by the ratio test; -4.11952700 . . . .

32. Diverges, $a_n \not\to 0$.   **33.** Converges, by the ratio test; 2.5707963 . . . .

34. Diverges by the ratio test.

35. Converges by comparison with $\sum 12/n^4$; 1.26079119 . . . .

36. Both tests have limit 1.

9.5   ALTERNATING SERIES AND ABSOLUTE CONVERGENCE

1. Convergers; $s_{32} = 0.82199\ldots < L < 0.82297\ldots = s_{31}$

2. Converges very slowly. $s_{1.97 \times 10^{434}}$ has error at most 0.001.

3. Diverges   **4.** Diverges   **5.** Converges; $s_{1,001,997}$ is within 0.001.

6. Converges; $(s_{102} + s_{103})/2 \approx 0.7651$.   **7.** Converges. $|L - s_{10000}| < 0.001$.

8. Diverges   **9.** Diverges   **10.** Converges

11. Converges absolutely   **12.** Converges conditionally

13. Converges absolutely   **14.** Diverges   **15.** Converges conditionally

16. Diverges   **17.** Converges absolutely   **18.** Converges conditionally

19. Converges conditionally **20.** Converges absolutely **21.** Converges absolutely

22. Diverges   **23.** Converges absolutely   **24.** Converges conditionally

25. Diverges   **26.** Converges absolutely   **27.** Diverges

28. Converges conditionally **29.** Converges absolutely **30.** Converges absolutely

31. Converges absolutely **32.** Converges absolutely **33.** Converges absolutely

34. Converges conditionally **35.** Converges conditionally

36. Converges absolutely   **37.** $|error| < 0.2$ **38.** $|error| < 10^{-5}$

39. $|error| < 2 \times 10^{-11}$ **40.** $|error| < t^4$ **41.** 0.540302

42. $\sum_{n=0}^{8} \frac{(-1)^n}{n!} = 0.3678819$

43. a) $|a_n|$ not strictly decreasing   b) $-1/2$ **44.** 0.69258

45. $(a_{n+1} - a_{n+2}) + (a_{n+3} - a_{n+4}) + \ldots$ has same sign as a_{n+1}.

46. Both series converge to 1.

47. a) $0.18226 < \text{sum} < 0.18233$ b) $0.4053 < \text{sum} < 0.4055$
   c) $0.5875 < \text{sum} < 0.5881$ d) $0.64147 < \text{sum} < 0.64218$

48. a) not alternating   c) 1.01396   d) probably within 0.00001

9.6 POWER SERIES

1. a) $-2 < x < 0$,   b) $-2 < x < 0$ **2.** a) $-1 < x < 1$,   b) $-1 < x < 1$

3. a) $-1 \le x \le 1$,   b) $-1 \le x \le 1$ **4.** a) $0 \le x < 2$,   b) $0 < x < 2$

5. a) All x,   b) All x **6.** a) All x,   b) All x

7. a) $-1 \le x < 1$,   b) $-1 < x < 1$ **8.** a) $-1 < x \le 1$,   b) $-1 < x < 1$

9. a) $-1 \le x < 1$,   b) $-1 < x < 1$ **10.** a) $2 < x < 4$,   b) $2 < x < 4$

11. a) $-3 < x < 3$,   b) $-3 < x < 3$ **12.** a) $0 < x < 2$,   b) $0 < x < 2$

13. a) $-1 < x < 1$,   b) $-1 < x < 1$ **14.** a) $-1 < x < 1$,   b) $-1 < x < 1$

15. a) $(-1, 1)$,   b) $(-1, 1)$,   c) $\frac{1}{1-x}$,   d) $-0.8 < x < 0.7$

16. a) $-6 < x < -4$,   b) $-6 < x < -4$,   c) $\frac{-1}{4+x}$,   d) $-5.8 < x < -4.3$

17. a) $(-8, 12)$,   b) $(-8, 12)$,   c) $\frac{10}{12-x}$,   d) $-6 \le x \le 9$

18. a) $-\frac{1}{2} < x < \frac{1}{2}$,   b) $-\frac{1}{2} < x < \frac{1}{2}$,   c) $\frac{1}{1-2x}$,   d) $-0.4 < x < 0.35$

19. a) $P_{20} = -3.597\ldots, P_{100} = -5.187\ldots$,   b) 0.19

20. b) 99,   c) $\frac{1}{2n-1} \approx \frac{1}{2}\left(\frac{1}{n}\right)$

21. - 24. a) Convergent, b) Absolutely convergent, c) Alternating on, d) Error < 0.01

21. a) $[1,3)$ b) $(1,3)$ c) $[1,2)$ d) P_{30} on $[1.1,2]$

22. a) $(-3,-1]$ b) $(-3,-1)$ c) $(-2,-1)$ d) P_{30} on $[-2.9,-2]$

23. a) $(2,4)$ b) $(2,4)$ c) $(2,3)$ d) P_{110} on $[2.1,3]$

24. a) $(1,3)$ b) $(1,3)$ c) $(1,2)$ d) P_{110} on $[1.1,2]$

25. b) $[-3.97,3.97], [-7.71,7.71], [-11.44,11.44]$

26. a) Compare with $D_x \sin x$,   b) all x

27. All x; $[-6.8,6.8]$ **28.** $e^{-x}, [-6.8,6.8]$ **29.** All x; $[-2.2,2.2]$

30. a) $-1 < x < 1$,   b) $[-0.69,0.67]$ **31.** d) $-0.80 < x < 0.74$

32. a) All x,   b) $x - \sin x$,   c) $|x| < 15.9$

33. b) Use $-\ln(3 - x) = -\ln(1 - (x - 2))$ and part a)   **34.** d) $-1 < x < 1$

35. a) $(-0.118,0.118)$ b) $(-0.142,0.142)$ c) $(-0.139,0.139)$ d) $x = 0$

37. $x = 0$ **38.** $x = 4$ **39.** Converges for $1 < x < 5$ to $\frac{2}{x-1}$

40. Converges on $1 < x \leq 5$, absolutely convergent on $1 < x < 5$, sum is $2\ln|x - 1| + 3 - \ln 4$.

41. a) $-0.873 < x < 0.873$,   b) $\frac{x^2}{2} + \frac{x^4}{12} + \frac{x^6}{45} + \frac{17x^8}{(8)(315)} + \cdots, -\frac{\pi}{2} < x < \frac{\pi}{2}$,

    c) $1 + x^2 + \frac{2x^4}{3} + \cdots, -\frac{\pi}{2} < x < \frac{\pi}{2}$

42. a) $|x| < 0.823$,   b) $x + \frac{x^3}{6} + \frac{x^5}{24} + \frac{61}{(7)(720)}x^7 + \cdots$,   c) $x + \frac{5}{6}x^3 + \frac{61}{120}x^5 + \cdots$

43. b) $|s_{30} - f(x)| < 0.01$ when $|x| < 1.172$ or $1.97 < |x| < \pi$

44. $1.471 < |x| < 2.319$ **45.** Compare $|a_n|$ with $\frac{1}{n^2}$

46. $s(x)$ looks like a sawtooth curve.

49. A smooth peak becomes an intricate "mountain range".

50. Vertical lines   **51.** Conjecture: $s(x)$ is not differentiable   **52.** 500

53. Diverges, by the Ratio Test   **54.** $3, 2, 1$ terms respectively. $|\pi \text{ error}| \approx 5 \times 10^{-7}$

9.7   TAYLOR SERIES AND MACLAURIN SERIES

1. $P_3 = (x - 1) - (x - 1)^2/2 + (x - 1)^3/3; \ 0.60 < x < 1.47$

2. $P_3 = 0 + x - (\frac{1}{2})x^2 + \frac{1}{3}x^3 \ ; \ -0.404 < x < 0.484$

3. $P_3 = \frac{1}{2} - \frac{1}{4}(x - 2) + \frac{1}{8}(x - 2)^2 - \frac{1}{16}(x - 2)^3 \ ; \ 1.322 < x < 2.819$

4. $P_3 = \frac{1}{2} - \frac{x}{4} + \frac{x^2}{8} - \frac{x^3}{16} \ ; \ -0.678 < x < 0.819$

5. $P_3 = \frac{1}{\sqrt{2}}[1 + (x - \pi/4) - (x - \pi/4)^2/2 - (x - \pi/4)^3/6] \ ; \ -0.016 < x < 1.526$

6. $P_3(x) = \frac{\sqrt{2}}{2} - \frac{\sqrt{2}}{2}(x - \frac{\pi}{4}) - \frac{\sqrt{2}}{2}\frac{1}{2!}(x - \frac{\pi}{4})^2 + \frac{\sqrt{2}}{2}\frac{1}{3!}(x - \frac{\pi}{4})^3; \ 0.045 < x < 1.587$

7. $P_3 = 2 + (x - 4)/4 - (x - 4)^2/64 + (x - 4)^3/512 \ ; \ 1.882 < x < 6.624$

8. $P_3(x) = 2 + \frac{x}{4} - \frac{x^2}{64} + \frac{x^3}{512}; \ -2.118 < x < 2.624$ **9.** $\sum_{n=0}^{\infty} \frac{(-x)^n}{n!}, \ (-3.14, 3.30)$

10. $e^{x/2} = \sum_{k=0}^{\infty} \frac{(x/2)^k}{k!}$; graphically $|\text{error}| < 0.01$ when $|x| < 6.605$; by R_{10} when $|x| < 5.1$

11. $\sin 3x = \sum_{0}^{\infty} \frac{(-1)^n (3x)^{2n+1}}{(2n+1)!}$; graphically, when $|x| < 1.083$; using R_{10}, when $|x| < 0.95$

12. $5\sum_{k=0}^{\infty} \frac{(-1)^k (\pi x)^{2k}}{(2k)!}$; graphically, when $|x| < 1.007$; analytically, when $|x| < 1.003$

13. $\sum_{n=0}^{\infty}(-1)^n x^{2n}/(2n)!$; graphically, when $|x| < 3.624$; analytically, when $|x| < 3.22$

14. $\sum_{k=0}^{\infty} \frac{(-1)^k x^{2k+2}}{(2k+1)!}$; graphically, when $|x| < 2.942$; analytically, when $|x| < 2.929$

15. $\sum_{n=0}^{\infty} x^{2n}/(2n)!$; graphically, when $|x| < 3.581$; analytically, when $|x| < 2.734$

16. $\sum_{j=0}^{\infty} \frac{x^{2j+1}}{(2j+1)!}$; graphically when $|x| < 3.210$; analytically when $|x| < 2.496$

17. $\sum_{n=2}^{\infty}(-1)^n x^{2n}/(2n)!$; graphically, when $|x| < 3.624$; analytically, when $|x| < 3.22$

18. $\frac{1}{2} + \frac{1}{2}\sum_{k=0}^{\infty} \frac{(-1)^k(2x)^{2k}}{(2k)!}$; graphically, when $|x| < 1.921$; analytically, when $|x| < 1.720$

19. $[1 - x + x^2] - x^3/(1+c)^4$, c between 0 and x

20. $1 + x(\frac{1}{2}) + x^2(\frac{-1}{4})(\frac{1}{2!}) + \frac{x^3}{3!}\frac{3}{8} \cdot \frac{1}{(1+c)^{5/2}}$

21. $[x - x^2/2] + x^3/(3(1+c)^3)$, c between 0 and x

22. $1 + x \cdot k + \frac{x^2}{2!}k(k-1) + \frac{x^3}{3!}k(k-1)(k-2)(1+c)^{k-3}$ **23.** $(x) - (x^3\cos c)/3!$

24. $1 - \frac{x^2}{2}$ is the quadratic approximation; error term can be expressed as $\frac{x^3}{3!}\sin c_1$ or $\frac{x^4}{4!}\cos c_2$

25. $\sum_{n=0}^{\infty}(x-a)^n e^a/n! = e^a[1 + (x-a) + (x-a)^2/2! + \cdots]$

26. $\sum_{k=0}^{\infty}\frac{(x-1)^k}{k!}e^1$ **27.** $|x| \leq 0.56$ **28.** Too small; $|\text{error}| < 0.0026$

29. $|\text{error}| < 1.67 \times 10^{-10}$, $x < 0$ **30.** $|\text{error}| < 1.26 \times 10^{-5}$

31. $|R_2| < 1.84 \times 10^{-4}$ **32.** $|\text{error}| < 0.00017$

33. 2.6×10^{-4} **34.** $\frac{h^2}{2}(1.01) < 0.0051h$

35. $\sin 0.1 = 0.0998334\ldots$ **36.** $\cos x$ at $\pi/4$

38. $\int$ series for $\sin x = (\text{series for } \cos x) + \text{const, etc.}$

39. $x + x^2 + (\frac{1}{3})x^3 - (\frac{1}{30})x^5 - (\frac{1}{90})x^6 + \cdots$ **40.** $1 + x - \frac{x^3}{3} - \frac{x^4}{6} - \frac{x^5}{30} + \cdots$

42. Start with $1 - \frac{x^2}{2} < \cos x < 1 - \frac{x^2}{2} + \frac{x^4}{24}$ **43.** a) -1, b) $\frac{1}{\sqrt{2}}(1+i)$, c) $-i$

9.8 FURTHER CALCULATIONS WITH TAYLOR SERIES

1. $\cos 1 - (x-1)\sin 1 - \frac{(x-1)^2}{2}\cos 1 + \frac{(x-1)^3}{6}\sin 1$; $|x-1|^4/4!$

2. $\sin x = (x - 2\pi) - \frac{(x-2\pi)^3}{3!} + \frac{(x-2\pi)^5}{5!} - \frac{(x-2\pi)^7}{7!} + \ldots$; $|\text{error at } 6.3| < 3 \cdot 10^{-22}$

3. $e^{0.4}[1 + (x-0.4) + (x-0.4)^2/2 + (x-0.4)^3/6]$; $|x-0.4|e^{0.4}/4!$

4. $\ln x = (x-1) - \frac{(x-1)^2}{2} + \frac{(x-1)^3}{3} - \frac{(x-1)^4}{4} + \ldots$; $|\text{error at } x = 1.3| < 5 \cdot 10^{-4}$

5. $\cos 69 - (x-69)\sin 69 - ((x-69)^2 \cos 69)/2 + ((x-69)^3 \sin 69)/3!$; $|x-69|^4/4!$

6. $\tan^{-1} x = \frac{\pi}{4} + \frac{(x-1)}{2} - \frac{(x-1)^2}{4} + \frac{(x-1)^3}{12} + \ldots$; at $x = 2$, error $= 0.988$

8. $k \geq m + 1 \Rightarrow \begin{pmatrix} m \\ k \end{pmatrix} = 0$

		x-Range	Viewing Window
	9.	$(-0.88, 1.14)$	$(-2,6)$ by $(-2,15)$
	10.	$(-1, 1.27)$	$(-1,10)$ by $(0,100)$
9. – 14.	**11.**	$(-0.35, 0.4)$	$(-1,6)$ by $(0,3)$
	12.	$(-0.35, 0.41)$	$(-1,6)$ by $(0,2)$
	13.	$(-0.27, 0.26)$	$(-1,4)$ by $(0,1.5)$
	14.	$(-0.33, 0.33)$	$(-1,3)$ by $(0,1.5)$

15. a) $2.005 \cdot 10^{-8}$, b) $9.93 \cdot 10^{-4}$, c) 0.169

16. $|x| < 0.848$ **17.** $\sum_{k=1}^{\infty} \frac{(-1)^{k+1} x^{2k-1}}{(2k-1)(2k)!}$

18. a) $x - \frac{x^2}{2 \cdot 2!} + \frac{x^3}{3 \cdot 3!} - \frac{x^4}{4 \cdot 4!} + \cdots$, c) for $0 \leq x \leq 1$, P_8 is within 10^{-6}

19. $\sum_{k=1}^{\infty} \frac{(-1)^{k+1}(0.1)^{2k-1}}{(2k-1)(2k-1)!}$; $\int_0^{0.1} P_{10}(x)\,dx = 0.0999444612$

20. $x - \frac{x^3}{3} + \frac{x^5}{5 \cdot 2!} - \frac{x^7}{7 \cdot 3!} + \cdots \Big]_0^{0.1} = \sum_{k=0}^{\infty} \frac{(-1)^k x^{(2k+1)}}{(2k+1)k!} \Big]_0^{0.1}$; evaluated from $k = 0$ to 5 gives $0.99667\ldots$

21. $\sum_{n=1}^{\infty} \frac{(-1)^{n+1} x^{2n-1}}{(2n-1)(2n)!}$; $\int_0^{0.1} P_{10}(x)\,dx = 0.49986114\ldots$

22. $\sum_{k=0}^{\infty} \begin{pmatrix} \frac{1}{2} \\ k \end{pmatrix} \frac{(0.1)^{4k+1}}{4k+1}$; $\sum_{k=0}^{2}$ gives 0.1000009999 **24.** 7 terms

PRACTICE EXERCISES, CHAPTER 9

1. Converges to 1 **2.** Converges to -1 **3.** Diverges

4. Converges to 1 **5.** Converges to 0 **6.** Converges to e^5

7. Converges to 3 **8.** Converges to 0 **9.** Converges to 0

10. Converges to 0   **11.** Diverges   **12.** Converges to $\frac{1}{2}$

13. Diverges   **14.** -1 **15.** $\frac{e}{e-1}$ **16.** $-\frac{3}{5}$

17. 2625   **18.** $e-1$ **19.** Diverges   **20.** Diverges

21. Conditionally convergent, approx value of S is 0.6

22. Converges to 0.601028 with error $< 2.5\ E - 7$

23. Conditionally convergent; -0.92 is within 0.5 of S

24. Converges; $S_{1000} = 1.965$ with $|\text{error}| < 0.145$

25. Absolutely convergent; $-0.55\ldots$

26. Converges conditionally   **27.** Converges, $2e - 1$ **28.** Diverges

29. Convergent, $e^{-3} - 1$ **30.** Converges to $32.024\ldots$

31. a) $-5 \le x < 1$,   b) $-5 < x < 1$, -4.78

32. a) $-1 \le x < 1$,   b) $-1 < x < 1$

33. all x, all x **34.** a) $-1 < x < 3$,   b) $-1 < x < 3$

35. a) $0 \le x \le 2$,   b) $0 \le x \le 2$ **36.** a) for all x,   b) for all x

37. $f(x) = 1/(1 + x)$; at $x = 1/4$, sum is 0.8

38. $f(x) = \ln(1 + x)$; at $x = 2/3$; sum is $\ln(\frac{5}{3})$

39. $f(x) = \sin x$; at $x = \pi$, sum is 0   **40.** $f(x) = \cos x$; at $x = \frac{\pi}{3}$, sum is $\frac{1}{2}$

41. $f(x) = e^x$; at $x = \ln 2$, sum is 2   **42.** $f(x) = \tan^{-1} x$; at $x = \frac{1}{\sqrt{3}}$; sum is $\frac{\pi}{6}$

43. $2 - \frac{1}{2}(x + 1) + \frac{3}{16}(x + 1)^2 + \frac{9}{192}(x + 1)^3 + \ldots$; $-2.143 < x < 0.238$

44. $-1 + (x - 2) - (x - 2)^2 + (x - 2)^3$; $1.710 < x < 2.340$

45. $(2x) - \frac{(2x)^3}{3!} + \frac{(2x)^5}{5!} - \frac{(2x)^7}{7!} + \cdots$ **46.** $\frac{2x^2}{2!} - \frac{2^3 x^4}{4!} + \frac{2^5 x^6}{6!} - \frac{2^7 x^8}{8!} + \cdots$

47. 0.48491714   **48.** 0.487222362

49. a) $\sum_{n=0}^{\infty} 0 \frac{x^n}{n!}$, converges for all x, converges to f only at $x = 0$

   b) for $x \neq 0$, $R_n(x) = e^{-1/x^2}$

50. $x = 0, x + 0.9286$

CHAPTER 10

PLANE CURVES, PARAMETRIZATIONS, AND POLAR COORDINATES

10.1 Conic Sections and Quadratic Equations

1. $y = \frac{x^2}{16}$ 2. $y = x^2$ 3. $y = -\frac{x^2}{12}$ 4. $y = -\frac{x^2}{2}$ 5. $x = -\frac{y^2}{12}$ 6. $x = \frac{y^2}{8}$

7. $F(0, \frac{1}{16})$, $y = -\frac{1}{16}$ 　　　　　　　8. Focus: $(0, \frac{3}{4})$. Directrix: $y = -\frac{3}{4}$

9. Focus: $(0, -\frac{1}{12})$. Directrix: $y = \frac{1}{12}$ 10. Focus: $(0, -1)$. Directrix: $y = 1$

11. Graph $y = \frac{x^2}{2}$ in $[-10.6, 10.6]$ by $[0, 12.5]$ to check your result. (We have used the "screen-squaring" feature of our calculator to help determine the viewing rectangle.)

12. Graph $y = -\frac{x^2}{6}$ in $[-4.25, 4.25]$ by $[-4, 1]$.

13. Graph $y = \sqrt{8x}$ and $y = -\sqrt{8x}$ together in $[-9.4, 14.4]$ by $[-7, 7]$ to check your result.

14. Graph $y_1 = 2\sqrt{-x}$ and $y_2 = -y_1$ in $[-11.7, 8.7]$ by $[-6, 6]$.

15. Graph $y = \frac{3}{2}\sqrt{4 - x^2}$ and $y = -\frac{3}{2}\sqrt{4 - x^2}$ in $[-5.1, 5.1]$ by $[-3, 3]$.

16. Check your result by graphing $y_1 = \sqrt{1 - x^2/2}$ and $y_2 = -y_1$ in $[-2, 2]$ by $[-1.2, 1.2]$.

17. Graph $y_1 = 2\sqrt{1 + x^2}$ and $y_2 = -y_1$ in $[-13.6, 13.6]$ by $[-8, 8]$.

18. Check your result by graphing $y_1 = \frac{3}{2}\sqrt{x^2 - 4}$ and $y_2 = -y_1$ in $[-17, 17]$ by $[-10, 10]$.

19. $\frac{x^2}{6^2} - \frac{y^2}{8^2} = 1$, $e = \frac{5}{3}$. Foci: $(\pm 10, 0)$, asymptotes: $y = \pm\frac{4}{3}x$. Graph $y_1 = (4/3)\sqrt{x^2 - 36}$, $y_2 = -y_1$, $y_3 = (4/3)x$ and $y_4 = -y_3$ in $[-34, 34]$ by $[-20, 20]$.

20. $\frac{x^2}{25} + \frac{y^2}{16} = 1$, $e = \frac{3}{5}$. Foci: $(\pm 3, 0)$. Check your sketch by graphing $y_1 = \frac{4}{5}\sqrt{25 - x^2}$ and $y_2 = -y_1$ in $[-6.8, 6.8]$ by $[-4, 4]$. Intercepts: $(\pm 5, 0)$, $(0, \pm 4)$.

21. $\frac{y^2}{2} - \frac{x^2}{8} = 1$, $e = \sqrt{5}$. Foci: $(0, \pm\sqrt{10})$, asymptotes: $y = \pm\frac{x}{2}$. Graph $y = \frac{\sqrt{x^2 + 8}}{2}$, $y = -\frac{\sqrt{x^2 + 8}}{2}$, $y = \frac{x}{2}$ and $y = -\frac{x}{2}$ in $[-8.5, 8.5]$ by $[-5, 5]$.

22. $\frac{x^2}{16} + \frac{y^2}{7} = 1$. Foci: $(\pm3,0)$, $e = \frac{3}{4}$. Check your sketch by graphing $y_1 = \frac{\sqrt{7}}{4}\sqrt{16-x^2}$ and $y_2 = -y_1$ in $[-4.5, 4.5]$ by $[-2.65, 2.65]$. Intercepts: $(\pm4, 0)$, $(0, \pm\sqrt{7})$.

23. $\frac{x^2}{25} + \frac{y^2}{169} = 1$, $e = \frac{12}{13}$. Foci: $(0, \pm12)$. Graph $y_1 = \frac{13}{5}\sqrt{25-x^2}$ and $y_2 = -y_1$ in $[-22, 22]$ by $[-13, 13]$.

24. $\frac{y^2}{3} - x^2 = 1$, $e = \frac{2}{\sqrt{3}}$. Foci: $(0, \pm2)$, asymptotes: $y = \pm\sqrt{3}x$. Graph $y_1 = \sqrt{3x^2 + 3}$, $y_2 = -y_1$, $y_3 = \sqrt{3}x$, $y_4 = -y_3$ in $[-8.5, 8.5]$ by $[-5, 5]$. Vertices: $(0, \pm\sqrt{3})$.

25. $\frac{x^2}{2} - \frac{y^2}{8} = 1$, $e = \sqrt{5}$. Foci: $(\pm\sqrt{10}, 0)$, asymptotes: $y = \pm2x$. Graph $y = 2\sqrt{x^2 - 2}$, $y = -2\sqrt{x^2 - 2}$, $y = 2x$ and $y = -2x$ in $[-17, 17]$ by $[-10, 10]$.

26. $\frac{x^2}{9} + \frac{y^2}{6} = 1$, $e = \frac{\sqrt{3}}{3}$. Foci: $(\pm\sqrt{3}, 0)$. Graph $y_1 = \sqrt{54 - 6x^2}/3$ and $y_2 = -y_1$ in $[-4.2, 4.2]$ by $[-2.5, 2.5]$. Intercepts: $(\pm3, 0)$, $(0, \pm\sqrt{6})$.

27. $\frac{x^2}{10} + \frac{y^2}{9} = 1$, $e = \frac{1}{\sqrt{10}}$. Foci: $(\pm1, 0)$. Graph $y_1 = \frac{3\sqrt{10-x^2}}{\sqrt{10}}$ and $y_2 = -y_1$ in $[-5.1, 5.1]$ by $[-3, 3]$.

28. $\frac{y^2}{8} - \frac{x^2}{8} = 1$, $e = \sqrt{2}$. Foci: $(0, \pm4)$, asymptotes: $y = \pm x$. Graph $y_1 = \sqrt{x^2 + 8}$, $y_2 = -y_1$, $y_3 = x$, $y_4 = -x$ in $[-13.6, 13.6]$ by $[-8, 8]$. Vertices: $(0, \pm\sqrt{8})$.

29. $x^2 - y^2 = 1$, $e = \sqrt{2}$. Foci: $(\pm\sqrt{2}, 0)$, asymptotes: $y = \pm x$. Graph $y = \sqrt{x^2 - 1}$, $y = -\sqrt{x^2 - 1}$, $y = x$ and $y = -x$ in $[-8.2, 8.2]$ by $[-4.9, 4.9]$.

30. $\frac{x^2}{2} + \frac{y^2}{4} = 1$, $e = \frac{\sqrt{2}}{2}$. Foci: $(0, \pm\sqrt{2})$. Graph $y_1 = \sqrt{4 - 2x^2}$ and $y_2 = -y_1$ in $[-3.4, 3.4]$ by $[-2, 2]$.

31. $\frac{y^2}{4} - \frac{x^2}{4} = 1$, $e = \sqrt{2}$. Foci: $(0, \pm2\sqrt{2})$, asymptotes: $y = \pm x$. Graph $y = \sqrt{x^2 + 4}$, $y = -\sqrt{x^2 + 4}$, $y = x$ and $y = -x$ in $[-8.2, 8.2]$ by $[-4.9, 4.9]$.

32. $x^2 + \frac{y^2}{2} = 1$, $e = \frac{1}{\sqrt{2}}$. Foci: $(0, \pm1)$. Graph $y_1 = \sqrt{2 - 2x^2}$ and $y_2 = -y_1$ in $[-2.4, 2.4]$ by $[-\sqrt{2}, \sqrt{2}]$. Intercepts: $(0, \pm\sqrt{2})$, $(\pm1, 0)$.

33. $\frac{x^2}{2} + \frac{y^2}{3} = 1$, $e = \frac{1}{\sqrt{3}}$. Foci: $(0, \pm1)$. Graph $y = \sqrt{1.5}\sqrt{2 - x^2}$ and $y = -\sqrt{1.5}\sqrt{2 - x^2}$ in $[-2.9, 2.9]$ by $[-\sqrt{3}, \sqrt{3}]$.

34. $\frac{x^2}{16} - \frac{y^2}{9} = 1$. Foci: $(\pm5, 0)$, $e = \frac{5}{4}$, asymptotes: $y = \pm\frac{3}{4}x$. Graph $y_1 = 0.75\sqrt{x^2 - 16}$, $y_2 = -y_1$, $y_3 = 0.75x$, $y_4 = -y_3$ in $[-17, 17]$ by $[-10, 10]$. Vertices: $(\pm4, 0)$.

35.

$$y = -x^2/4 \qquad x = -y^2/4$$

Focal axis:	The y-axis	The x-axis
Focus:	$(0, -1)$	$(-1, 0)$
Vertex:	$(0, 0)$	$(0, 0)$
Directrix:	$y = 1$	$x = 1$

36.

$$8y^2 - 2x^2 = 16 \qquad\qquad 8x^2 - 2y^2 = 16$$
$$\frac{y^2}{2} - \frac{x^2}{8} = 1 \qquad\qquad \frac{x^2}{2} - \frac{y^2}{8} = 1$$

Focal axis:	The y-axis	The x-axis
Center-to-focus distance: $c = \sqrt{a^2 + b^2}$	$c = \sqrt{2 + 8} = \sqrt{10}$	$c = \sqrt{2 + 8} = \sqrt{10}$
Foci:	$(0, \pm c) = (0, \pm\sqrt{10})$	$(\pm c, 0) = (\pm\sqrt{10}, 0)$
Vertices:	$(0, \pm a) = (0, \pm\sqrt{2})$	$(\pm a, 0) = (\pm\sqrt{2}, 0)$
Center:	$(0, 0)$	$(0, 0)$
Asymptotes:	$y = \pm\frac{a}{b}x = \pm\sqrt{\frac{2}{8}}x = \pm\frac{x}{2}$	$y = \pm\frac{b}{a}x = \pm 2x$

38. $y = \frac{wx^2}{2H}$

39. One example is the graph of $\frac{x^2}{25} + \frac{y^2}{9} = 1$.

40. The orbit has the shape of $\frac{x^2}{16} + \frac{y^2}{15} = 1$. Graph $y_1 = \frac{\sqrt{15}}{4}\sqrt{16 - x^2}$ and $y_2 = -y_1$ in $[-6.58, 6.58]$ by $[-\sqrt{15}, \sqrt{15}]$.

41. Dimensions: $2\sqrt{2}$ (horizontal) by $\sqrt{2}$. Area $= 4$.

42. $(0, \frac{16}{3\pi})$.   **43.** 24π **44.** $\sqrt{2}\pi[\sqrt{5} + \frac{1}{2}\sinh^{-1} 2]$

10.2   THE GRAPHS OF QUADRATIC EQUATIONS IN x AND y

1. Hyperbola. Graph $y_1 = \sqrt{x^2 - 1}$ and $y_2 = -y_1$ in $[-17, 17]$ by $[-10, 10]$.

2. Ellipse. Graph $y_1 = \frac{5}{3}\sqrt{9 - x^2}$ and $y_2 = -y_1$ in $[-8.5, 8.5]$ by $[-5, 5]$.

3. Parabola. Graph $y_1 = 2\sqrt{x+1}$ and $y_2 = -y_1$ in $[-5.8, 7.8]$ by $[-4, 4]$. Shift the graph of $x = \frac{y^2}{4}$ horizontally left one unit.

4. Ellipse (circle). Graph $y_1 = \sqrt{10 - x^2}$ and $y_2 = -y_1$ in $[-5.37, 5.37]$ by $[-\sqrt{10}, \sqrt{10}]$.

5. Ellipse. Let $y_1 = \sqrt{64 - 16(x^2 - 4x + 4)}$. Graph $y_2 = (8 + y_1)/8$ and $y_3 = (8 - y_1)/8$ in $[0, 4]$ by $[-3.8, 2.3]$.

6. Hyperbola. $\theta = \frac{1}{2}\tan^{-1}\frac{4}{3} = 0.464$. Let $y_1 = \sqrt{(4x+3)^2 - 4(-2x^2 + 2x + 6)}$. Graph $y_2 = \frac{1}{2}(4x + 3 + y_1)$ and $y_3 = \frac{1}{2}(4x + 3 - y_1)$ in $[-17, 17]$ by $[-10, 10]$.

7. Parabola. Let $y_1 = \sqrt{(4x)^2 - 16(x^2 - 3x - 6)}$. Graph $y_2 = (-4x + y_1)/8$ and $y_3 = (-4x - y_1)/8$ in $[-8.4, 13.6]$ by $[-9.1, 3.9]$. $\theta = -0.464$.

8. Ellipse (circle). Let $y_1 = \sqrt{4 - 4(x^2 + 3x - 10)}$. Graph $y_2 = \frac{1}{2}(2 + y_1)$ and $y_3 = \frac{1}{2}(2 - y_1)$ in $[-8.6, 5.6]$ by $[-3.2, 5.2]$.

9. Hyperbola. Let $y_1 = \sqrt{x^2 + 12x + 20}$. Graph $y_2 = (-x + y_1)/2$ and $y_3 = (-x - y_1)/2$ in $[-49, 43]$ by $[-27.4, 26.8]$. $\theta = -\frac{\pi}{8}$.

10. Parabola. Let $y_1 = \sqrt{(6x + 5)^2 - 4(3)(3x^2 - 4x - 12)}$. Graph $y_2 = \frac{1}{6}[-(6x + 5) + y_1]$ and $y_3 = \frac{1}{6}[-(6x + 5) - y_1]$ in $[-7.4, 15.1]$ by $[-10, 3.2]$. $\theta = \frac{\pi}{4}$.

11. Hyperbola. Graph $y = \sqrt{x^2 - 1}$ and $y = -\sqrt{x^2 - 1}$ in $[-8.5, 8.5]$ by $[-5, 5]$.

12. Ellipse. Graph $y_1 = \sqrt{(7 + 4x - 2x^2)/3}$ and $y_2 = -y_1$ in $[-2.8, 4.9]$ by $[-2.3, 2.3]$.

13. Hyperbola. Graph $y = \frac{1}{x}$ in $[-5.1, 5.1]$ by $[-3, 3]$. $\theta = \frac{\pi}{4}$.

14. Hyperbola. Graph $y = -\frac{3}{x}$ in $[-10, 10]$ by $[-5.9, 5.9]$. $\theta = \frac{\pi}{4}$.

15. Hyperbola. Graph $y = -(2x^2 + x + 1)/(x - 1)$ in dot format in $[-8, 8.7]$ by $[-19, 9.1]$. $\theta = 0.232$.

16. Hyperbola. Graph $y = -(x^2 - 2x - 3)/(2x + 3)$ in dot format in $[-8, 8.7]$ by $[-19, 20]$. $\theta = 0.554$.

17. Ellipse. Let $y_1 = \sqrt{(6 - 3x)^2 - 4(3)(x^2 - 7)}$. Graph $y_2 = \frac{-(6-3x) + y_1}{6}$ and $y_2 = \frac{-(6-3x) - y_1}{6}$ in $[-20.3, 8.2]$ by $[-12.9, 3.9]$. $\theta = 0.491$.

18. Hyperbola. Graph $y_1 = \frac{5}{2}\sqrt{x^2 - 14}$ and $y_2 = -y_1$ in $[-17, 17]$ by $[-10, 10]$.

19. Ellipse. Let $y_1 = \sqrt{(3x + 17)^2 - 4(2)(6x^2 + 2)}$. Graph $y_2 = \frac{-(3x+17)+y_1}{4}$ and $y_3 = \frac{-(3x+17)-y_1}{4}$ in $[-11.9, 14.4]$ by $[-12.6, 2.9]$. $\theta = 0.322$.

20. Parabola. Let $y_1 = \sqrt{(12x - 9)^2 - 4(12)(3x^2 + 435x + 72)}$. Graph $y_2 = \frac{1}{24}[-(12x - 9) + y_1]$ and $y_3 = \frac{1}{24}[-(12x - 9) - y_1]$ in $[-2.4, 1.3]$ by $[-6.1, 5.7]$. $\theta = -0.464$.

21. Graph the hyperbola $y = \frac{2}{x}$ in $[-8.5, 8.5]$ by $[-5, 5]$. $\theta = \frac{\pi}{4}$. $x^2 - y^2 = 4$.

22. Ellipse. Let $y_1 = \sqrt{x^2 - 4(x^2 - 1)}$. Graph $y_2 = \frac{1}{2}(-x + y_1)$ and $y_3 = \frac{1}{2}(-x - y_1)$ in $[-2.4, 2.4]$ by $[-1.4, 1.4]$. $\frac{3}{2}x^2 + \frac{1}{2}y^2 = 1$. $\theta = \frac{\pi}{4}$.

23. Let $y_1 = \sqrt{3x^2 - 4(2)(x^2 - 1)}$. Graph $y_2 = (\sqrt{3}x + y_1)/4$ and $y_3 = (\sqrt{3}x - y_1)/4$ in $[-2.6, 2.1]$ by $[-1.5, 1.3]$ obtaining an ellipse. $\theta = \frac{\pi}{6}$. $x^2 + 5y^2 = 2$.

24. Degenerate parabola consisting of the two lines $y - x = \pm\sqrt{2}$. $\theta = \frac{\pi}{4}$. $y = \pm 1$.

25. Let $y_1 = \sqrt{9x^2 - 4(x^2 - 5)}$. Graph $y_2 = (3x + y_1)/2$ and $y_3 = (3x - y_1)/2$ in $[-17, 17]$ by $[-10, 10]$ obtaining a hyperbola. $\theta = \frac{\pi}{4}$. $5y^2 - x^2 = 10$.

26. Degenerate hyperbola consisting of two lines. $\theta = \frac{\pi}{4}$. The original equation is equivalent to $x = 1$, $y = 1$. The transformed equation is equivalent to $y = \pm(x - \sqrt{2})$.

27. Ellipse. Let $y_1 = \sqrt{4x^2 - 12(3x^2 - 19)}$. Graph $y_2 = (-2x + y_1)/6$ and $y_3 = (-2x - y_1)/6$ in $[-5.1, 5.1]$ by $[-3, 3]$. $\theta = \frac{\pi}{4}$. $4x^2 + 2y^2 = 19$.

28. Hyperbola. Let $y_1 = \sqrt{48x^2 - 4(7 - 3x^2)}$. Graph $y_2 = \frac{1}{2}(4\sqrt{3}x + y_1)$ and $y_3 = \frac{1}{2}(4\sqrt{3}x - y_1)$ in $[-5, 5]$ by $[-30, 30]$. $5x^2 - 3y^2 = 7$. $\theta = \frac{\pi}{6}$.

29. $x = x'\cos\theta + y'\sin\theta$, $y = -x'\sin\theta + y'\cos\theta$.

31. $x^2 + 6xy + y^2 - 16 = 0$.   **32.** $5x^2 - 2\sqrt{3}xy + 7y^2 - 40 = 0$.

33. $x^2 + 10\sqrt{3}xy + 11y^2 - 40 = 0$.   **34.** $5x^2 - 6xy + 5y^2 - 7 = 0$.

10.3   PARAMETRIC EQUATIONS FOR PLANE CURVES

1. Graph $x_1 = \cos t$, $y_1 = \sin t$, $0 \le t \le \pi$ in $[-1.7, 1.7]$ by $[-1, 1]$. The upper half of the unit circle, $x^2 + y^2 = 1$, is traced out in the counterclockwise direction from $(1, 0)$ to $(-1, 0)$.

2. Graph $x_1 = \cos 2t$, $y = \sin 2t$, $0 \le t \le \pi$ in $[-1.7, 1.7]$ by $[-1, 1]$. The unit circle $x^2 + y^2 = 1$ is traced out in the counterclockwise direction.

3. Graph $x_1 = \sin 2\pi t$, $y_1 = \cos 2\pi t$, $0 \le t \le 1$ in $[-1.7, 1.7]$ by $[-1, 1]$. The unit circle is traced out once in the clockwise direction starting at $(0, 1)$.

4. Graph $x_1 = \cos(\pi - t)$, $y_1 = \sin(\pi - t)$, $0 \le t \le \pi$ in $[-1.7, 1.7]$ by $[-1, 1]$. The top half of the unit circle $x^2 + y^2 = 1$ is traced out in the clockwise direction.

5. $x = 4 \cos t$, $y = 2 \sin t$, $0 \le t \le 2\pi$. Graph this with t-step $= 0.1$ in $[-4, 4]$ by $[-2.4, 2.4]$. The ellipse $\frac{x^2}{16} + \frac{y^2}{4} = 1$ is traced out once in the counterclockwise direction.

6. Graph $x = 4 \sin t$, $y = 2 \cos t$, $0 \le t \le \pi$ in $[-4, 4]$ by $[-2.35, 2.35]$. The right-hand side of the ellipse $\frac{x^2}{16} + \frac{y^2}{4} = 1$ is traced out in the clockwise direction.

7. Graph in $[-8.5, 8.5]$ by $[-5, 5]$. The upper half of the ellipse $\frac{x^2}{16} + \frac{y^2}{25} = 1$ is traced out in the counterclockwise direction.

8. Graph $x_1 = 4 \sin t$, $y_1 = 5 \cos t$, $0 \le t \le 2\pi$ in $[-8.5, 8.5]$ by $[-5, 5]$. The entire ellipse $\frac{x^2}{16} + \frac{y^2}{25} = 1$ is traced out in the clockwise direction starting at $(0, 5)$.

9. Graph for $-1 \le t \le 1$ in $[-7.6, 7.6]$ by $[0, 9]$. The parabola $y = x^2$ is traced out from left to right.

10. Graph $x_1 = -\sqrt{t}$, $y_1 = t$, $t \ge 0$ (use $0 \le t \le 9$) in $[-9.2, 6.2]$ by $[0, 9]$. The curve $x = -\sqrt{y}$ (the left side of $y = x^2$) is traced out from right to left.

11. Graph for $0 \le t \le 10$ in $[0, 10]$ by $[-1.4, 4.5]$. The upper half of the parabola $y^2 = x$ is traced out from left to right.

12. Graph $x_1 = \sec^2 t - 1$, $y_1 = \tan t$, $-\frac{\pi}{2} < t < \frac{\pi}{2}$ in $[-2.6, 5.1]$ by $[-2.3, 2.3]$. The parabola $x = y^2$ is traced out, the bottom half from right to left, then the top from left to right.

13. Graph in $[-17, 17]$ by $[-10, 10]$. The left branch of the hyperbola $x^2 - y^2 = 1$ is traced out from bottom to top.

14. Graph $x = \csc t$, $y = \cot t$, $0 < t < \pi$ in $[-1.9, 4.9]$ by $[-1, 3]$. The right branch of the hyperbola $x^2 - y^2 = 1$ is traced out from top to bottom.

15. Graph for $-5 \leq t \leq 5$ in $[-16.6, 17.4]$ by $[-7, 13]$. The graph of the line $y = 2x + 3$ is traced out from left to right.

16. Graph $x = 1 - t$, $y = 1 + t$, $-\infty < t < \infty$ (use $-3 \leq t \leq 3$) in $[-4, 6]$ by $[-2, 4]$. The line $x + y = 2$ is traced out from right to left.

17. Graph in $[-2, 3]$ by $[-1, 2]$. The line segment from $(0, 1)$ to $(1, 0)$ is traced out from left to right. It is part of $y = 1 - x$.

18. Graph $x = 3t$, $y = 2 - 2t$, $0 \leq t \leq 1$ in $[-1.9, 4.9]$ by $[-1, 3]$. The segment of the line $y = -\frac{2}{3}x + 2$, $(0, 2)$ to $(3, 0)$, is traced out from left to right.

19. Graph in $[-1, 1]$ by $[-0.1, 1.1]$. The upper half of the unit circle, $y = \sqrt{1 - x^2}$, is traced out from left to right.

20. Graph $x = t$, $y = \sqrt{4 - t^2}$, $0 \leq t \leq 2$ in $[-0.7, 2.7]$ by $[0, 2]$. The quarter-circle of radius 2 with center $(0, 0)$ is traced out from $(0, 2)$ to $(2, 0)$ in the clockwise direction.

21. Graph for $0 \leq t \leq 4$ in $[-6.9, 21.9]$ by $[0, 17]$. The top half of the hyperbola $y^2 - x^2 = 1$ for $x \geq 0$ is traced out from left to right.

22. Graph $x = \sqrt{t + 1}$, $y = \sqrt{t}$, $t \geq 0$ (use $0 \leq t \leq 20$) in $[-1.83, 5.83]$ by $[0, 4.5]$. The upper half of the right branch of the hyperbola $x^2 - y^2 = 1$ is traced out from left to right starting at $(1, 0)$.

23. Graph for $-3 \leq t \leq 3$ in $[-17, 17]$ by $[-10, 10]$. The right branch of the hyperbola $x^2 - y^2 = 1$ is traced out from bottom to top.

24. Graph $x = 2\sinh t$, $y = 2\cosh t$, $-\infty < t < \infty$ (use $-2.3 \leq t \leq 2.3$) in $[-10, 10]$ by $[-10, 10]$. The upper branch of the hyperbola $\frac{y^2}{4} - \frac{x^2}{4} = 1$ is traced out from left to right.

25. a) $x = a\cos t$, $y = -a\sin t$, $0 \leq t \leq 2\pi$ b) $x = a\cos t$, $y = a\sin t$, $0 \leq t \leq 2\pi$ c) $x = a\cos(2t)$, $y = -a\sin(2t)$, $0 \leq t \leq 2\pi$ d) $x = a\cos t$, $y = a\sin t$, $0 \leq t \leq 4\pi$

26. $a = \pi$. The curve is also closed for $a = 2\pi$ and this gives the complete curve.

27. $a = \pi$. $a = 2\pi$ is required for the complete graph.

28. $a = \pi/3$. A complete graph is obtained using $a = \pi$.

29. $a = \pi/2$. For a complete graph use $a = 2\pi$.

30. $a = \pi/2.5$. Use $a = 4\pi$ for a complete graph.

31. $a = \pi/1.5$. A complete graph is obtained if $a = 4\pi$.

32. No such a exists.   **33.** No such a exists.

34. The following use $0 \leqq t \leqq 2\pi$.   a) $x = a\cos t$, $y = -b\sin t$ b) $x = a\cos t$, $y = b\sin t$ c) $x = a\cos 2t$, $y = -b\sin 2t$ d) $x = a\cos 2t$, $y = b\sin 2t$.

35. $x = \cos t + t\sin t$, $y = \sin t - t\cos t$. Graph this and $x_2 = \cos t$, $y_2 = \sin t$, $0 \leqq t \leqq 2\pi$ in $[-10.2, 10.2]$ by $[-6, 6]$.

36. $x = 2\cot t$, $y = 2\sin^2 t$, $0 < t < \pi$. Graph in $[-10, 10]$ by $[-1, 3]$.

37. $(1, 1)$ **38.** $(1, \frac{\sqrt{3}}{2})$ and $(1, -\frac{\sqrt{3}}{2})$

39. b) $x = x_1 t$, $y = y_1 t$ c) $x = -1 + t$, $y = t$. Graph in $[-2, 2]$ by $[-1, 3]$, $-1 \leqq t \leqq 3$.

40. Use the viewing window $[-4, 4]$ by $[-2.36, 2.36]$ for each of these graphs.

41. a) Use $[-18, 32]$ by $[-15, 15]$.   b) Use $[-0.13, 2]$ by $[-0.55, 0.55]$.   c) Use $[-50, 1]$ by $[-55, 15]$.

42. $[-3, 9]$ by $[-2.6, 4.5]$ a possible viewing window.

43. The three graphs can be compared in the viewing window $[0, 4\pi]$ by $[-2.7, 4.7]$.

44. The two graphs in a) and b) may be compared in the viewing window $[-1.7, 1.7]$ by $[-1, 1]$.   c) Graph $x_1 = \cos t$, $y_1 = \sin t$, $x_2 = 0.75 + 0.25\cos t$, $y_2 = 0.25\sin t$, $0 \leqq t \leqq 2\pi$ in $[-1.7, 1.7]$ by $[-1, 1]$. If the small circle rolls through 2π, it travels $2\pi r = \pi/2$ which is exactly 1/4 of the circumference of the unit circle. Graphing all three curves together is also helpful.

45. Graph in $[-5.1, 5.9]$ by $[-3.2, 3.2]$. The new equations amount to $x = -2\cos t + \cos(2t)$, $y = -2\sin t + \sin(2t)$. Graph in the same window. The original curve had three cusps. The new curve appears to be a cardioid.

46. Compare the graphs in the viewing window $[-6.8, 6.8]$ by $[-4, 4]$.

47. Graph a), b), c) in $[0, 128]$ by $[-21, 54]$. In d) the curve is part of the y-axis traced from $(0, 0)$ to $(0, 64)$ and back down to $(0, 0)$.

48. The curves a), b), c) may be graphed in $[-18.7, 18.7]$ by $[-11, 11]$. Graph d) in $[-11.5, 11.5]$ by $[-6.75, 6.75]$. Graph e) in $[-1.5, 1.5]$ by $[-1.5, 1.5]$. In e) $0 \leq t \leq \pi$ is sufficient.

49. Graph $x_1 = t$, $y_1 = t^2 + 1$, $x_2 = (\sqrt{3}t - (t^2 + 1))/2$, $y_2 = (t + \sqrt{3}(t^2 + 1))/2$, $-4 \leq t \leq 4$ in $[-16.1, 16.1]$ by $[-2, 17]$. $3x^2 + 2\sqrt{3}xy + y^2 + 2x - 2\sqrt{3}y + 4 = 0$.

50. Graph $x_1 = t$, $y_1 = t^2 + 1$, $x_2 = -t^2 - 1$, $y_2 = t$, $-3 \leq t \leq 3$ in $[-21, 16]$ by $[-11, 11]$. The rotated curve has equation $x = -y^2 - 1$.

51. The rotated curve has equation $y = x^2$. Graph $x_1 = t^2$, $y_1 = t$, $x_2 = t$, $y_2 = t^2$, $-3 \leq t \leq 3$ in $[-15.3, 15.3]$ by $[-9, 9]$.

52. Graph $x_1 = t^2$, $y_1 = t$, $x_2 = (t^2 - t)/\sqrt{2}$, $y_2 = (t^2 + t)/\sqrt{2}$, $-3 \leq t \leq 3$ in $[-15.3, 15.3]$ by $[-9, 9]$. The rotated curve has equation $x^2 - 2xy + y^2 = \sqrt{2}x + \sqrt{2}y$.

53. Graph $x_1 = 2\cos t$, $y_1 = 3\sin t$, $x_2 = \cos t - (3\sqrt{3}/2)\sin t$, $y_2 = \sqrt{3}\cos t + (3/2)\sin t$, $0 \leq t \leq 2\pi$ in $[-5.1, 5.1]$ by $[-3, 3]$. The rotated curve has equation $21x^2 + 10\sqrt{3}xy + 31y^2 = 144$.

54. Graph $x_1 = 2\cos t$, $y_1 = 3\sin t$, $x_2 = (2\cos t - 3\sin t)/\sqrt{2}$, $y_2 = (2\cos t + 3\sin t)/\sqrt{2}$, $0 \leq t \leq 2\pi$ in $[-5.1, 5.1]$ by $[-3, 3]$. The rotated curve has equation $13x^2 + 10xy + 13y^2 = 72$.

55. Graph $x_1 = 4\sec t$, $y_1 = 5\tan t$, $x_2 = (4\sec t - 5\sqrt{3}\tan t)/2$, $y_2 = (4\sqrt{3}\sec t + 5\tan t)/2$, $0 \leq t \leq 2\pi$ in $[-34, 34]$ by $[-20, 20]$ (dot format may help). The rotated curve has equation $-23x^2 + 82\sqrt{3}xy + 59y^2 = 1600$.

56. Graph $x_1 = 4\sec t$, $y_1 = 5\tan t$, $x_2 = (4\sqrt{3}\sec t - 5\tan t)/2$, $y_2 = (4\sec t + 5\sqrt{3}\tan t)/2$, $0 \leq t \leq 2\pi$ in $[-34, 34]$ by $[-20, 20]$ (dot format suggested). The rotated curve has equation $59x^2 + 82\sqrt{3}xy - 23y^2 = 1600$.

10.4   THE CALCULUS OF PARAMETRIC EQUATIONS

1. Tangent line: $y = -x + 2\sqrt{2}$. $\left.\frac{d^2y}{dx^2}\right|_{t=\pi/4} = -\sqrt{2}$. Graph $x_1 = 2\cos t$, $y_1 = 2\sin t$, $x_2 = t$, $y_2 = -t + 2\sqrt{2}$, $-3.5 \le t \le 9$, T step $= 0.05$ in $[-10.5, 10, 5]$ by $[-6.1, 6.1]$.

2. Tangent line: $y = \sqrt{3}x + 2$. $\left.\frac{d^2y}{dx^2}\right|_{t=-\frac{1}{6}} = -8$. Graph $x_1 = \sin 2\pi t$, $y_1 = \cos 2\pi t$, $x_2 = t$, $y_2 = \sqrt{3}t + 2$, $-2.2 \le t \le -0.4$ in $[-2.7, 2.6]$ by $[-1.74, 1.39]$.

3. $y = -\frac{1}{2}x + 2\sqrt{2}$. $\left.\frac{d^2y}{dx^2}\right|_{t=\pi/4} = -\frac{\sqrt{2}}{4}$. Graph $x_1 = 4\sin t$, $y_1 = 2\cos t$, $x_2 = t$, $y_2 = -\frac{1}{2}x + 2\sqrt{2}$, $-10.5 \le t \le 10.5$ in $[-10.5, 10.5]$ by $[-6.1, 6.1]$.

4. The line $y = \sqrt{3}x$ is its own tangent. $y'' = 0$.

5. $y = -\frac{1}{2}x - \frac{1}{2}$. $\left.\frac{d^2y}{dx^2}\right|_{t=-\frac{\pi}{4}} = \frac{1}{4}$. Graph $x_1 = \sec^2 t - 1$, $y_1 = \tan t$, $x_2 = t$, $y_2 = -\frac{1}{2}t - \frac{1}{2}$, $-7 \le t \le 15$ in $[-6.2, 14.2]$ by $[-8, 4]$.

6. $y = 2x - \sqrt{3}$. $\left.\frac{d^2y}{dx^2}\right|_{t=\pi/6} = -3\sqrt{3}$. Graph $x_1 = (\cos t)^{-1}$, $y_1 = \tan t$, $x_2 = t$, $y_2 = 2t - \sqrt{3}$, $-\pi \le t \le \pi$ in $[-4.1, 4.4]$ by $[-2.3, 2.7]$ in Dot Format.

7. $y = x + \frac{1}{4}$. $\left.\frac{d^2y}{dx^2}\right|_{t=1/4} = -2$. Graph $x_1 = t$, $y_1 = \sqrt{t}$, $x_2 = t$, $y_2 = t + 0.25$, $-10.5 \le t \le 10.5$ in $[-10.5, 10.5]$ by $[-6.1, 6.1]$.

8. $y = -2x - 1$. $\left.\frac{d^2y}{dx^2}\right|_{t=3} = -\frac{1}{3}$. Graph $x_1 = -\sqrt{t+1}$, $y_1 = \sqrt{3t}$, $x_2 = t$, $y_2 = -2t - 1$, $-10 \le t \le 10$ in $[-9.5, 7.5]$ by $[-5, 5]$.

9. $y = x - 4$. $\frac{d^2y}{dx^2} = \frac{1}{2}$ for all $t \ne 0$. Graph $x_1 = 2t^2 + 3$, $y_1 = t^4$, $x_2 = t$, $y_2 = t - 4$, $-2 \le t \le 20$ in $[-13.2, 24.2]$ by $[-6, 16]$.

10. $y = -x - 1$. $\left.\frac{d^2y}{dx^2}\right|_{t=1} = 1$. Graph $x_1 = \frac{1}{t}$, $y_1 = -2 + \ln t$, $x_2 = t$, $y_2 = -t - 1$, $-10 \le t \le 10$ in $[-10, 10]$ by $[-10, 10]$.

11. $y = \sqrt{3}\, x + 2 - \frac{\sqrt{3}}{3}\pi$. $\left.\frac{d^2y}{dx^2}\right|_{t=\pi/3} = -4$. Graph $x_1 = t - \sin t$, $y_1 = 1 - \cos t$, $x_2 = t$, $y_2 = \sqrt{3}\, t + 2 - \frac{\sqrt{3}}{3}\pi$, $-17 \le t \le 17$ in $[-17, 17]$ by $[-10, 10]$.

12. $y = 2$. $\left.\frac{d^2y}{dx^2}\right|_{t=\pi/2} = -1$. Graph $x_1 = \cos t$, $y_1 = 1 + \sin t$, $x_2 = t$, $y_2 = 2$, $-\pi \le t \le \pi$ in $[-2.55, 2.55]$ by $[0, 3]$.

13. Graph in $[-1, 1]$ by $[0, \pi]$. $L = 4$ 14. Graph in $[0, 3\sqrt{3}]$ by $[0, 4.5]$. $L = 7$

15. Graph in $[0,8]$ by $[1/3,9]$. $L = 12$ **16.** Graph in $[\sqrt{3},9]$ by $[0,7.5]$. $L = \frac{21}{2}$

17. Graph in $[8,4\pi]$ by $[0,8]$. $L = \pi^2$

18. Graph, $0 \leq t \leq \pi/3$, in $[0,0.5]$ by $[0.5,1]$ or, for a bigger picture, $-\pi/2 < t < \pi/2$, in $[-3,3]$ by $[0,1]$. $L = \ln 2$

19. $8\pi^2$ **20.** $\frac{28\pi}{9}$ **21.** $\frac{52\pi}{3}$ **22.** π

23. $3\sqrt{5}\,\pi$ **24.** $\pi r\sqrt{h^2 + r^2}$ **25.** a) π b) π

26. a) TRAP yields 5.8698, NINT yields 5.8699 b) $|E_T| < 0.013$. $(M \leq 4 \cdot 1)$

27. 19.377 **28.** 13.808 **29.** 2505.105

30. 19.134 **31.** 159.485 **32.** 888.703

33. Graph $x_1 = \sin t$, $y_1 = \sin 2t$, $0 \leq t \leq 2\pi$ in $[-1.86, 1.86]$ by $[-1.1, 1.1]$. Horizontal tangent at $(\frac{\sqrt{2}}{2}, 1)(t = \frac{\pi}{4})$. Tangents at origin: $y = \pm 2x$. To confirm, we graph x_1, y_1, $x_2 = t$, $y_2 = 2t$, $x_3 = t$, $y_3 = -2t$, $-2\pi \leq t \leq 2\pi$ in the viewing rectangle given above.

34. Graph $x_1 = \sin 2t$, $y_1 = \sin 3t$, $0 \leq t \leq 2\pi$ in $[-1.86, 1.86]$ by $[-1.1, 1.1]$. Horizontal tangent at $(\frac{\sqrt{3}}{2}, 1)$. Tangents at origin: $y = \pm\frac{3}{2}x$. To confirm, we graph x_1, y_1, $x_2 = t$, $y_2 = 1.5t$, $x_3 = t$, $y_3 = -1.5t$, $-2\pi \leq t \leq 2\pi$ in the rectangle above.

35. through 41. For each of these we may use $0 \leq t \leq 2\pi$ in $[-1.86, 1.86]$ by $[-1.1, 1.1]$. For 38 and 39, $\frac{\pi}{2} \leq t \leq \frac{3\pi}{2}$ suffices.

42. Graph $x = 5\cos t + 10\cos(ct)$, $y = 5\sin t + 10\sin(ct)$, $0 \leq t \leq 2\pi$ in $[-34, 34]$ by $[-20, 20]$ for each $c = 2, 4, 6, 8$.

43. Graph $x = 12\cos t + 6\cos(ct)$, $y = 12\sin t + 6\sin(ct)$, $0 \leq t \leq 2\pi$ in $[-34, 34]$ by $[-20, 20]$ for each $c = 2, 4, 6, 8$.

44. 503.14 **45.** 306.324

10.5   POLAR COORDINATES

1. {a,c},   {b,d},   {e,k},   {f,h},   {g,j},   {i,l},   {m,o},   {n,p}

2. a) $(3,0)$ b) $(-3,0)$ c) $(3,0)$ d) $(-3,0)$ e) $(-1,\sqrt{3})$ f) $(-1,-\sqrt{3})$ g) $(1,\sqrt{3})$ h) $(-1,-\sqrt{3})$ i) $(1,-\sqrt{3})$ j) $(1,\sqrt{3})$ k) $(-1,\sqrt{3})$ l) $(1,-\sqrt{3})$

3.

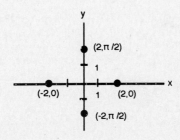

a) $(2,\frac{\pi}{2}+2n\pi)$, $(-2,-\frac{\pi}{2}+2n\pi)$ b) $(2,2n\pi)$, $(-2,(2n+1)\pi)$ c) $(-2,\frac{\pi}{2}+2n\pi)$, $(2,-\frac{\pi}{2}+2n\pi)$ d) $(-2,2n\pi)$, $(2,(2n+1)\pi)$. $n=0,\pm1,\pm2,\ldots$

4.

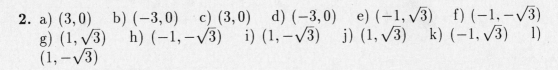

a) $(3,\frac{\pi}{4}+2n\pi)$, $(-3,\frac{5\pi}{4}+2n\pi)$ b) $(-3,\frac{\pi}{4}+2n\pi)$, $(3,\frac{5\pi}{4}+2n\pi)$ c) $(3,-\frac{\pi}{4}+2n\pi)$, $(-3,\frac{3\pi}{4}+2n\pi)$ d) $(-3,-\frac{\pi}{4}+2n\pi)$, $(3,\frac{3\pi}{4}+2n\pi)$

5. a) $(1,1)$ b) $(1,0)$ c) $(0,0)$ d) $(-1,-1)$ e) $(\frac{3\sqrt{3}}{2},-\frac{3}{2})$ f) $(3,4)$ g) $(1,0)$ h) $(-\sqrt{3},3)$

6. $(0,\theta)$, any real θ

7. Graph $r=2, 0\leqq\theta\leqq2\pi$ in a square window containing $[-2,2]$ by $[-2,2]$ in polar mode.

8.

9.

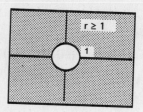

10.

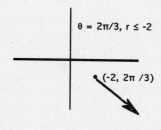

11.

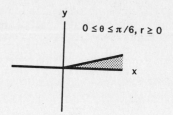

12.

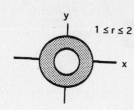

13.

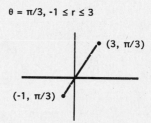

14.

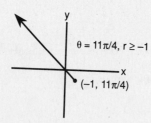

15. The graph consists of the origin and the positive y-axis.

16. The graph consists of the origin and the negative y-axis.

17. The graph consists of the upper half of the unit circle including $(-1,0)$ and $(1,0)$.

18. The graph consists of the lower half of the unit circle including $(-1,0)$ and $(1,0)$.

19.   **20.**

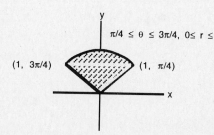

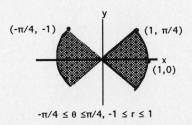

21.   **22.**

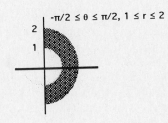

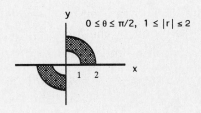

23. $x = 2$. Vertical line consisting of all points with x-coordinate 2.

24. $y = -1$, horizontal line through $(0,-1)$.

25. $y = 4$, the horizontal line through $(1,4)$.

26. $x = 0$, the y-axis.   **27.** $y = 0$, the x-axis.

28. $x = -3$, the vertical line through $(-3,0)$.

29. $x + y = 1$, the line through $(1,0)$ and $(0,1)$.

30. $y = x$ **31.** $x^2 + y^2 = 1$, the unit circle.

32. $x^2 + y^2 = 4y$. Circle with center $(0,2)$ and radius 2.

33. $y = 2x + 5$, line with slope 2 through $(0, 5)$.

34. $y = \frac{1}{4}x^2$, the parabola with vertex $(0, 0)$ which passes through $(\pm 2, 1)$.

35. $r = 7 \sec \theta$, $-\frac{\pi}{2} < \theta < \frac{\pi}{2}$, the vertical line through $(7, 0)$.

36. $r = \csc \theta$ **37.** $\theta = \frac{\pi}{4}$ **38.** $r = \frac{3}{\cos \theta - \sin \theta}$ **39.** $r = 2$, circle.

40. $r = \pm\sqrt{\sec 2\theta}$, hyperbola   **41.** $r = \frac{\pm 6}{\sqrt{4 \cos^2 \theta + 9 \sin^2 \theta}}$, ellipse.

42. $r = \frac{\pm\sqrt{2}}{\sqrt{\cos \theta \sin \theta}}$, hyperbola.   **43.** $r = \frac{4 \cos \theta}{\sin^2 \theta}$, parabola.

44. The graph consists of the origin plus the graph of $r = 25 \sec 2\theta$.

10.6   GRAPHING IN POLAR COORDINATES

1. In Exercises 1 through 12 the student should use the method of Example 1 including a table of values, use of symmetries and "slope at $(0, \theta_0) = \tan \theta_0$" as a guide as to how the curve goes into and out of the origin. The student's results can then be checked on a grapher. One way of carrying out this check is given in the answers. It is assumed that a graphing utility with a polar graphing mode and with a screen "squaring" function is being used.

Graph $r = 1 + \cos \theta$, $0 \le \theta \le 2\pi$, $\theta\text{Step} = 0.1$ in a "squared" rectangle containing $[-0.25, 2]$ by $[-1.3, 1.3]$, for example $[-1.33, 3.08]$ by $[-1.3, 1.3]$.

2. Graph $r = 2 - 2 \cos \theta$, $0 \le \theta \le 2\pi$ in $[-6.8, 3.7]$ by $[-3.1, 3.1]$.

3. Graph $r = 1 - \sin \theta$, $0 \le \theta \le 2\pi$ in $[-2.4, 2.4]$ by $[-2.2, 0.7]$.

4. Graph $r = 1 + \sin \theta$, $0 \le \theta \le 2\pi$ in $[-2.1, 2.1]$ by $[-0.45, 2]$.

5. Graph $r = 2 + \sin \theta$, $0 \le \theta \le 2\pi$ in $[-3.5, 3.6]$ by $[-1.2, 3]$.

6. Graph $r = 1 + 2 \sin \theta$, $0 \le \theta \le 2\pi$ in $[-3, 3]$ by $[-0.45, 3]$.

7. Graph $r = 2\sqrt{\cos 2\theta}$ and $r = -2\sqrt{\cos 2\theta}$ in $[-2, 2]$ by $[-1.2, 1.2]$. Use $\theta\text{Step} = 0.01$, $-\frac{\pi}{4} \le \theta \le \frac{\pi}{4}$.

8. Graph $r_1 = 2\sqrt{\sin \theta}$, $r_2 = -r_1$, $0 \le \theta \le \pi$ in $[-3.6, 3.6]$ by $[-2.13, 2.13]$.

9. Graph $r = \theta$ in $[-33, 33]$ by $[-18.4, 20]$ first using $0 \le \theta \le 20$ then $-20 \le \theta \le 0$ and then $-20 \le \theta \le 20$.

10. Graph $r = \sin(\theta/2)$, $0 \leq \theta \leq 4\pi$ in $[-1.7, 1.7]$ by $[-1, 1]$.

11. Graph $r = 8\cos 2\theta$, $0 \leq \theta \leq 2\pi$ in $[-13.6, 13.6]$ by $[-8, 8]$. A complete graph requires a minimum of 2π for the range of θ. The factor 8 stretches the graph of $r = \cos 2\theta$ away from the origin by a factor of 8. The range, $\frac{\pi}{4} \leq \theta \leq \frac{3\pi}{4}$, for example, produces a closed curve. Replacing θ by 2θ produces 3 more leaves.

12. Graph $r = 8\cos 3\theta$, $0 \leq \theta \leq \pi$ in $[-13.6, 13.6]$ by $[-8, 8]$. A complete graph requires a minimum of π units for the range of θ. The factor 8 stretches the graph of $r = \cos 3\theta$ away from the origin by a factor of 8. The range $\frac{\pi}{6} \leq \theta \leq \frac{\pi}{2}$, for example, produces a closed curve. Replacing θ by 3θ has tripled the number of leaves.

13. $m = \pm 1$. Graph $r = -1 + \cos\theta$, $r = -(\sin\theta + \cos\theta)^{-1}$ and $r = (\sin\theta - \cos\theta)^{-1}$, $-\pi \leq \theta \leq \pi$ in $[-2.6, 4.3]$ by $[-2, 2]$.

14. The slopes at $0, \frac{\pi}{2}$, π are, respectively, -1, undefined, 1. Graph $r_1 = -1 + \sin\theta$, $r_2 = \frac{-1}{\sin\theta + \cos\theta}$, $r_3 = \frac{-1}{\sin\theta - \cos\theta}$, $0 \leq \theta \leq 2\pi$ in $[-3.4, 3.4]$ by $[-2, 2]$. Regard the y-axis as the tangent at the origin.

15. $\theta = \frac{\pi}{4}$, $m = -1$; $\theta = \frac{-\pi}{4}$, $m = 1$; $\theta = \frac{3\pi}{4}$, $m = 1$; $\theta = \frac{-3\pi}{4}$, $m = -1$. $\theta = 0$, $m = 0$; $\theta = \frac{\pi}{2}$, $m = \infty$; $\theta = \pi$, $m = 0$; $\theta = \frac{3\pi}{2}$, $m = -\infty$. Graph $r = \sin 2\theta$, $r = \pm\sqrt{2}/(\sin\theta + \cos\theta)$, $r = \pm\sqrt{2}/(\sin\theta - \cos\theta)$, $0 \leq \theta \leq 2\pi$ in $[-1.9, 1.9]$ by $[-1.2, 1.2]$ and regard the x- and y-axes as tangent lines also.

16. $\theta = 0$, slope undefined; $\theta = \pm\frac{\pi}{2}$, slope $= 0$; $\theta = \pi$, slope undefined. Going into the origin in the first and third quadrant, the slope is 1 while in the second and fourth it is -1. Graph $r = \cos 2\theta$, $r = \pm\sec\theta$, $r = \pm\csc\theta$, $0 \leq \theta \leq 2\pi$ in $[-3.4, 3.4]$ by $[-2, 2]$. Use the line-drawing feature of your grapher to draw in $y = \pm x$.

17. Graph $r = \pm 2\sqrt{\cos 2\theta}$, $-\frac{\pi}{4} \leq \theta \leq \frac{\pi}{4}$, θStep $= 0.01$ in $[-2, 2]$ by $[-1.2, 1.2]$. $\frac{\pi}{2}$ is a minimum range of θ, but it must be over an interval in which $\cos 2\theta$ is non-negative.

18. Graph $r = \pm 2\sqrt{\sin 2\theta}$, $0 \leq \theta \leq \frac{\pi}{2}$ in $[-3.4, 3.4]$ by $[-2, 2]$. $\frac{\pi}{2}$ is a minimum range of θ.

19. a) Graph $r = \frac{1}{2} + \cos\theta$, $0 \leq \theta \leq 2\pi$, θStep $= 0.1$ in $[-0.9, 2.3]$ by $[-0.94, 0.94]$.
    b) Graph $r = 0.5 + \sin\theta$, $0 \leq \theta \leq 2\pi$ in $[-1.5, 1.5]$ by $[-0.2, 1.6]$.

20. a) Graph $r = 1 - \cos\theta$, $0 \leq \theta \leq 2\pi$ in $[-3.3, 1.55]$ by $[-1.43, 1.42]$.
    b) Graph $r = -1 + \sin\theta$, $0 \leq \theta \leq 2\pi$ in $[-2.1, 2.1]$ by $[-0.5, 2]$.

21. a) Graph $r = 1.5 + \cos\theta$, $0 \le \theta \le 2\pi$ in $[-2,4]$ by $[-1.8, 1.9]$.   b) Graph $1.5 - \sin\theta$, $0 \le \theta \le 2\pi$ in $[-3.1, 3.1]$ by $[-2.7, 1]$.

22. a) Graph $r = 2 + \cos\theta$, $0 \le \theta \le 2\pi$ in $[-4.1, 6.1]$ by $[-3, 3]$.   b) Graph $r = -2 + \sin\theta$, $0 \le \theta \le 2\pi$ in $[-4.2, 4.2]$ by $[-1.5, 3.5]$.

23. Graph $r = 2 - 2\cos\theta$, $0 \le \theta \le 2\pi$ in $[-6.5, 3.2]$ by $[-2.8, 2.8]$. The region consists of this closed curve (a cardioid) and every point inside it.

24. Graph $r_1 = \sqrt{\cos\theta}$, $r_2 = -\sqrt{\cos\theta}$, $-\frac{\pi}{2} \le \theta \le \frac{\pi}{2}$ in $[-1.7, 1.7]$ by $[-1, 1]$. The region consists of this closed curve and every point inside it.

27. The origin, $(1, \frac{\pi}{2})$ and $(1, \frac{3\pi}{2})$ **28.** The origin, $(1, 0)$ and $(1, \pi)$.

29. $(2(\sqrt{2}-1), \sin^{-1}(3 - 2\sqrt{2}))$, $(2(\sqrt{2}-1), \pi - \sin^{-1}(3 - 2\sqrt{2}))$, the origin and $(2, \frac{3\pi}{2}) = (-2, \frac{\pi}{2})$.

30. The origin, $(\pm 1, \frac{\pi}{4})$ and $(\pm 1, \frac{3\pi}{4})$.   **31.** $(\pm 2^{-1/4}, \frac{\pi}{8})$ and the origin.

32. The origin, $(1 \pm \frac{1}{\sqrt{2}}, \frac{\pi}{2})$, $(1 \pm \frac{1}{\sqrt{2}}, \frac{3\pi}{2})$. Check the graphs, $0 \le \theta \le 4\pi$ in $[-2, 2]$ by $[-2, 2]$.

33. $(1, \frac{\pi}{12})$, $(1, \frac{5\pi}{12})$, $(-1, \frac{19\pi}{12})$, $(-1, \frac{23\pi}{12})$, $(1, \frac{13\pi}{12})$, $(1, \frac{17\pi}{12})$, $(-1, \frac{7\pi}{12})$, $(-1, \frac{11\pi}{12})$

34. $(1, \frac{\pi}{4})$, $(1, \frac{5\pi}{4})$

35. Graph $y = 5\sin\theta$, $0 \le \theta \le \pi$ in $[-5, 5]$ by $[-0.44, 5.44]$. Period π.

36. Graph $r = 5\cos\theta$, $0 \le \theta \le \pi$ in $[-3.1, 7.1]$ by $[-3, 3]$. Period π.

37. Graph $r = 5\sin 2\theta$, $0 \le \theta \le 2\pi$ in $[-8.5, 8.5]$ by $[-5, 5]$. Period 2π.

38. Graph $r = 5\cos 2\theta$, $0 \le \theta \le 2\pi$ in $[-8.5, 8.5]$ by $[-5, 5]$. Period 2π.

39. Graph $r = 5\sin 5\theta$, $0 \le \theta \le \pi$ in $[-8.5, 8.5]$ by $[-5, 5]$. Period π.

40. Graph $r = 5\cos 5\theta$, $0 \le \theta \le \pi$ in $[-8.5, 8.5]$ by $[-5, 5]$. Period π.

41. Graph $r = 5\sin(2.5\theta)$, $0 \le \theta \le 4\pi$ in $[-8.5, 8.5]$ by $[-5, 5]$. Period 4π.

42. Graph $r = 5\cos 2.5\theta$, $0 \le \theta \le 4\pi$ in $[-8.5, 8.5]$ by $[-5, 5]$. Period 4π.

43. Graph $r = 5\sin 1.5\theta$, $0 \le \theta \le 4\pi$ in $[-8.5, 8.5]$ by $[-5, 5]$. Period 4π.

44. Graph $r = 5\cos 1.5\theta$, $0 \le \theta \le 4\pi$ in $[-8.5, 8.5]$ by $[-5, 5]$. Period 4π.

45. Graph $r = 1 - 2\sin 3\theta$, $0 \leq \theta \leq 2\pi$ in $[-4.7, 4.7]$ by $[-2.1, 3.4]$. Period 2π.

46. Graph $r = 1 + 2\sin\frac{\theta}{2}$, $0 \leq \theta \leq 4\pi$ in $[-5.1, 3.7]$ by $[-2.6, 2.6]$. Period $= 4\pi$. Kidney.

47. a) Graph $r = e^{\theta/10}$, $-20 \leq \theta \leq 10$ in $[-4.3, 3.6]$ by $[-2, 2.7]$. b) Graph $r = 8/\theta$, $-20 \leq \theta \leq 20$ in the same window. c) Graph $r = 10/\sqrt{\theta}$ and $r = -10/\sqrt{\theta}$, $0 \leq \theta \leq 200$, θStep $= 0.5$ in the same window.

49. Infinite period

50. Here is a possible conjecture for a special case: if m and n are odd with no common factor, $r = 5\sin(\frac{m}{n}\theta)$ is a rose with m overlapping petals having period $n\pi$.

51. Graph $r = 1.75 + (0.06/2\pi)\theta$, $0 \leq \theta \leq 10\pi$ in $[-3, 3]$ by $[-3, 3]$.

53. 741.420cm

54. b) $S_a = 741.416$cm compared with $S = 741.420$cm.

55. a) $n = (-\pi r_0 + \sqrt{(\pi r_0)^2 + \pi S_a b})/\pi b$. b) The speed of the take-up reel steadily decreases.

56. The counter value is an increasing function of time with decreasing derivative.

58. a) $r = f(\theta - \alpha)$ b) Graph $r = 1 - \cos\theta$, $r = 1 - \cos(\theta - \pi/6)$, $r = 1 - \cos(\theta - \pi/2)$ and $r = 1 - \cos(\theta - 2\pi/3)$, $0 \leq \theta \leq 2\pi$ in $[-3.4, 3.4]$ by $[-2, 2]$.

10.7   POLAR EQUATIONS OF CONIC SECTIONS

1. $r\cos(\theta - \frac{\pi}{6}) = 5$, $\sqrt{3}x + y = 10$ **2.** $r\cos(\theta - \frac{3\pi}{4}) = 2$, $y = x + 2\sqrt{2}$.

3. Graph $r = \frac{\sqrt{2}}{\cos(\theta - \frac{\pi}{4})}$, $0 \leq \theta \leq \pi$ in $[-5.8, 7.8]$ by $[-3, 5]$. $x + y = 2$.

4. Graph $r = \frac{3}{\cos(\theta - \frac{2\pi}{3})}$, $0 \leq \theta \leq \pi$ in $[-8.5, 8.5]$ by $[-5, 5]$. $y = \frac{\sqrt{3}}{3}x + 2\sqrt{3}$.

5. $r = 8\cos\theta$ **6.** $r = 2\sqrt{2}\sin\theta$

7. Check your sketch by graphing $r = 4\cos\theta$, $0 \leq \theta \leq \pi$ in $[-1.4, 5.4]$ by $[-2, 2]$. Center: $(2, 0)$, radius $= 2$.

8. Center: $(3, \frac{\pi}{2})$, radius 3. Check your sketch by graphing $r = 6\sin\theta$, $0 \le \theta \le \pi$ in $[-5.1, 5.1]$ by $[0, 6]$.

9. $r = \frac{2}{1+\cos\theta}$ 10. $r = \frac{2}{1+\sin\theta}$ 11. $r = \frac{8}{1+2\cos\theta}$ 12. $r = \frac{30}{1-5\sin\theta}$

13. $r = \frac{1}{2+\cos\theta}$ 14. $r = \frac{2}{4-\cos\theta}$ 15. $r = \frac{10}{5-\sin\theta}$ 16. $r = \frac{6}{3+\sin\theta}$

17. Directrix: $x = 1$, vertex: $(\frac{1}{2}, 0)$. Graph for $-\pi \le \theta \le \pi$ in $[-7.4, 2.8]$ by $[-3, 3]$. Include the directrix $r = 1/\cos\theta$.

18. Graph $r = \frac{6}{2+\cos\theta}$, $0 \le \theta \le 2\pi$ in $[-8.5, 8.5]$ by $[-5, 5]$. Also include the directrix $r = 6/\cos\theta$. Vertices: $(2, 0)$, $(6, \pi)$, center: $(2, \pi)$.

19. Graph $r_1 = \frac{5}{2-\cos\theta}$ and $r_2 = -5/\cos\theta$, $-\pi \le \theta \le \pi$ in $[-8.5, 8.5]$ by $[-5, 5]$. Directrix concerned is $x = -5$. Vertices: $(\frac{5}{3}, \pi)$, $(5, 0)$, center: $(\frac{5}{3}, 0)$.

20. Directrix: $x = -2$, vertex: $(1, \pi)$. Graph $r_1 = 2/(1-\cos\theta)$, $r_2 = -2/\cos\theta$, $-\pi \le \theta \le \pi$ in $[-8.5, 8.5]$ by $[-5, 5]$.

21. Graph $r = \frac{25}{(1+0.5\sin\theta)}$, $0 \le \theta \le 2\pi$ in $[-93, 9]$ by $[-50, 60]$. Also include $r = 50/\sin\theta$. Vertices: $(\frac{50}{3}, \frac{\pi}{2})$, $(-50, \frac{\pi}{2})$, center: $(-\frac{50}{3}, \frac{\pi}{2})$.

22. Directrix: $y = 4$, vertex: $(2, \frac{\pi}{2})$. Check your sketch by graphing $r_1 = \frac{4}{1+\sin\theta}$ and $r_2 = 4/\sin\theta$, $-\pi \le \theta \le \pi$ in $[-8.5, 8.5]$ by $[-5, 5]$.

23. Graph $r = 4/(1-\sin\theta)$ and $r = -4/\sin\theta$, $0 \le \theta \le 2\pi$ in $[-13, 13]$ by $[-5, 12]$. Vertex: $(2, \frac{3\pi}{2})$.

24. Graph $r_1 = \frac{4}{2-\sin\theta}$, $r_2 = -4/\sin\theta$, $-\pi \le \theta \le \pi$ in $[-8.5, 8.5]$ by $[-5, 5]$. Directrix: $y = -4$, center: $(\frac{4}{3}, \frac{\pi}{2})$, vertices: $(\frac{4}{3}, \frac{3\pi}{2})$ and $(4, \frac{\pi}{2})$.

25. Graph the ellipses sequentially in $[-2, 1.4]$ by $[-1, 1]$, $0 \le \theta \le 2\pi$, θStep $= 0.1$. The last two require a larger rectangle. As e increases, the center moves to the left, the ellipse increases in size. The ellipse also flattens out horizontally as can be seen by graphing in $[-11.3, 2.3]$ by $[-4, 4]$.

26. Graph r, $0 \le \theta \le 2\pi$ in $[-8.7, 17]$ by $[-7.5, 7.5]$ in dot format. In each case the graph is a hyperbola with the x-axis being the focal axis. The point $(1, 0)$ lies between the two vertices, the left vertex starting out at $(0.524, 0)$. As e increases both vertices (and the center) converge to $(1, 0)$.

27. Graph these sequentially in $[-27, 27]$ by $[-16, 16]$. As k becomes more negative, the parabola opens up wider and wider to the right. As k becomes more and more positive, the parabola opens to the left wider and wider.

28. Parabola opens downward for $k < 0$, upward for $k > 0$; becomes wider as $|k|$ increases.

29. Graph $r = 3\sec(\theta - \pi/3) = 3/\cos(\theta - \pi/3)$, $0 \leq \theta \leq 2\pi$ in $[-11, 19]$ by $[-6, 11.7]$. $x + \sqrt{3}y = 6$ in rectangular coordinates.

30. (Circle) Graph $r = 4\sin\theta$, $0 \leq \theta \leq \pi$ in $[-3.4, 3.4]$ by $[0, 4]$.

31. Graph $r = 8/(4 + \cos\theta)$, $0 \leq \theta \leq 2\pi$ in $[-4.9, 3.9]$ by $[-2.6, 2.6]$.

32. Graph $r = 1/(1 - \sin\theta)$, $0 \leq \theta \leq 2\pi$ in $[-5.95, 5.95]$ by $[-2, 5]$.

33. Graph $r = 1/(1 + 2\sin\theta)$, $0 \leq \theta \leq 2\pi$ in $[-2.7, 2.7]$ by $[-0.93, 2.27]$ in dot format, $\theta\text{Step} = 0.01$.

34. $r = 4\sec(\theta + \frac{\pi}{6})$. $r\cos(\theta + \frac{\pi}{6}) = 4$ leads to $y = \sqrt{3}x - 8$. Graph $r = 4\sec(\theta + \frac{\pi}{6})$, $-\frac{2\pi}{3} \leq \theta \leq \frac{\pi}{3}$ in $[-5, 10]$ by $[-12, 5]$.

35. Graph $r = -2\cos\theta$, $0 \leq \theta \leq \pi$ in $[-2.7, 0.7]$ by $[-1, 1]$.

36. Graph $8/(4 + \sin\theta)$, $0 \leq \theta \leq 2\pi$ in $[-4.1, 4.1]$ by $[-3, 2]$.

37. Graph $r = 1/(1 + \cos\theta)$, $0 \leq \theta \leq 2\pi$, $\theta\text{Step} = 0.1$ in $[-7.7, 5.9]$ by $[-4, 4]$.

38. Graph $r = 1/(1 + 2\cos\theta)$, $0 \leq \theta \leq 2\pi$ in $[-2.7, 4.04]$ by $[-4, 4]$. Use dot format.

39. Graph $r = 2\cos\theta$, $0 \leq \theta \leq \pi$ in $[-0.7, 2.7]$ by $[-1, 1]$. The region consists of the circle and all points within it.

40. Graph $r = -3\cos\theta$, $0 \leq \theta \leq \pi$ in $[-4.1, 1.1]$ by $[-1.5, 1.5]$. The region is the circle and all points inside the circle.

41. b)

Planet	$a(1-e)AU$	$a(1+e)AU$
Mercury	0.3075	0.4667
Venus	0.7184	0.7282
Earth	0.9833	1.017
Mars	1.382	1.666
Jupiter	4.951	5.455
Saturn	9.021	10.057
Uranus	18.30	20.06
Neptune	29.81	30.31
Pluto	29.65	49.23

42.

Mercury: $r = \dfrac{0.3707}{1 + 0.2056 \cos \theta}$ 　　　　Jupiter: $r = \dfrac{5.191}{1 + 0.0484 \cos \theta}$

Venus: $r = \dfrac{0.7233}{1 + 0.0068 \cos \theta}$ 　　　　Saturn: $r = \dfrac{9.511}{1 + 0.0543 \cos \theta}$

Earth: $r = \dfrac{0.9997}{1 + 0.0617 \cos \theta}$ 　　　　Uranus: $r = \dfrac{19.14}{1 + 0.0460 \cos \theta}$

Mars: $r = \dfrac{1.511}{1 + 0.0934 \cos \theta}$ 　　　　Neptune: $r = \dfrac{30.06}{1 + 0.0082 \cos \theta}$

Pluto: $r = \dfrac{37.012}{1 + 0.2481 \cos \theta}$

Using $0 \le \theta \le 2\pi$, graph the first four in $[-2.72, 2.72]$ by $[-1.6, 1.6]$ and the second four in $[-52.7, 52.7]$ by $[-40, 40]$. If a viewing window includes the largest orbits, the smallest orbits can't be seen due to the limited size and number of pixels.

43. a) $x^2 + (y - 1)^2 = 1$, $y = 1$ 　　b) Graph $r = 2 \sin \theta$, $r = 1/\sin \theta$, $0 \le \theta \le \pi$ in $[-1.7, 1.7]$ by $[0, 2]$. Label the points of intersection $(1, 1)$, $(\sqrt{2}, \frac{\pi}{4})$ and $(-1, 1)$, $(\sqrt{2}, \frac{3\pi}{4})$.

44. a) $(x - 1)^2 + y^2 = 1$, $x = 1$ 　　b) Graph $r = 2 \cos \theta$, $r = 1/\cos \theta$, $0 \le \theta \le \pi$ in $[-2.9, 2.9]$ by $[-2, 2]$. Label the points of intersection $(1, 1)$, $(\sqrt{2}, \frac{\pi}{4})$ and $(1, -1)$, $(-\sqrt{2}, \frac{3\pi}{4})$.

45. $r = \frac{4}{1 + \cos \theta}$ 　　　　　　　　　　**46.** $r = \frac{2}{1 + \sin \theta}$

47. Assume a and b are non-zero. Then $P_0 = \left(\frac{ca}{a^2 + b^2}, \frac{cb}{a^2 + b^2} \right)$ and $r = \frac{|c|}{\sqrt{a^2 + b^2} \cos(\theta - \theta_0)}$ where $\theta_0 = \tan^{-1} \frac{b}{a}$ if P_0 is in the 1st or 4th quadrant and $\theta_0 = \pi + \tan^{-1} \frac{b}{a}$ if P_0 is in the 2nd or 3rd quadrant.

48. $r = \frac{\sqrt{5}}{\cos(\theta - \pi + \tan^{-1} 0.5)}$ 　　　**49.** $r = \frac{6}{\sqrt{13} \cos(\theta - \tan^{-1} \frac{2}{3})}$

50. $r = \frac{4}{\sqrt{5} \cos(\theta + \tan^{-1} 0.5)}$ 　　　**51.** $r = \frac{12}{5 \cos(\theta - (\pi + \tan^{-1}(3/4)))}$

52.

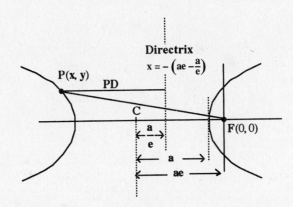

10.8   INTEGRATION IN POLAR COORDINATES

1. Graph $r = \cos\theta$, $0 \le \theta \le \frac{\pi}{4}$ in $[0,1]$ by $[0,0.5]$. Then draw a line segment connecting $(0,0)$ and the rectangular point $(\frac{1}{2},\frac{1}{2})$. $A = \frac{\pi+2}{16}$.

2. Graph $r = e^\theta$, $0 \le \theta \le \ln 25$ in $[-25,2]$ by $[-5.2,10.8]$. Then draw a line from the origin to the terminal point of the graph. $A = 156$.

3. Graph $r = 4 + 2\cos\theta$, $0 \le \theta \le 2\pi$ in $[-8.2,12.2]$ by $[-6,6]$. $A = 18\pi$.

4. For one example take $a = 2$ and graph $r = 2(1 + \cos\theta)$, $0 \le \theta \le 2\pi$ in $[-3.6,6.6]$ by $[-3,3]$. $A = \frac{3}{2}a^2\pi$.

5. Graph $r = \cos 2\theta$, $-\frac{\pi}{4} \le \theta \le \frac{\pi}{4}$ in $[-0.09,1.12]$ by $[-0.35,0.35]$ for one leaf. $A = \frac{\pi}{8}$.

6. For one example take $a = 2$ and graph $r = 4\sin\theta$, $0 \le \theta \le \pi$ in $[-3.4,3.4]$ by $[0,4]$. $A = \pi a^2$.

7. For the purpose of graphing let $a = 2$. For the entire graph use $r = \sqrt{8\cos 2\theta}$, $0 \le \theta \le 2\pi$ in $[-3,3]$ by $[-1.7,1.7]$. $A = 2a^2$.

8. Graph $r = 2\sqrt{\sin 2\theta}$, $0 \le \theta \le \frac{\pi}{2}$ in $[-0.7,2.7]$ by $[0,2]$. $A = 2$.

9. Graph $r_1 = \sqrt{2\sin 3\theta}$ and $r_2 = -r_1$, $0 \le \theta \le 2\pi$ in $[-2.5,2.5]$ by $[-1.5,1.5]$. $A = 4$.

10. Graph $r_1 = 2\sin\theta$, $r_2 = 2\cos\theta$, $0 \le \theta \le \pi$ in $[-2.05,3.05]$ by $[-1,2]$ to see the region inside both circles. $A = \frac{\pi}{2} - 1$.

11. Graph $r = 1$ and $r = 2\sin\theta$, $0 \leq \theta \leq 2\pi$ in $[-2.5, 2.5]$ by $[-1, 2]$. $A = \frac{2\pi}{3} - \frac{\sqrt{3}}{2}$.

12. Graph $r_1 = 2$ and $r_2 = 2(1 - \cos\theta)$, $-\frac{\pi}{2} \leq \theta \leq \frac{3\pi}{2}$ in $[-7.8, 5.8]$ by $[-4, 4]$. For $-\frac{\pi}{2} \leq \theta \leq \frac{\pi}{2}$ the region is bounded by $r = 2(1 - \cos\theta)$ and for $\frac{\pi}{2} \leq \theta \leq \frac{3\pi}{2}$ the region is bounded by $r = 2$. $A = 5\pi - 8$.

13. Graph $r = 2(1 + \cos\theta)$ and $r = 2(1 - \cos\theta)$, $0 \leq \theta \leq 2\pi$ in $[-6.8, 6.8]$ by $[-4, 4]$. $A = 6\pi - 16$.

14. Graph $r_1 = (\sqrt{6})\sqrt{\cos 2\theta}$ and $r_2 = \sqrt{3}$, $0 \leq \theta \leq 2\pi$ in $[-2.7, 2.7]$ by $[-1.8, 1.8]$. $A = 3\sqrt{3} - \pi$.

15. Graph $r = 3a\cos\theta$ and $r = a(1 + \cos\theta)$, with $a = 2$, $0 \leq \theta \leq 2\pi$ in $[-3, 8.3]$ by $[-3.3, 3.3]$. $A = \pi a^2$.

16. Graph $r_1 = -2\cos\theta$ and $r_2 = 1$, $0 \leq \theta \leq 2\pi$ in $[-2.2, 1.2]$ by $[-1, 1]$. $A = \frac{\pi}{3} + \frac{\sqrt{3}}{2}$.

17. a) $2\pi + \frac{3\sqrt{3}}{2}$ b) $\pi + 3\sqrt{3}$

18. Graph $r_1 = 6$ and $r_2 = 3(\sin\theta)^{-1}$, $0 \leq \theta \leq 2\pi$ in $[-10.2, 10.2]$ by $[-6, 6]$. $A = 12\pi - 9\sqrt{3}$.

19. Graph $r = \theta^2$, $0 \leq \theta \leq \sqrt{5}$ in $[-4.9, 2.5]$ by $[0, 4.4]$. $L = \frac{19}{3}$.

20. Graph $r = e^\theta/\sqrt{2}$, $0 \leq \theta \leq \pi$ in $[-16.6, 1.57]$ by $[-3.4, 7.4]$. $L = e^\pi - 1$.

21. The graph is the line segment from $(1, 0)$ to $(1, 1)$ which has length 1.

22. $\sqrt{3} = $ length of line segment from $(\sqrt{3}, 1)$ to $(0, 1)$.

23. Graph $r = 1 + \cos\theta$, $0 \leq \theta \leq 2\pi$ in $[-1.7, 3.4]$ by $[-1.5, 1.5]$. $L = 8$.

24. a) $2\pi a$ b) πa c) πa assuming $a > 0$

25. $\sqrt{2}\pi$ **26.** $\sqrt{5}\pi(e^{\pi/2} + 1)$ **27.** $2(2 - \sqrt{2})\pi$ **28.** $4\pi^2 a^2$

29. b) $y_1 \to \infty$ as $x \to 0^+$ c) The integral is improper because y_1 has a vertical asymptote at the endpoint $x = 0$.

30. $f(x) \to 39.356\ldots$ as $x \to 0^+$.   b) $f(x)$ decreases as $x \to 5$.   c) $39.356\ldots$

31. $((0.8333\ldots)a, 0) = \left(\frac{5a}{6}, 0\right)$ **32.** $\left(0, \frac{4a}{3\pi}\right)$

PRACTICE EXERCISES, CHAPTER 10

1. Graph $y = \pm 2\sqrt{2x}$ in $[-11.8, 16.8]$ by $[-8.4, 8.4]$. Use the line-drawing feature to include the directrix $x = -2$. Focus: $(2, 0)$.

2. Graph $y_1 = -x^2/4$ and $y_2 = 1$ in $[-3.73, 3.73]$ by $[-2.4, 2]$. Focus: $(0, -1)$.

3. Vertices $(0, \pm 4)$, foci: $(0, \pm 3)$. Graph $y = \pm 4\sqrt{1 - \frac{x^2}{7}}$, $y = \pm \frac{16}{3}$ (directrices) in $[-10.2, 10.2]$ by $[-6, 6]$.

4. Vertices: $(\pm 2, 0)$, foci: $(\pm\sqrt{2}, 0)$, directrices: $x = \pm 2\sqrt{2}$. In polar mode graph $r_1 = 2/\sqrt{\cos^2\theta + 2\sin^2\theta}$, $r_2 = 2(\sqrt{2})(\cos\theta)^{-1}$, $r_3 = -r_2$, $0 \leqq \theta \leqq 2\pi$ in $[-3.4, 3.4]$ by $[-2, 2]$.

5. Vertices: $(\pm 1, 0)$, foci: $(\pm 2, 0)$, directrices: $x = \pm\frac{1}{2}$. Graph $y = \pm\sqrt{3x^2 - 3}$ in $[-15, 15]$ by $[-10, 10]$.

6. Vertices: $(0, \pm 2\sqrt{2})$, foci: $(0, \pm\sqrt{10})$, directrices: $y = \pm\frac{4\sqrt{10}}{5}$. Check your sketch by graphing $y = \pm 2\sqrt{x^2 + 2}$, $y = \pm\frac{4\sqrt{10}}{5}$ in $[-17, 17]$ by $[-10, 10]$.

7. $B^2 - 4AC = -3 < 0$ indicates ellipse but there is no solution and no graph.

8. Hyperbola. Graph $y = [-(3x+1) \pm \sqrt{(3x+1)^2 - 8(x^2+x+1)}]/4$ in $[-17, 17]$ by $[-10, 10]$.

9. Parabola. Graph $y = \frac{-(4x+1)\pm\sqrt{-8x-15}}{8}$ in $[-13.5, 3.5]$ by $[0, 10]$.

10. Hyperbola. Graph $y = [-(2x + 1) \pm \sqrt{(2x + 1)^2 + 8(x^2 + x + 1)}]/(-4)$ in $[-17, 17]$ by $[-10, 10]$.

11. Ellipse, $\theta = \frac{\pi}{4}$. Equivalent conic: $\frac{x^2}{6} + \frac{y^2}{10} = 1$. Graph $y = \pm\sqrt{10(1 - \frac{x^2}{6})}$ and $y = \frac{-x\pm\sqrt{x^2 - 8(2x^2 - 15)}}{4}$ in $[-7.5, 7.5]$ by $[-4, 5]$.

12. Hyperbola, $\theta = \frac{\pi}{6}$. Equivalent conic: $x^2 - y^2 = 2$. Let $y_1 = 4\sqrt{x^2 - 1}$. Graph $y_2 = (2\sqrt{3}x + y_1)/2$, $y_3 = (2\sqrt{3}x - y_1)/2$, $y_4 = \sqrt{x^2 - 2}$, $y_5 = -y_4$ in $[-8.5, 8.5]$ by $[-4, 6]$.

13. $e = \sqrt{2}$ 14. $\frac{x^2}{4} - \frac{y^2}{12} = 1$ 15. a) 24π b) 16π 16. 24π 17. $(\pm 2, 1)$

19. $y = 2x + 1$. The entire line is traced out from left to right.

20. $y = 1 - x$, $x \geqq 0$. The half-line is traced out from left to right.

21. $\frac{y^2}{(0.5)^2} - \frac{x^2}{(0.5)^2} = 1$, hyperbola. The graph is the upper branch traced out from left to right. This may be confirmed by graphing in parametric mode in $[-25.5, 25.5]$ by $[-10, 20]$.

22. $x^2 + y^2 = 4$, the semi-circle of radius 2 with center at the origin is traced out in the clockwise direction from $(-2, 0)$ to $(2, 0)$.

23. The portion of the parabola $y = x^2$ determined by $-1 \leq x \leq 1$ is traced out from left to right.

24. The ellipse $\frac{x^2}{16} + \frac{y^2}{81} = 1$ is traced out in the counterclockwise direction.

25. $x = 3\cos t,\ y = 4\sin t,\ 0 \leq t \leq 2\pi$

26. One possible answer: $x = 2\cos t,\ y = -2\sin t,\ \pi \leq t \leq 7\pi$.

27. $y - 1 = (\sqrt{3}/2)(x - \sqrt{3}/2)$. At $t = \pi/3,\ d^2y/dx^2 = 1/4$.

28. $y + \frac{1}{2} = -3(x - \frac{5}{4})$. $\left.\frac{d^2y}{dx^2}\right|_{t=2} = 6$.

29. Graph in $[-0.16, 4.4]$ by $[-0.26, 2.5]$. Length $= 3 + \ln 2/8$.

30. Graph $x = t^2,\ y = \frac{t^3}{3} - t,\ -2.5 \leq t \leq 2.5$ in $[-1, 5]$ by $[-1.8, 1.8]$. $L = 4\sqrt{3}$.

31. $76\pi/3$ **32.** $2\pi\left(2 - \frac{3\sqrt{2}}{4}\right)$

33. Graph $r = \cos 2\theta,\ 0 \leq \theta \leq 2\pi$ in $[-1.7, 1.7]$ by $[-1, 1]$. Period $= 2\pi$. Four-leaved rose.

34. This is the vertical line $x = 1$. $r = \sec\theta$ has period π.

35. Graph $r = 6/(1 - 2\cos\theta),\ 0 \leq \theta \leq 2\pi$ in $[-30, 22]$ by $[-13, 18]$ in dot format. Period $= 2\pi$. Hyperbola.

36. Four-leaved rose. Period $= 2\pi$. Graph $r = \sin 2\theta,\ 0 \leq \theta \leq 2\pi$ in $[-1.7, 1.7]$ by $[-1, 1]$.

37. Graph $r = \theta,\ -4\pi \leq \theta \leq 4\pi$ in $[-18.6, 18.6]$ by $[-12.3, 9.7]$. Infinite period. Spiral.

38. $r^2 = \cos 2\theta$. Lemniscate. The period is 2π if we use $r = \sqrt{\cos 2\theta}$; it is π if we use $r = \pm\sqrt{\cos 2\theta}$. Graph $r = \sqrt{\cos 2\pi},\ 0 \leq \theta \leq 2\pi$ in $[-1.7, 1.7]$ by $[-1, 1]$.

39. Graph $r = 1 + \cos\theta,\ 0 \leq \theta \leq 2\pi$ in $[-1.6, 3.2]$ by $[-1.4, 1.4]$. Period 2π. Cardioid.

40. Cardioid. Period $= 2\pi$. Graph $r = 1 - \sin\theta$, $0 \le \theta \le 2\pi$ in $[-2.5, 2.5]$ in $[-2.35, 0.65]$.

41. Graph $r = 2/(1 - \cos\theta)$, $0 \le \theta \le 2\pi$ in $[-10, 17]$ by $[-8, 8]$. Period 2π. Parabola.

42. Lemniscate. The period is $\frac{3\pi}{2}$ if $r = \sqrt{\sin 2\theta}$ is used; it is $\frac{\pi}{2}$ if $r = \pm\sqrt{\sin 2\theta}$ is used. Graph $r = \sqrt{\sin 2\theta}$, $0 \le \theta \le 2\pi$ in $[-1.7, 1.7]$ by $[-1, 1]$.

43. Graph $r = -\sin\theta$, $0 \le \theta \le \pi$ in $[-1, 1]$ by $[-1.1, 0.1]$. Period π. Circle.

44. Limaçon. Period $= 2\pi$. Graph $r = 2\cos\theta + 1$, $0 \le \theta \le 2\pi$ in $[-2, 4.8]$ by $[-2, 2]$.

45. Graph $r = 2\sqrt{3}/\cos(\theta - \pi/3)$, $0 \le \theta \le 2\pi$ in $[-17, 17]$ by $[-5, 15]$. $y = -\frac{1}{\sqrt{3}}x + 4$.

46. Graph $r = \sqrt{2}/(2\cos(\theta - \frac{3\pi}{4}))$, $0 \le \theta \le \pi$ in $[-5.5, 6.5]$ by $[-2, 5]$. $y = x + 1$.

47. Center $(0, 1)$, radius $= 1$ **48.** Center $(-2, 0)$, radius $= 2$

49. The region consists of all points on and within the circle with center $(3, 0)$ and radius 3. Graph the circle $r = 6\cos\theta$, $0 \le \theta \le \pi$ in $[-2.1, 8.1]$ by $[-3, 3]$.

50. Graph $r = -4\sin\theta$, $0 \le \theta \le \pi$ in $[-3.4, 3.4]$ by $[-4, 0]$. The region consists of all points on and within the circle with center $(0, -2)$ and radius 2.

51. The origin is the only point of intersection.

52. The origin, $(\frac{1}{2}, \frac{\pi}{3})$ and $(\frac{1}{2}, \frac{5\pi}{3})$.

53. All points on the curve since the two curves are identical.

54. The origin, $(1, \frac{\pi}{2}) = (-1, \frac{3\pi}{2})$ and $(1, \frac{3\pi}{2}) = (-1, \frac{\pi}{2})$.

55. Graph the parabola $r = 2/(1 + \cos\theta)$, $0 \le \theta \le 2\pi$ in $[-26.5, 7.5]$ by $[-10, 10]$. $(1, 0)$ is the vertex.

56. Graph $r = \frac{8}{2 + \cos\theta}$, $0 \le \theta \le 2\pi$ in $[-10.51, 5.2]$ by $[-4.62, 4.62]$. Vertices: $(-8, 0)$, $(\frac{8}{3}, 0)$, center: $(-\frac{8}{3}, 0)$

57. Graph r, $0 \le \theta \le 2\pi$ in $[-13, 4]$ by $[-5, 5]$ in dot format. Vertices: $(-6, 0)$, $(2, \pi)$.

58. Graph $r = 12/(3 + \sin\theta)$, $0 \le \theta \le 2\pi$ in $[-8.2, 8.2]$ by $[-6.2, 3.5]$. Vertices: $(-6, \frac{\pi}{2})$, $(3, \frac{\pi}{2})$, center: $(-\frac{3}{2}, \frac{\pi}{2})$.

59. $r = \frac{4}{1+2\cos\theta}$ **60.** $r = \frac{4}{1-\cos\theta}$ **61.** $r = \frac{2}{2+\sin\theta}$ **62.** $r = \frac{6}{3-\sin\theta}$

63. $\theta = \frac{\pi}{4}$ and $\theta = \frac{3\pi}{4}$ or $y = \pm x$ **64.** $\theta = \frac{2\pi}{3}$ and $\theta = \frac{4\pi}{3}$ or $y = \pm\sqrt{3}x$

65. $r\cos(\theta-\theta_0) = 1$ where $\theta_0 = \frac{\pi}{4}, \frac{3\pi}{4}, \frac{5\pi}{4}$ and $\frac{7\pi}{4}$ **66.** $r = \frac{-1}{\sin\theta\pm\cos\theta}$

67. Graph $r = 2 - \cos\theta$, $0 \le \theta \le 2\pi$ in $[-4.7, 2.7]$ by $[-2.2, 2.2]$. $A = \frac{9\pi}{2}$

68. Graph $r = \sin 3\theta$, $0 \le \theta \le \pi/3$ in $[-0.04, 0.92]$ by $[0, 0.56]$. $A = \frac{\pi}{12}$

69. Graph $r = 1 + \cos\theta$ and $r = 1$, $0 \le \theta \le 2\pi$ in $[-2, 2]$ by $[-1.2, 1.2]$. $A = 2 + \frac{\pi}{4}$

70. Graph $r = 2(1 + \sin\theta)$ and $r = 2\sin\theta$, $0 \le \theta \le 2\pi$ in $[-4, 4]$ by $[-0.5, 4]$. $A = 5\pi$

71. $(2 - \sqrt{2})\pi$ **72.** 4π **73.** 8

74. Graph $r = \sin\theta$, $0 \le \theta \le \pi$ in $[-0.85, 0.85]$ by $[0, 1]$. $L = \pi$ **75.** $(\pi+3)/8$

76. Graph $r = \sqrt{1 + \sin 2\pi}$, $0 \le \theta \le 2\pi$ in $[-2.2, 2.2]$ by $[-1.3, 1.3]$. $L = 2\sqrt{2}\pi$

77. Graph $x_1 = t$, $y_1 = t^2 - 1$, $x_2 = x_1\cos(\pi/6) - y_1\sin(\pi/6)$, $y_2 = x_1\sin(\pi/6) + y_1\cos(\pi/6)$, $-3 \le t \le 3$ in $[-6.6, 3]$ by $[-1, 8.4]$. $3x^2 + 2\sqrt{3}xy + y^2 + 2x - 2\sqrt{3}y - 4 = 0$

78. Graph $x_1 = 3\cos t$, $y_1 = 2\sin t$, $x_2 = x_1\cos(\pi/3) - y_1\sin(\pi/3)$, $y_2 = x_1\sin(\pi/3) + y_1\cos(\pi/3)$, $0 \le \theta \le 2\pi$ in $[-4.7, 4.7]$ by $[-2.8, 2.8]$. $31x^2 - 10\sqrt{3}xy + 21y^2 = 144$

79. a) a b) a c) $2a/\pi$

81. We use Fig. 10.9. $\frac{r_{max}-r_{min}}{r_{max}+r_{min}} = \frac{(c+a)-(a-c)}{(c+a)+(a-c)} = \frac{2c}{2a} = \frac{c}{a} = e$.

82. a) $e = \frac{7}{93}$ b) $r = \frac{430000}{93+7\cos\theta}$

CHAPTER 11
VECTORS AND ANALYTIC GEOMETRY IN SPACE

11.1 Vectors in the Plane

1. a) 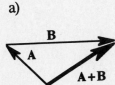 b) 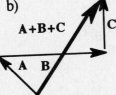 c) 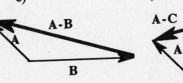 d)

2. a) 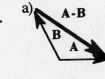 b) 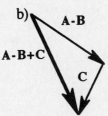 c) 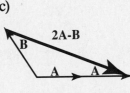 d)

3. 9 and 6   4. 4 and -10 5. 1 and 3   6. 5 and -7

7. 12 and -19 8. -16 and 29

9. $i - 4j$

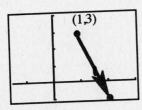

10. $-i + j$

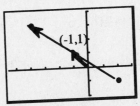

11. $-2i - 3j$

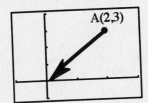

12. 0

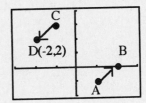

13. $\theta = \frac{\pi}{6}: \frac{\sqrt{3}}{2}i + \frac{1}{2}j$;

$\theta = \frac{2\pi}{3}: -\frac{1}{2}i + \frac{\sqrt{3}}{2}j$

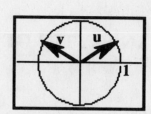

14. $\theta = \frac{\pi}{4}: \frac{\sqrt{2}}{2}i - \frac{\sqrt{2}}{2}j$; $\theta = -\frac{3\pi}{4}: -\frac{\sqrt{2}}{2}i - \frac{\sqrt{2}}{2}j$ **15.** $\frac{\sqrt{3}}{2}i - \frac{1}{2}j$

16. $-\frac{\sqrt{2}}{2}i + \frac{\sqrt{2}}{2}j$ **17.** $\sqrt{13}$ **18.** 5   **19.** 1   **20.** 1

21. 1   **22.** 1   **23.** $\frac{3}{5}i + \frac{4}{5}j$ **24.** $\frac{4}{5}i - \frac{3}{5}j$ **25.** $\frac{12}{13}i - \frac{5}{13}j$

26. $-\frac{15}{17}i + \frac{8}{17}j$ **27.** $\frac{2}{\sqrt{13}}i + \frac{3}{\sqrt{13}}j$ **28.** $\frac{5}{\sqrt{29}}i - \frac{2}{\sqrt{29}}j$

29. $\sqrt{2}\left(\frac{1}{\sqrt{2}}i + \frac{1}{\sqrt{2}}j\right)$ **30.** $\sqrt{13}\left[\frac{2}{\sqrt{13}}i - \frac{3}{\sqrt{13}}j\right]$ **31.** $2\left(\frac{\sqrt{3}}{2}i + \frac{1}{2}j\right)$

32. $\sqrt{13}\left[-\frac{2}{\sqrt{13}}i + \frac{3}{\sqrt{13}}j\right]$ **33.** $13\left[\frac{5}{13}i + \frac{12}{13}j\right]$ **34.** $13\left[-\frac{5}{13}i - \frac{12}{13}j\right]$

35. $\frac{A}{|A|} = \frac{1}{\sqrt{5}}i + \frac{2}{\sqrt{5}}j$; $\frac{B}{|B|} = -\frac{1}{\sqrt{5}}i - \frac{2}{\sqrt{5}}j$ **36.** Both have direction $\frac{1}{\sqrt{5}}[i + 2j]$.

37. $\pm\frac{1}{\sqrt{17}}(i + 4j)$ are unit tangent vectors; $\pm\frac{1}{\sqrt{17}}(4i - j)$ are unit normal vectors.

38. Unit tangent vectors are $\pm\frac{1}{\sqrt{5}}(i + 2j)$; unit normal vectors are $\pm\frac{1}{\sqrt{5}}(2i - j)$.

39. Unit tangent vectors are $\pm\frac{1}{\sqrt{2}}(i - j)$; unit normal vectors are $\pm\frac{1}{\sqrt{2}}(i + j)$.

40. Unit tangent vectors are $\pm\frac{1}{\sqrt{5}}(i + 2j)$; unit normal vectors are $\pm\frac{1}{\sqrt{5}}(2i - j)$.

41. Unit tangent vectors are $\pm\frac{1}{\sqrt{5}}(2i + j)$; unit normal vectors are $\pm\frac{1}{\sqrt{5}}(i - 2j)$.

42. Unit tangent vectors are $\pm\frac{1}{\sqrt{3}}(i + \sqrt{2}j)$; unit normal vectors are $\pm\frac{1}{\sqrt{3}}(\sqrt{2}i - j)$.

43. The slopes are the same.   **44.** Only the zero vector has length 0.

11.2 CARTESIAN (RECTANGULAR) COORDINATES AND VECTORS IN SPACE

1. Line through $(2,3,0)$ parallel to the z-axis.

2. Line through $(-1,2,0)$ parallel to the y-axis.

3. The x-axis

4. Line through $(1,0,6)$ parallel to the z-axis.

5. Circle in xy-plane, center at $(0,0,0)$, radius 2.

6. Circle in plane $z = -2$, center at $(0,0,-2)$, radius 2.

7. Circle in xz-plane, center at $(0,0,0)$, radius 2.

8. Circle in yz-plane, center at $(0,0,0)$, radius 1.

9. Circle in yz-plane, center at $(0,0,0)$, radius 1.

10. Circle in the plane $y = -4$, center at $(0,-4,0)$, radius 3.

11. Circle in xy-plane, center at $(0,0,0)$, radius 4.

12. Circle in xz-plane, center at $(0,0,0)$, radius $\sqrt{3}$.

13. a) The first quadrant in the xy-plane   b) The fourth quadrant in the xy-plane

14. a) Slab parallel to the yz-plane, 1 unit thick, between the planes $x = 0$ and $x = 1$,   b) Square column of side 1, parallel to z-axis,   c) The unit cube in the corner of the first octant.

15. a) The interior and surface of the unit sphere (center at $(0,0,0)$),

    b) All of 3-space <u>but</u> the interior and surface of the unit sphere

16. a) The interior and boundary of the circle $x^2 + y^2 = 1$ in the xy-plane,

    b) The interior and boundary of the circle $x^2 + y^2 = 1$ in the plane $z = 3$,

    c) A cylindrical column with both a) and b) as cross-sections

17. a) The surface of the top half $(z \geq 0)$ of the unit sphere,   b) The interior and surface of the top half of the unit sphere

18. a) The line $y = x$ in the xy-plane,   b) The plane $y = x$

19. a) $x = 3$,   b) $y = -1$,   c) $z = -2$ **20.** a) $x = 3$,   b) $y = -1$,   c) $z = 2$

21. a) $z = 1$,   b) $x = 3$,   c) $y = -1$

22. a) $x^2 + y^2 = 4$, $z = 0$;   b) $y^2 + z^2 = 4$, $x = 0$;   c) $x^2 + z^2 = 4$, $y = 0$

23. a) $x^2 + (y-2)^2 = 4$, $z = 0$;   b) $(y-2)^2 + z^2 = 4$, $x = 0$;   c) $x^2 + z^2 = 4$, $y = 2$

24. a) $(x+3)^2 + (y-4)^2 = 1$, $z = 1$;   b) $(y-4)^2 + (z-1)^2 = 1$, $x = -3$;
    c) $(x+3)^2 + (z-1)^2 = 1$, $y = 4$

25. a) $y = 3$, $z = -1$;   b) $x = 1$, $z = -1$,   c) $x = 1$, $y = 3$

26. $y = 1$ **27.** $x^2 + y^2 = 16$, $z = 3$ **28.** $x^2 + y^2 = 3$, $z = 0$

29. $0 \leq z \leq 1$ **30.** $0 \leq x \leq 2$, $0 \leq y \leq 2$, $0 \leq z \leq 2$

31. $z \leq 0$ **32.** $x^2 + y^2 + z^2 = 1$, $z \geq 0$

33. a) $(x-1)^2 + (y-1)^2 + (z-1)^2 < 1$;   b) $(x-1)^2 + (y-1)^2 + (z-1)^2 > 1$

34. $1 \leq x^2 + y^2 + z^2 \leq 4$ **35.** Length 3, direction $\frac{2}{3}\boldsymbol{i} + \frac{1}{3}\boldsymbol{j} - \frac{2}{3}\boldsymbol{k}$

36. 7, $\frac{3}{7}\boldsymbol{i} - \frac{6}{7}\boldsymbol{j} + \frac{2}{7}\boldsymbol{k}$ **37.** 9, $\frac{1}{9}\boldsymbol{i} + \frac{4}{9}\boldsymbol{j} - \frac{8}{9}\boldsymbol{k}$ **38.** 11, $\frac{9}{11}\boldsymbol{i} - \frac{2}{11}\boldsymbol{j} + \frac{6}{11}\boldsymbol{k}$

39. 5, $\boldsymbol{k}$ **40.** 6, $\boldsymbol{i}$ **41.** $4, -\boldsymbol{j}$ **42.** 1, $\frac{3}{5}\boldsymbol{i} + \frac{4}{5}\boldsymbol{k}$

43. $\frac{5}{12}$, $-\left(\frac{4}{5}\right)\boldsymbol{i} + \left(\frac{3}{5}\right)\boldsymbol{j}$ **44.** 1, $\frac{1}{\sqrt{2}}\boldsymbol{i} - \frac{1}{\sqrt{2}}\boldsymbol{k}$

45. $\frac{1}{\sqrt{2}}$, $\left(\frac{1}{\sqrt{3}}\right)\boldsymbol{i} - \left(\frac{1}{\sqrt{3}}\right)\boldsymbol{j} - \left(\frac{1}{\sqrt{3}}\right)\boldsymbol{k}$ **46.** 1, $\frac{1}{\sqrt{3}}\boldsymbol{i} + \frac{1}{\sqrt{3}}\boldsymbol{j} + \frac{1}{\sqrt{3}}\boldsymbol{k}$

47. a) 3,   b) $\frac{2}{3}\boldsymbol{i} + \frac{2}{3}\boldsymbol{j} - \frac{1}{3}\boldsymbol{k}$,   c) $(2, 2, \frac{1}{2})$

48. a) $5\sqrt{2}$,   b) $\frac{3}{5\sqrt{2}}\boldsymbol{i} + \frac{4}{5\sqrt{2}}\boldsymbol{j} - \frac{5}{5\sqrt{2}}\boldsymbol{k}$,   c) $(\frac{1}{2}, 3, \frac{5}{2})$

49. a) 7,   b) $\frac{3}{7}\boldsymbol{i} - \frac{6}{7}\boldsymbol{j} + \frac{2}{7}\boldsymbol{k}$,   c) $(\frac{5}{2}, 1, 6)$

50. a) $\sqrt{3}$,   b) $-\frac{1}{\sqrt{3}}\boldsymbol{i} - \frac{1}{\sqrt{3}}\boldsymbol{j} - \frac{1}{\sqrt{3}}\boldsymbol{k}$,   c) $(\frac{5}{2}, \frac{7}{2}, \frac{9}{2})$

51. a) $2\sqrt{3}$,   b) $\frac{1}{\sqrt{3}}\boldsymbol{i} - \frac{1}{\sqrt{3}}\boldsymbol{j} - \frac{1}{\sqrt{3}}\boldsymbol{k}$,   c) $(1, -1, -1)$

52. a) $\sqrt{38}$,   b) $-\frac{5}{\sqrt{38}}\boldsymbol{i} - \frac{3}{\sqrt{38}}\boldsymbol{j} + \frac{2}{\sqrt{38}}\boldsymbol{k}$,   c) $(\frac{5}{2}, \frac{3}{2}, -1)$

53. a) $2\boldsymbol{i}$,   b) $-\sqrt{3}\boldsymbol{k}$,   c) $\frac{3}{10}\boldsymbol{j} + \frac{4}{10}\boldsymbol{k}$,   d) $6\boldsymbol{i} - 2\boldsymbol{j} + 3\boldsymbol{k}$

54. a) $-7\boldsymbol{j}$,   b) $-\frac{3\sqrt{2}}{5}\boldsymbol{i} - \frac{4\sqrt{2}}{5}\boldsymbol{k}$,   c) $\frac{1}{4}\boldsymbol{i} - \frac{1}{3}\boldsymbol{j} - \boldsymbol{k}$,   d) $\frac{a}{\sqrt{2}}\boldsymbol{i} + \frac{a}{\sqrt{3}}\boldsymbol{j} - \frac{a}{\sqrt{6}}\boldsymbol{k}$

55. $\frac{84}{13}\boldsymbol{i} - \frac{35}{13}\boldsymbol{k}$ **56.** $\sqrt{\frac{5}{3}}\boldsymbol{i} + \sqrt{\frac{5}{3}}\boldsymbol{j} + \sqrt{\frac{5}{3}}\boldsymbol{k}$ **57.** $-\frac{10}{7}\boldsymbol{i} + \frac{15}{7}\boldsymbol{j} - \frac{30}{7}\boldsymbol{k}$

58. $-\sqrt{3}\boldsymbol{i} + \sqrt{3}\boldsymbol{j} + \sqrt{3}\boldsymbol{k}$

59. a) $C(-2,0,2)$, radius $= \sqrt{8} = 2\sqrt{2}$,   b) $C(-\frac{1}{2}, -\frac{1}{2}, -\frac{1}{2})$, radius $= \frac{\sqrt{21}}{2}$,

   c) $C(\sqrt{2}, \sqrt{2}, -\sqrt{2})$, radius $= \sqrt{2}$,   d) $C(0, -\frac{1}{3}, \frac{1}{3})$, radius $= \frac{\sqrt{29}}{3}$

60. a) $(x-1)^2 + (y-2)^2 + (z-3)^2 = 14$;   b) $x^2 + (y+1)^2 + (z-5)^2 = 4$,

   c) $(x+2)^2 + y^2 + z^2 = 3$,   d) $x^2 + (y+7)^2 + z^2 = 49$

61. Center $(-2,0,2)$, radius $\sqrt{8}$ **62.** Center $(-\frac{1}{4}, -\frac{1}{4}, -\frac{1}{4})$, radius $\frac{5}{4}\sqrt{3}$

63. Center $(0,0,1)$, radius 1   **64.** Center $(0, -\frac{1}{3}, \frac{1}{3})$, radius $\frac{\sqrt{29}}{3}$

65. a) $x^2 + z^2 = 5$ in the plane $y = -2$, $x^2 + z^2 = 9$ in the plane $y = 0$, $x^2 + z^2 = 8$
   in the plane $y = 1$

   b) the areas are 5π, 9π, 8π

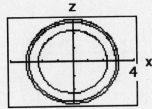

66. a) $y^2 + z^2 = 8$ in $x = 2$, $y^2 + z^2 = 9$ in $x = 0$, $y^2 + z^2 = 5$ in $x = 2$

   b) areas in 8π, 9π, 5π

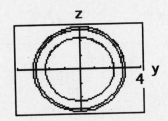

67. a) In $z = 2$, $(x+2)^2 + y^2 = 8$; in $z = 4$, $(x+2)^2 + y^2 = 4$

   b)

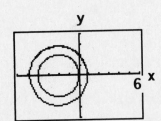

68. a) In $x = -2$, $y^2 + (z-2)^2 = 8$; in $x = 0$, $y^2 + (z-2)^2 = 4$

b)

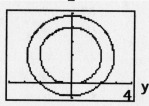

69. a) $\sqrt{y^2 + z^2}$, b) $\sqrt{x^2 + z^2}$, c) $\sqrt{x^2 + y^2}$ **70.** a) z, b) x, c) y

11.3 DOT PRODUCTS

	$A \cdot B$	$|A|$	$|B|$	$\cos\theta$	$|B|\cos\theta$	$\mathrm{Proj}_A B = \dfrac{A \cdot B}{A \cdot A} A$
1.	10	$\sqrt{13}$	$\sqrt{26}$	$\frac{10}{13\sqrt{2}}$	$\frac{10}{\sqrt{13}}$	$\frac{10}{13}[3i + 2j]$
2.	0	1	$\sqrt{34}$	0	0	$\mathbf{0}$
3.	4	$\sqrt{14}$	2	$\frac{2}{\sqrt{14}}$	$\frac{4}{\sqrt{14}}$	$\frac{2}{7}[3i - 2j - k]$
4.	0	$\sqrt{53}$	1	0	0	$\mathbf{0}$
5.	2	$\sqrt{34}$	$\sqrt{3}$	$\frac{2}{\sqrt{3}\sqrt{34}}$	$\frac{2}{\sqrt{34}}$	$\frac{1}{17}[5j - 3k]$
6.	0	1	$\sqrt{\frac{3}{2}}$	0	0	$\mathbf{0}$
7.	$\sqrt{3} - \sqrt{2}$	$\sqrt{2}$	3	$\frac{\sqrt{3}-\sqrt{2}}{3\sqrt{2}}$	$\frac{\sqrt{3}-\sqrt{2}}{\sqrt{2}}$	$\frac{\sqrt{3}-\sqrt{2}}{2}[-i + j]$
8.	2	$\sqrt{2}$	$\sqrt{3}$	$\sqrt{\frac{2}{3}}$	$\sqrt{2}$	$i + k$
9.	-25	5	5	-1	-5	$-2i + 4j - \sqrt{5}k$
10.	$\sqrt{17} - 10$	$\sqrt{26}$	11	$\frac{\sqrt{17}-10}{11\sqrt{26}}$	$\frac{\sqrt{17}-10}{\sqrt{26}}$	$\frac{\sqrt{17}-10}{26}[-5i + j]$
11.	25	15	5	$\frac{1}{3}$	$\frac{5}{3}$	$\frac{1}{9}[10i + 11j - 2k]$
12.	13	15	3	$\frac{13}{45}$	$\frac{13}{15}$	$\frac{13}{225}[2i + 10j - 11k]$

13. $[\frac{3}{2}i + \frac{3}{2}j] + [-\frac{3}{2}i + \frac{3}{2}j + 4k]$ **14.** $[\frac{1}{2}i + \frac{1}{2}j] + [-\frac{1}{2}i + \frac{1}{2}j + k]$

15. $\frac{14}{3}[i + 2j - k] + \frac{2}{3}[5i - 8j - 11k]$ **16.** Yes

17. $x + 2y = 4$ **18.** $x - y = -3$

19. $2x + y = 0$

20. $2x - 3y = -8$

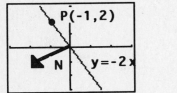

21. $2\sqrt{10}$ **22.** $6/\sqrt{10}$ **23.** $\sqrt{2}$ **24.** $\sqrt{5}$

25. $A \cdot B = A \cdot C = B \cdot C = 0$

26. $\text{proj}_A D = \frac{1}{3}(i - j + k)$, $\text{proj}_B D = j + k$), $\text{proj}_C D = \frac{1}{3}(2i + j - k)$

27. $i \cdot j = i \cdot k$ but $j \neq k$ **28.** v_1 and v_2 must have the same length

29. $< A = 71.068°$, $< B = 37.864°$, $< C = 71.068°$

30. $73.209°$ **31.** $35.264°$ **32.** $54.736°$ **33.** $-5\ N \cdot m$

34. $6 \times 10^7\ N \cdot m$ **35.** $3018.838\ N \cdot m$ **36.** $2{,}000{,}000\ N \cdot m$

37. $45°$ or $135°$ **38.** $142.125°$ **39.** $59.156°$ **40.** $45°$, $90°$

41. $63.4°$ at $x = 0$ and $83.7°$ at $x = -1.41$

42. $86.36°$ at $x = 0.386$ and $83.39°$ at $x = 1.962$

43. $|A|^2 + |B|^2 - |C|^2 = a_1^2 + a_2^2 + a_3^2 + b_1^2 + b_2^2 + b_3^2 - [(b_1 - a_1)^2 + (b_2 - a_2)^2 + (b_3 - a_3)^2] = 2(a_1 b_1 + a_2 b_2 + a_3 b_3)$.

11.4 CROSS PRODUCTS

1. $A \times B$: length $= 3$, direction $= [\frac{2}{3}i + \frac{1}{3}j + \frac{2}{3}k]$; $B \times A$: length $= 3$, direction $= -[\frac{2}{3}i + \frac{1}{3}j + \frac{2}{3}k]$

2. $A \times B = 5k$, length 5, direction k; $B \times A = -5k$, length 5, direction $-k$

3. $A \times B = B \times A = 0$, both have length 0 and no direction

4. $A \times B = B \times A = 0$, length 0, no direction

5. $A \times B$: length $= 6$, direction $= -k$; $B \times A$ has same length, opposite direction

6. $A \times B = i - j + k$, length $\sqrt{3}$, direction $\frac{1}{\sqrt{3}}(i - j + k)$; $B \times A$ has length $\sqrt{3}$, opposite direction

7. $A \times B$ has length $6\sqrt{5}$, direction $\frac{1}{\sqrt{5}}(i - 2k)$; $B \times A$ has same length, opposite direction

8. $A \times B = -2i - 2j + 2k$, length $2\sqrt{3}$, direction $\frac{1}{\sqrt{3}}(-i - j + k)$; $B \times A$ has length $2\sqrt{3}$, opposite direction

9. $A \times B = k$

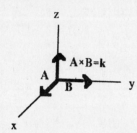

10. $A \times B = -i + k$

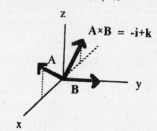

11. $A \times B = i - j + k$

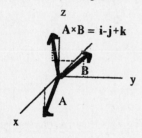

12. $A \times B = 5k$

13. $A \times B = 3i - j$

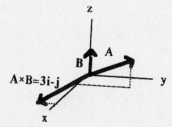

14. $A \times B = 2i - j + 2k$

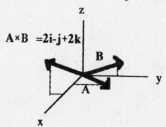

15. a) $\pm(8i + 4j + 4k)$,   b) $2\sqrt{6}$,   c) $\pm\frac{1}{\sqrt{6}}(2i + j + k)$

16. a) $\pm(6i + 4j - 3k)$,   b) $\frac{\sqrt{61}}{2}$,   c) $\pm\frac{1}{\sqrt{61}}(6i + 4j - 3k)$

17. a) $\pm(-i + j)$,   b) $1/\sqrt{2}$,   c) $\pm\frac{1}{\sqrt{2}}(-i + j)$

18. a) $\pm(2i + 3j + k$, b) $\frac{1}{2}\sqrt{14}$, c) $\pm\frac{2}{\sqrt{14}}(2i + 3j + k)$

19. a) none b) A and C **20.** a) $A \perp B$, $A \perp C$, $B \perp C$, b) none

21. $2i + 4j + 7k, 0, 0$ **22.** Yes, $(A \times B) \perp A$ and $(A \times B) \perp B$.

23. a) $\frac{A \cdot B}{B \cdot B} B$, b) $A \times B$, c) $\frac{\sqrt{A \cdot A}}{\sqrt{B \cdot B}} B$, d) $(A \times B) \times C$, e) $(B \times C) \times A$

24. $i \times i = i \times 7i$ but $i \neq 7i$

25. 16.383 foot-pounds **26.** 16.383 foot-pounds

27. $-$ **30.**

	$A \times B$	$(A \times B) \cdot C$	$B \times C$	$(B \times C) \cdot A$	$C \times A$	$(C \times A) \cdot B$, Vol.
27.	$4k$	8	$4i$	8	$4j$	8, 8
28.	$i + 4j + 3k$	4	$3i + 4j + 5k$	4	$i - k$	4, 4
29.	$i - 2j - 4k$	-7	$-2i - 3j + k$	-7	$-2i + 4j + k$	-7, 7
30.	$-i + 3j + k$	8	$4(i - j - k)$	8	$-6i + 2j - 2k$	8, 8

11.5 LINES AND PLANES IN SPACE

1. $x = 3 + 1 \cdot t, y = -4 + 1 \cdot t, z = -1 + 1 \cdot t$

2. $x = 2 + 4t, y = 3 - 2t, z = -1 + 3t$ **3.** $x = 1 - 2t,\ y = 2 - 2t,\ z = -1 + 2t$

4. $x = -2 + t,\ y = t,\ z = 3 - t$ **5.** $x = 1,\ y = 2 - t,\ z = -t$

6. $x = 3 + (e - 3)t,\ y = \pi + (\sqrt{2} - \pi)t,\ z = -2 + 9t$

7. $x = 0,\ y = 2t,\ z = t$ **8.** $x = 3 + 2t,\ y = -2 - t,\ z = 1 + 3t$

9. $x = 1,\ y = 1,\ z = 1 + t$ **10.** $x = 2 + 3t,\ y = 4 + 7t,\ z = 5 - 5t$

11. $x = t,\ y = -7 + 2t,\ z = 2t$ **12.** $x = 2 - 2t,\ y = 3 + 4t,\ z = -2t$

13. $x = t,\ y = 0,\ z = 0$ **14.** $x = 0,\ y = 0,\ z = t$

15. $x = t, y = t, z = t, 0 \leq t \leq 1,$

$t = 0$ corresponds to $(0, 0, 0)$

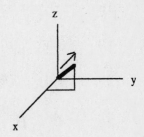

16. $x = t, \ y = 0, \ z = 0,$

$0 \leq t \leq 1$

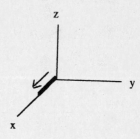

17. $x = 1, \ y = t, \ z = 0,$

$0 \leq t \leq 1$

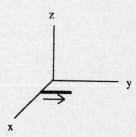

18. $x = 1, \ y = 1, \ z = t,$

$0 \leq t \leq 1$

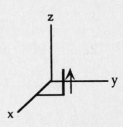

19. $x = 0, \ y = -1 + 2t, \ z = 1,$

$0 \leq t \leq 1$

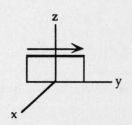

20. $x = 3 - 3t,\ y = 2t,\ z = 0,$
$\quad 0 \le t \le 1$

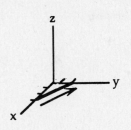

21. $x = 2 - t,\ y = 2,\ z = -2t,$
$\quad 0 \le t \le 1$

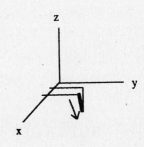

22. $x = 1 - t,\ y = -1 + 3t,$
$\quad z = -2 + 3t,\ 0 \le t \le 1$

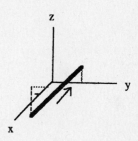

23. $3x - 2y - z = -3$ **24.** $3x + y + z = 5$ **25.** $7x - 5y - 4z = 6$

26. $x + 3y - z = 9$ **27.** $x + 3y + 4z = 34$ **28.** $x - 2y + z = 6$

29. $\sqrt{120}$ **30.** 3 **31.** 0 **32.** $\sqrt{\frac{14}{3}}$ **33.** 3

34. $\frac{6}{7}$ **35.** $\frac{19}{5}$ **36.** $\frac{8}{3}$ **37.** $\frac{5}{3}$ **38.** $\frac{3}{\sqrt{2}}$

39. $\left(\frac{3}{2}, -\frac{3}{2}, \frac{1}{2}\right)$ **40.** $\left(2, -\frac{20}{7}, \frac{27}{7}\right)$ **41.** $(1, 1, 0)$

42. $(-4, -2, -5)$ **43.** $45°$ **44.** $90°$ **45.** $101.096°$

46. $54.736°$ **47.** $47.124°$ **48.** $42.025°$

49. $x = -t,\ y = 2 + t,\ z = -1$ **50.** $x = 1 + 14t,\ y = 2t,\ y = 15t$

51. $x = 4,\ y = 1 + 6t,\ z = 3t$ **52.** $x = 2t,\ y = -\frac{11}{2} + 5t,\ z = -1 + 4t$

53. $4x - y - 12z = -34$ **54.** $-3x + 8y + z = 18$

55. $(1, -1, 0), (0, -\frac{1}{2}, -\frac{3}{2}), (-1, 0, -3)$

56. $x = \sqrt{3}t, \; y = t, \; z = 3$ **57.** No, $\boldsymbol{N} \cdot (-2\boldsymbol{i} + 5\boldsymbol{j} - 3\boldsymbol{k}) \neq 0$

58. parallel if $\frac{A_1}{A_2} = \frac{B_1}{B_2} = \frac{C_1}{C_2}$; perpendicular if $A_1 A_2 + B_1 B_2 + C_1 C_2 = 0$

11.6 SURFACES IN SPACE

1.   **2**   **3.**

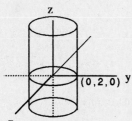

$x^2 + y^2 = 4$

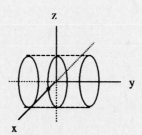

$x^2 + z^2 = 4$

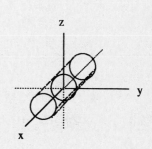

$y^2 + z^2 = 1$

4.   **5.**   **6.**

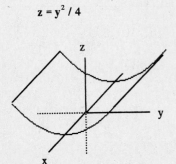

$z = y^2 / 4$

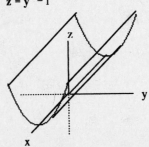

$z = y^2 - 1$

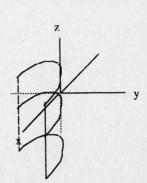

$x = y^2$

7.

$z = 4 - x^2$

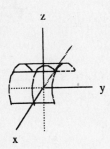

8.

$x = 4 - y^2$

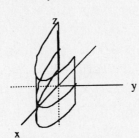

9.

$y = x^2$

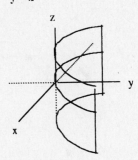

10.

$y = x^2 - 2$

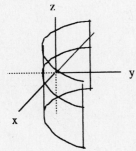

11.

$y^2 + 4z^2 = 16$

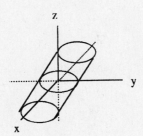

12.

$4x^2 + y^2 = 36$

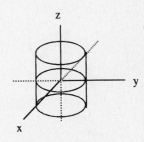

13.

$z^2 + 4y^2 = 9$

14.

$y^2 - z^2 = 4$

15.

$z^2 - y^2 = 1$

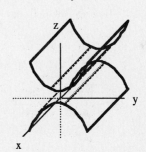

16.

$yz = 1$

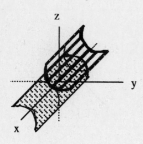

17.

$9x^2 + y^2 + z^2 = 9$

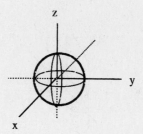

18.

$4x^2 + 4y^2 + z^2 = 16$

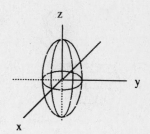

19.

$x^2 + y^2 + z^2 = 4$

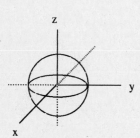

20.

$9x^2 + 4y^2 + z^2 = 36$

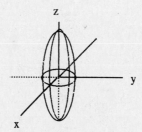

21.

$4x^2 + 9y^2 + 4z^2 = 36$

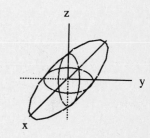

22.

$9x^2 + 4y^2 + 36z^2 = 36$

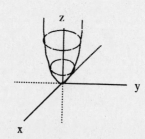

23.

$x^2 + y^2 = z$

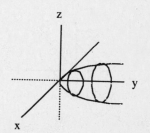

24.

25.

$$x^2 + 4y^2 = z$$

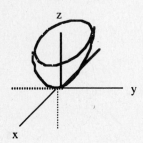

26.

$$x^2 + 9y^2 = z$$

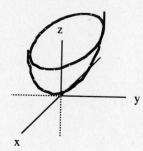

27.

$$z = 8 - x^2 - y^2$$

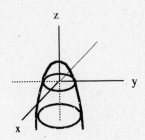

28.

$$z = 18 - x^2 - 9y^2$$

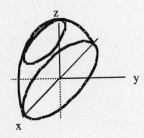

29.

$$x = 4 - 4y^2 - z^2$$

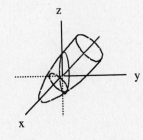

30.

$$y = 1 - x^2 - z^2$$

31.

$$z = x^2 + y^2 + 1$$

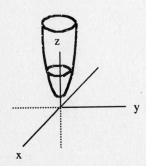

32.

$$z = 4x^2 + y^2 - 4$$

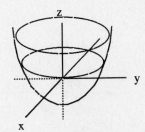

33.

$$x^2 + y^2 = z^2$$

34.

$$y^2 + z^2 = x^2$$

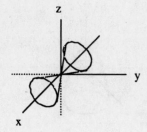

35.

$$x^2 + z^2 = y^2$$

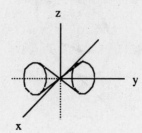

36.

$$4x^2 + 9y^2 = z^2$$

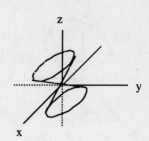

37.

$$9x^2 + 4y^2 = 36z^2$$

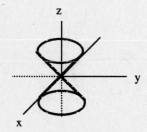

38.

$$4x^2 + 9z^2 = 9y^2$$

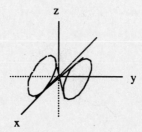

39.

$$x^2 + y^2 - z^2 = 1$$

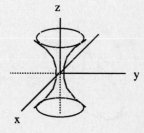

40.

$$y^2 + z^2 - x^2 = 1$$

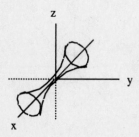

41.

$$(y^2/4) + (z^2/9) - (x^2/4) = 1$$

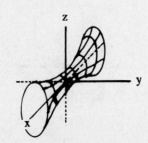

42.

$$(x^2/4) + (y^2/4) - (z^2/9) = 1$$

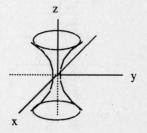

43.

$(x^2/4) + y^2 - z^2 = 1$

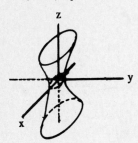

44.

$z^2 - x^2 - y^2 = 1$

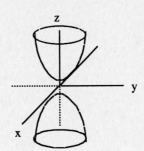

45.

$z^2 - (x^2/4) - y^2 = 1$

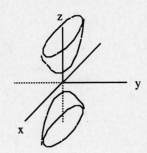

46.

$(y^2/4) - (x^2/4) - z^2 = 1$

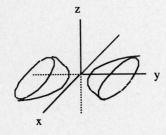

47.

$x^2 - y^2 - (z^2/4) = 1$

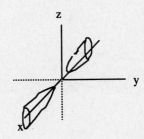

48.

$(x^2/4) - (z^2/4) - y^2 = 1$

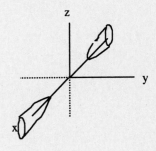

49.

$y^2 - x^2 = z$

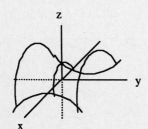

50.

$x^2 - y^2 = z$

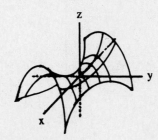

51.   **52.**

Ellipsoid $9x^2 + 36y^2 + 4z^2 = 36$ Paraboloid $3y^2 + 3z^2 = 2x$

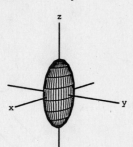   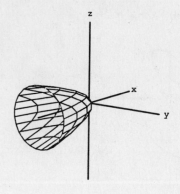

53.

Cone $9x^2 + 36z^2 = 4y^2$

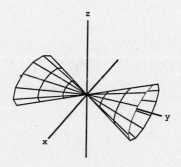

54.

Hyperboloid of two sheets $16y^2 - 9x^2 - 144z^2 = 144$

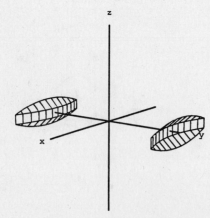

55.

Paraboloid $9x^2 + 16z^2 = 72y$

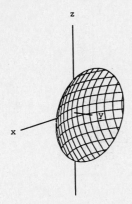

56.

Hyperboloid of one sheet - $4x^2 + 9y^2 + 36z^2 = 36$

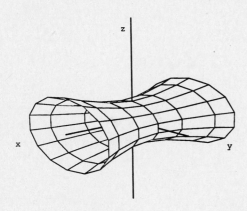

57.

Hyperbolic paraboloid $z^2 - 9y^2 = 3x$

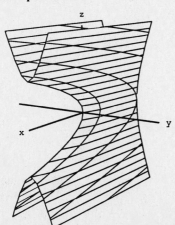

58.

Ellipsoid $36x^2 + 4y^2 + 9z^2 = 36$

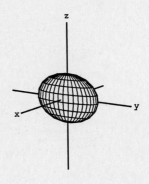

59.

Paraboloid $2x^2 + 2z^2 = 3y$

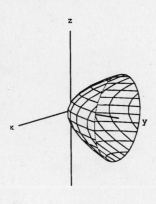

60.

Paraboloid $12y^2 + 3z^2 = 16x$

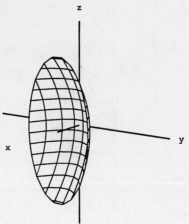

61.

Hyperboloid of two sheets $9x^2 - 36y^2 - 4z^2 = 36$

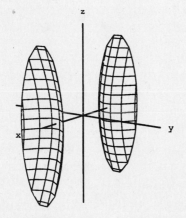

62.

Hyperbolic paraboloid $x^2 - 4z^2 = 2y$

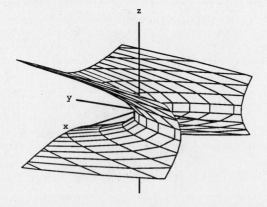

63.

Hyperboloid of one sheet $25x^2 - 100y^2 + 4z^2 = 100$

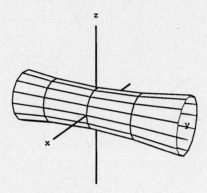

64.

Cone $16y^2 + z^2 = 4x^2$

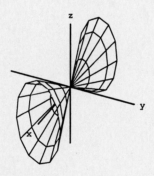

65.   66.

$z = y^2$ $z = 1 - y^2$

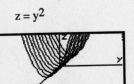   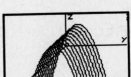

67.

$$z = x^2 + y^2$$

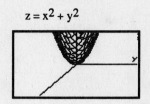

68.

$$z = x^2 + 2y^2$$

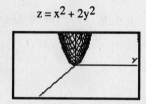

69.

$$z = \sqrt{1 - x^2}$$

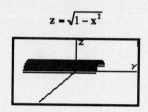

70.

$$z = \sqrt{1 - (y^2 / 4)}$$

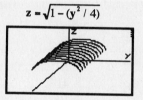

71.

$$z = \sqrt{x^2 + 2y^2 + 4}$$

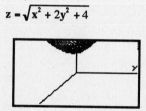

72. Source: 12 inches from the center; patient: 12 inches from the center on the other side.

11.7 CYLINDRICAL AND SPHERICAL COORDINATES

1. – 10.

	Rectangular (x,y,z)	Cylindrical (r,θ,z)	Spherical (ρ,ϕ,θ)
1.	$(0,0,0)$	$(0,0^*,0)$	$(0,0^*,0^*)$
2.	$(1,0,0)$	$(1,0,0)$	$(1,\pi/2,0)$
3.	$(0,1,0)$	$(1,\pi/2,0)$	$(1,\pi/2,\pi/2)$
4.	$(0,0,1)$	$(0,0^*,1)$	$(1,0,0^*)$
5.	$(1,0,0)$	$(1,0,0)$	$(1,\pi/2,0)$
6.	$(\sqrt{2},0,1)$	$(\sqrt{2},0,1)$	$(\sqrt{3},\cos^{-1}(1/\sqrt{3}),0)$
7.	$(0,1,1)$	$(1,\pi/2,1)$	$(\sqrt{2},\pi/4,\pi/2)$
8.	$(0,-3/2,\sqrt{3}/2)$	$(3/2,-\pi/2,\sqrt{3}/2)$	$(\sqrt{3},\pi/3,-\pi/2)$
9.	$(0,-2\sqrt{2},0)$	$(2\sqrt{2},3\pi/2,0)$	$(2\sqrt{2},\pi/2,3\pi/2)$
10.	$(0,0,-\sqrt{2})$	$(0,0^*,-\sqrt{2})$	$(\sqrt{2},\pi,3\pi/2)$

0^* can be any angle

11. Rectangular: $x=0$, $y=0$; spherical: $\phi=0$ or $\phi=\pi$; z-axis

12. Cylindrical: $r=\sqrt{5}$; spherical: $\rho\sin\varphi=\sqrt{5}$, circular cylinder

13. Rectangular: $z=0$; cylindrical: $z=0$; spherical: $\phi=\pi/2$; the xy-plane

14. Cylindrical: $z=-2$; spherical: $\rho\cos\varphi=-2$; the plane $z=-2$

15. Rectangular, cylindrical: $z=3$; the plane $z=3$

16. Cylindrical: $r=z$; spherical: $\varphi=\pi/4$; a cone

17. Rectangular: $x=0$; cylindrical: $\theta=\pi/2$ or $3\pi/2$; the yz-plane

18. Rectangular: $x^2+y^2=z^2$; cylindrical: $r^2=z^2$; a cone

19. Cylindrical: $r^2+z^2=4$; spherical: $\rho=2$; sphere of radius 2, center at origin

20. Spherical: $\rho=\cos\varphi$; cylindrical: $(z-\frac{1}{2})^2=\frac{1}{4}-r^2$; a sphere

21. Rectangular: $x^2+y^2+z^2=2y$; cylindrical: $r^2+z^2=2r\sin\theta$; a sphere

22. Rectangular: $x^2 + y^2 + z^2 = 6z$; cylindrical: $r^2 + z^2 = 6z$; a sphere

23. Rectangular: $y = 1$; spherical: $\rho \sin \varphi \sin \theta = 1$; the plane $y = 1$

24. Rectangular: $x = -3$; spherical: $\rho \sin \varphi \cos \theta = -3$; the plane $x = -3$

25. Spherical: $\rho = 2 \cos \varphi$, $\pi/4 < \varphi$; cylindrical: $r^2 = 2z - z^2$, $0 \le z \le 1$; lower half of a sphere

26. Spherical: $\rho = \sqrt{3}$, $\pi/3 \le \varphi \le \pi/2$; cylindrical: $z = 3 - r^2$, $0 \le z \le \sqrt{3}/2$; the upper half of a sphere with its "top" sliced off.

27. Rectangular: $x^2 + y^2 + z^2 = 4$, $1 \le z \le 2$; cylindrical: $r^2 + z^2 = 4$, $1 \le z \le 2$; top third of a sphere

28. Rectangular: $x^2 + y^2 + z^2 = 4$, $z \le -\sqrt{2}$; spherical: $\rho = 2$, $3\pi/4 \le \varphi \le \pi$; bottom part of a sphere

29. Rectangular: $x^2 + y^2 = 3z^2$, $0 \le z \le 1$; cylindrical: $r^2 = 3z^2$, $0 \le z \le 1$; truncated top half of a cone

30. Rectangular: $z = 0$, $x^2 + y^2 \le 7$; cylindrical: $r^2 \le 7$, $z = 0$; the interior and boundary of a circle in the xy-plane

31. Right circular cylinder generated by $x^2 + y^2 = 16$

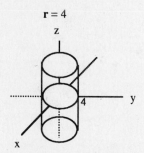

32. A sphere of radius 1, center at $(0,0,0)$

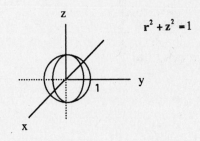

33. Right circular cylinder generated by the cardioid $r = 1 - \cos \theta$

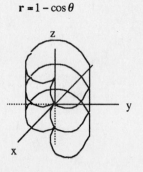

34. A cylinder generated by the circle $(x - 1)^2 + y^2 = 1$

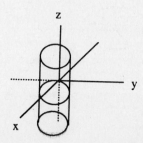

35. Circle of radius 2, center
at $(0, 0, 3)$,
parallel to the xy-plane

$r = 2, z = 3$

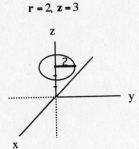

36. The intersection of the plane
$\theta = \pi/6$ and the upper nappe
of the cone $z = x^2 + y^2$

$\theta = \pi/6, z = r$

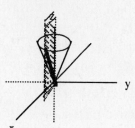

37. A spiral up the side of
the cylinder $r = 3$

$r = 3, \quad z = \theta/2$

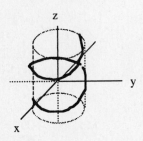

38. A spiral around the cylinder
$x^2 + y^2 = 1$

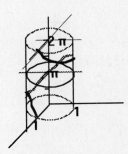

39. A circle in the xy-plane

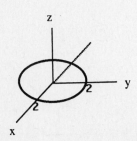

40. A circle of radius $3\sqrt{2}$
in the plane $z = 3\sqrt{2}$

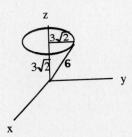

41. The intersection of the upper nappe of the cone $\varphi = \pi/4$ and the plane $\theta = \pi/4$; intersecting rays

42. The intersection of the yz-plane and the lower nappe of a cone

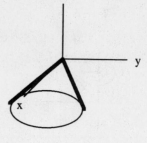

43. Circle in yz-plane: $(y-2)^2 + z^2 = 4$

44. The torus generated by revolving the circle $(y - \frac{1}{2})^2 + z^2 = \frac{1}{4}$ about the z-axis

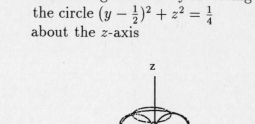

45. There will by symmetry about the z-axis. In the yz-plane, $\rho = \cos\varphi \Rightarrow$ $\rho^2 = \rho\cos\varphi \Rightarrow y^2 + z^2 = z$ or, $y^2 + (z - \frac{1}{2})^2 = \frac{1}{4}$. When revolved about the z-axis, this becomes a sphere.

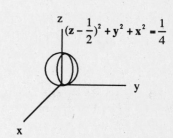

$(z - \frac{1}{2})^2 + y^2 + x^2 = \frac{1}{4}$

46. In the yz-plane this is half the cardioid $r = 1 - \cos\varphi$; revolved about the x-axis, it resembles an apple.

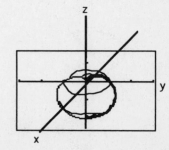

PRACTICE EXERCISES, CHAPTER 11

1.

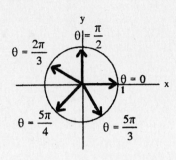

2. a) $\frac{1}{\sqrt{2}}\mathbf{i} - \frac{1}{\sqrt{2}}\mathbf{j}$;   b) $-\frac{\sqrt{3}}{2}\mathbf{i} - \frac{1}{2}\mathbf{j}$

3. tangents: $\pm\frac{1}{\sqrt{5}}(\mathbf{i} + 2\mathbf{j})$; normals: $\pm\frac{1}{\sqrt{5}}(2\mathbf{i} - \mathbf{j})$

4. tangents: $\pm\frac{1}{5}(4\mathbf{i} - 3\mathbf{j})$; normals: $\pm\frac{1}{5}(3\mathbf{i} + 4\mathbf{j})$

5. $2, (1/\sqrt{2})(\mathbf{i} + \mathbf{j})$ 6. $\sqrt{2}, \frac{-1}{\sqrt{2}}(\mathbf{i} + \mathbf{j})$ 7. $7, (1/7)(2\mathbf{i} - 3\mathbf{j} + 6\mathbf{k})$

8. $\sqrt{2}, \frac{1}{\sqrt{6}}(\mathbf{i} + 2\mathbf{j} - \mathbf{k})$ 9. $(2/\sqrt{33})(4\mathbf{i} - \mathbf{j} + 4\mathbf{k})$ 10. $-3\mathbf{i} - 4\mathbf{k}$

11. $|\mathbf{A}| = \sqrt{2}, |\mathbf{B}| = 3, \mathbf{A} \cdot \mathbf{B} = 3 = \mathbf{B} \cdot \mathbf{A}, \mathbf{A} \times \mathbf{B} = -2\mathbf{i} + 2\mathbf{j} - \mathbf{k}, \mathbf{B} \times \mathbf{A} = 2\mathbf{i} - 2\mathbf{j} + \mathbf{k}, |\mathbf{A} \times \mathbf{B}| = 3, \theta = \pi/4, |\mathbf{B}| \cos\theta = 3/\sqrt{2}, \text{proj}_\mathbf{A}\mathbf{B} = \frac{3}{2}(\mathbf{i} + \mathbf{j})$

12. $|\mathbf{A}| = 3\sqrt{3}, |\mathbf{B}| = \sqrt{14}, \mathbf{A} \cdot \mathbf{B} = \mathbf{B} \cdot \mathbf{A} = 6, \mathbf{A} \times \mathbf{B} = 5\mathbf{i} - 14\mathbf{j} - 11\mathbf{k} = -\mathbf{A} \times \mathbf{B}, |\mathbf{A} \times \mathbf{B}| = \sqrt{342}, \theta = 72.025°, |\mathbf{B}| \cos\theta = \frac{2}{\sqrt{3}}, \text{proj}_\mathbf{A}\mathbf{B} = \frac{2}{9}(5\mathbf{i} + \mathbf{j} + \mathbf{k})$

13. $(4/3)(2\mathbf{i} + \mathbf{j} - \mathbf{k}) - (1/3)(5\mathbf{i} + \mathbf{j} + 11\mathbf{k})$

14. $-\frac{1}{5}(\mathbf{i} - 2\mathbf{j}) + \frac{1}{5}(6\mathbf{i} + 3\mathbf{j} + 5\mathbf{k})$.

15.   **16.**

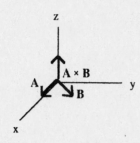   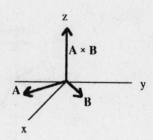

17. 3   **18.** 2   **19.** $\sqrt{2}$ **20.** $\sqrt{14}$ **21.** $2x + y - z = 3$

22. $x - 2y + 3z = -13$ **23.** $-9x + y + 7z = 4$ **24.** $x + y + z = 1$

25. $x = 1 - 3t, y = 2, z = 3 + 7t$ **26.** $(1, -1, 0), (0, -\frac{1}{2}, -\frac{3}{2}), (-1, 0, -3)$

27. $(4/3, -2/3, -2/3)$ **28.** $x = 1, y = 2 + t, z = -t, 0 \le t \le 1$

29. $x = 10 - 15t, y = 3t, z = -9 + 9t$ **30.** $60°$ **31.** 2

32. $7\sqrt{3}$ **33.** 28254.323 ft $\cdot$ lb   **34.** 20 pounds

35. a) $\sqrt{14}$,   b) 1   **36.** a) 1,   b) 1

37. (b) and (e) are not always true; others are always true.

38. All are always true.

39. y-axis in plane, yz-plane in 3-space.

40. Line in the plane, plane in 3-space.

41. In plane: circle; in 3-space: cylinder generated by the circle with axis parallel to z-axis.

42. Ellipse in the plane, in 3-space an elliptical cylinder, generated by the ellipse.

43. Parabola opening to the right, cylinder generated by the parabola.

44. Hyperbola, hyperbolic cylinder

45. Cardioid with dimple on right; cylinder generated by the cardioid.

46. Circle with center at $(0, \frac{1}{2})$, radius 1; circular cylinder.

47. Horizontal lemniscate; cylinder generated by the lemniscate.

48. Four-leafed rose; cylinder generated by the rose.

49. Surface of sphere centered at origin with radius 2.

50. Plane parallel to z-axis, generated by the line $y = x$.

51. The upper nappe of a cone whose surface makes an angle of $\pi/6$ with the z-axis.

52. Circle of radius 1, center at $(0,0,0)$ in the xy-plane.

53. The upper hemisphere of the unit sphere.

54. The region between the spheres $x^2 + y^2 + z^2 = 1$ and $x^2 + y^2 + z^2 = 2$ as well as the surfaces of these spheres.

	Rectangular	Cylindrical	Spherical
55.	$(1,0,0)$	$(1,0,0)$	$(1, \frac{\pi}{2}, 0)$
56.	$(0,1,0)$	$(1, \frac{\pi}{2}, 0)$	$(1, \frac{\pi}{2}, \frac{\pi}{2})$
57.	$(0,1,1)$	$(1, \frac{\pi}{2}, 1)$	$(\sqrt{2}, \frac{\pi}{4}, \frac{\pi}{2})$
58.	$(1, 0, -\sqrt{3})$	$(1, 0, -\sqrt{3})$	$(2, \frac{5\pi}{6}, 0)$
59.	$(1,1,1)$	$(\sqrt{2}, \frac{\pi}{4}, 1)$	$(\sqrt{3}, \cos^{-1}(\frac{1}{\sqrt{3}}), \frac{\pi}{4})$
60.	$(0, -1, 1)$	$(1, \frac{3\pi}{2}, 1)$	$(\sqrt{2}, \frac{\pi}{4}, \frac{3\pi}{2})$

61. Cylindrical: $z = 2$, spherical: $\rho \cos \phi = 2$; plane parallel to xy-plane.

62. Cylindrical: $z = r$; spherical: $\varphi = \frac{\pi}{4}$; upper nappe of a cone.

63. Rectangular: $z = x^2 + y^2$; spherical: $\rho = \cos \phi / \sin^2 \phi$; paraboloid opening up.

64. Rectangular: $(x - \frac{1}{2})^2 + y^2 = (\frac{1}{2})^2$; spherical: $\rho \sin \varphi = \cos \theta$; circular cylinder parallel to z axis.

65. Rectangular: $x^2 + y^2 + z^2 = 16$, cylindrical $r^2 + z^2 = 16$; sphere of radius 4.

66. Rectangular: $z = 1$; cylindrical; $z = 1$; the plane $z = 1$.

67. sphere

$$x^2 + y^2 + z^2 = 4$$

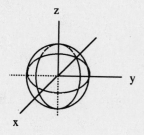

68. sphere

$$x^2 + (y-1)^2 + z^2 = 1$$

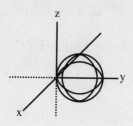

69. ellipsoid

$$4x^2 + 4y^2 + z^2 = 4$$

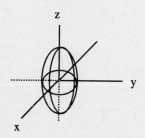

70. ellipsoid

$$36x^2 + 9y^2 + 4z^2 = 36$$

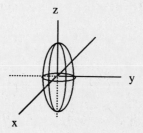

71. circular paraboloid

$$z = -(x^2 + y^2)$$

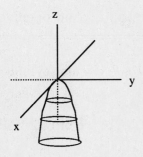

72. circular paraboloid

$$y = -(x^2 + z^2)$$

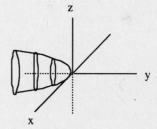

73. cone about z-axis

$$x^2 + y^2 = z^2$$

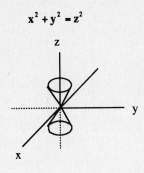

74. cone about y-axis

$$x^2 + z^2 = y^2$$

75. hyperboloid of one sheet

$$x^2 + y^2 - z^2 = 4$$

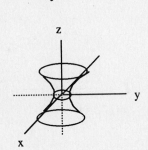

76. hyperboloid of one sheet

$$4y^2 + z^2 - 4x^2 = 4$$

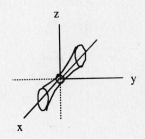

77. hyperboloid of two sheets

$$y^2 - x^2 - z^2 = 1$$

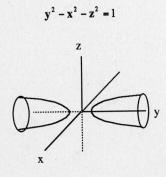

78. hyperboloid of two sheets

$$z^2 - x^2 - y^2 = 1$$

CHAPTER 12

VECTOR-VALUED FUNCTIONS, PARAMETRIZA-TIONS, AND MOTION IN SPACE

12.1 Vector-Valued Functions and Curves in Space; Derivatives and Integrals

1. a) $v = (-2\sin t)i + (3\cos t)j + 4k$ b) $a = (-2\cos t)i + (-3\sin t)j$ c) At $t = \pi/2$: speed $= 2\sqrt{5}$ d) direction $= (-2i + 4k)/2\sqrt{5}$ e) $v = 2\sqrt{5}[-(1/\sqrt{5})i + (2/\sqrt{5})k]$.

2. a) $v = i + 2tj + 2k$ b) $a = 2j$ c) At $t = 1$; speed $= 3$ d) direction $= \frac{1}{3}i + \frac{2}{3}j + \frac{2}{3}k$ e) $v = 3(\frac{1}{3}i + \frac{2}{3}j + \frac{2}{3}k)$.

3. a) $v = (-2\sin 2t)j + (2\cos t)k$ b) $a = (-4\cos 2t)j + (-2\sin t)k$ c) At $t = 0$: speed $= 2$ d) direction $= k$ e) $v = 2k$.

4. a) $v = e^t i + \frac{4}{9}e^{2t}j$ b) $a = e^t i + \frac{8}{9}e^{2t}j$ c) At $t = \ln 3$: speed $= 5$ d) direction $= (3i + 4j)/5$ e) $v = 5[\frac{3}{5}i + \frac{4}{5}j]$.

5. a) $v = (\sec t \tan t)i + (\sec^2 t)j + (4/3)k$ b) $a = (\sec t \tan^2 t + \sec^3 t)i + (2\sec^2 t \tan t)j$ c) At $t = \pi/6$, speed $= 2$ d) direction $= (1/3)i + (2/3)j + (2/3)k$ e) $v = 2[(1/3)i + (2/3)j + (2/3)k]$.

6. a) $v = \frac{2}{t+1}i + 2tj + tk$ b) $a = -\frac{2}{(t+1)^2}i + 2j + k$ c) At $t = 1$: $v = i + 2j + k$, speed $= \sqrt{6}$ d) direction $= \frac{1}{\sqrt{6}}i + \frac{2}{\sqrt{6}}j + \frac{1}{\sqrt{6}}k$ e) $v = \sqrt{6}(\frac{1}{\sqrt{6}}i + \frac{2}{\sqrt{6}}j + \frac{1}{\sqrt{6}}k)$.

7. a) $v = (-e^{-t})i + (-6\sin 3t)j + (6\cos 3t)k$ b) $a = (e^{-t})i + (-18\cos 3t)j + (-18\sin 3t)k$ c) At $t = 0$: speed $= \sqrt{37}$ d) direction $= (-i + 6k)/\sqrt{37}$ e) $v = \sqrt{37}[(-i + 6k)/\sqrt{37}]$.

8. a) $v = i + \sqrt{2}tj + t^2 k$ b) $a = \sqrt{2}j + 2tk$ c) At $t = 1$: speed $= 2$ d) direction $= \frac{1}{2}i + \frac{\sqrt{2}}{2}j + \frac{1}{2}k$ e) $v = 2(\frac{1}{2}i + \frac{\sqrt{2}}{2}j + \frac{1}{2}k)$.

9. $\pi/2$ 10. $\frac{3\pi}{4}$ 11. $\pi/2$ 12. $\frac{\pi}{2}$ 13. $t = 0, \pi, 2\pi$

14. v and a are orthogonal for all $t \geq 0$.   15. $\frac{1}{4}i + 7j + \frac{3}{2}k$

16. $-3i + 2(2\sqrt{2} - 1)j + 2k$ 17. $(\pi/2 + \sqrt{2})j + 2k$ 18. $i + (\ln 2)j + \frac{3}{4}k$

19. $(\ln 4)i + (\ln 4)j + (\ln 2)k$ 20. $\pi i + \sqrt{3}\frac{\pi}{4}k$

21. $v(\pi/4)=(\sqrt{2}/2)(i-j),\ a(\pi/4)=-(\sqrt{2}/2)(i+j),\ v(\pi/2)=-j,\ a(\pi/2)=-i.$

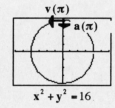 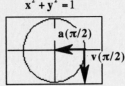

22. $v(\pi)=-2i,\ a(\pi)=-j,\ v(3\pi/2)=-\sqrt{2}i-\sqrt{2}j,\ a(3\pi/2)=\frac{\sqrt{2}}{2}i-\frac{\sqrt{2}}{2}j.$

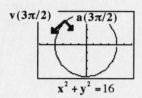

23. $v(\pi)=2i,\ a(\pi)=-j,\ v(3\pi/2)=i-j,\ a(3\pi/2)=-i.$

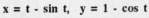

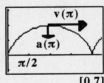 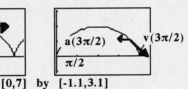

24. $v(-1)=i-2j,\ a(-1)=2j,\ v(0)=i,\ a(0)=2j,\ v(1)=i+2j,\ a(1)=2j.$

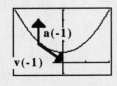 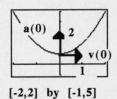 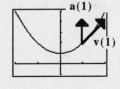

25. $r = (1 - \frac{t^2}{2})i + (2 - \frac{t^2}{2})j + (3 - \frac{t^2}{2})k$ **26.** $r = 90t^2 i + (90t^2 - \frac{16}{3}t^3 + 100)j$

27. $r = [(t+1)^{3/2} - 1]i + (1 - e^{-t})j + [\ln(t+1) + 1]k$

28. $r = (\frac{t^4}{4} + 2t^2 + 1)i + (\frac{t^2}{2} + 1)j + \frac{2}{3}t^3 k$

29. $r = 8ti + 8tj + (100 - 16t^2)k$ **30.** $r(t) = (10 - \frac{t^2}{2})(i + j + k)$.

31. $|\mathbf{v}|$ has maximum and minimum values 2 and 0. $|a| = 1 =$ maximum $|a| =$ minimum $|a|$.

32. $\text{Max}|v| = \max|a| = 3$, $\min|v| = \min|a| = 2$

12.2   MODELING PROJECTILE MOTION

1. 50 sec   **2.** 490 m/sec

3. a) 72.15 sec, 25.51 km   b) 4.02 km   c) 6377.55 m

4. $y = 0$ when $t = 2$ sec. $x(2) = 32\sqrt{3}$ ft ≈ 55.426 ft

6. 39.26° and 50.74°   **7.** 9.9 m/sec; 18.43° and 71.57°

8. 3.136×10^{-12} cm   **9.** 189.56 mph

10. To double the height and range the initial speed should be increased by about 41%.

12. The cannon's angle of elevation should be 32.079°. The performer will have maximum height 31.339 ft so will not strike the ceiling.

13. In flight, the ball passes just above the base of the pin.

14. $y = 29.942$ ft at $t = \sqrt{3}$ sec. It won't clear the tree.

15. It takes $t_1 \approx 2.245$ sec to reach the wall. The initial speed is $v_0 \approx 149.31$ ft/sec. The speed at t_1 is about 141.83 ft/sec neglecting all forces except gravity.

16. a) $r(t) = (145t\cos 23° - 14.67t)i + (2.5 + 145t\sin 23° - 16t^2)j$. $x(t) = 145t\cos 23° - 14.67t$, $y(t) = 2.5 + 145t\sin 23° - 16t^2$ b) In parametric mode graph $x(t)$, $y(t)$, $0 \leq t \leq 3.6$ in $[0, 428]$ by $[0, 52.66]$.   c) We use TRACE and tStep $= 0.1$ for the following estimates.   I) $y_{max} = 52.64$ ft at $t = 1.8$ sec.   II) It travels up to about $x = 427$ ft in about $t = 3.6$ sec when it hits the ground. III) The ball is 18.06 ft high at $t = 0.3$ sec when it is 35.64 ft from home plate. It is 19.96 ft high at $t = 3.2$ sec, 380.17 ft from home plate. IV) By drawing in the fence, LINE$(300, 0, 300, 15)$, we see it is easily a home run. In fact when $x = 300$ ft, $y > 40$ ft.

17. a) $r = [13 + (35 \cos 27°)t]i + [4 + (35 \sin 27°)t - 16t^2]j$. $x = 13 + (35 \cos 27°)t$, $y = 4 + (35 \sin 27°)t - 16t^2$ b) Graph x, y above, $0 \le t \le 1.2$ in $[0, 51]$ by $[-9.7, 19.7]$. Also draw in the net: Line$(25, 0, 25, 6)$. c) I) $y_{max} \approx 7.9$ ft occurs at $t \approx 0.5$ sec. II) It travels 37.4 ft and hits the ground at $t = 1.2$ sec approximately. III) $t \approx 0.25$ sec and 0.75 sec at 7.8 ft and 23.4 ft from the point of impact. IV) The ball hits the net.

18. (c-1) $y_{max} = 43.07$ ft at $t = 1.56$ sec (c-2) $y = 35$ ft at about $t = 0.86$ sec and $t = 2.28$ sec, 119.69 ft and 307.78 ft from home plate, respectively. (c-3) The ball travels 426.02 ft hitting the ground at $t = 3.23$ sec. A 15-ft fence placed 386.82 ft from home plate would prevent a home run. A 12-ft fence placed 395.45 ft from home plate would prevent a home run.

19. a) $y_{max} = 40.435$ ft at $t = 1.48$ sec b) It travels about 373 ft hitting ground at $t = 3.13$ sec c) $y = 30$ ft at about $t = 0.69$ sec and $t = 2.3$ sec, 94.59 ft and 287.08 ft from home plate, respectively. d) Yes

20. We first convert: $\frac{12\,mi}{hr} = \frac{12\,mi}{hr} \frac{1\,hr}{3600\,sec} \frac{5280\,ft}{1\,mi} = 17.6$ ft/sec. a) $x = \frac{152(\cos 20°)}{0.08}(1 - e^{-0.08t}) - 17.6t$, $y = 3 + \frac{152(\sin 20°)}{0.08}(1 - e^{-0.08t}) + \frac{32}{0.08^2}(1 - 0.08t - e^{-0.08t})$. Using these values of x and y, the vector form of the flight function is $r(t) = xi + yj$. b) We use x, y above. In parametric mode graph $x_1 = x$, $y_1 = y$, tstep $= 0.1$, $0 \le t \le 3.2$ in $[0, 410]$ by $[0, 50]$ to simulate the motion with the wind and use $x_2 = x_1 + 17.6t$, $y_2 = y_1$ without wind. c) I) With and without the wind (using TRACE) we obtain $y_{max} = 41.88$ at $t = 1.5$. II) With the wind the ball travels in the air about 345 ft and without the wind about 401 ft. In each case it hits the ground at approximately $t = 3.2$ sec. III) With the wind: $y = 35.489$ ft when $x = 108.191$ ft, $t = 0.9$ sec and $y = 34.782$ ft when $x = 249.414$ ft and $t = 2.2$ sec. Without the wind: $y = 35.489$ ft when $x = 124.031$ ft and $t = 0.9$ sec and $y = 34.782$ ft when $x = 288.134$ ft and $t = 2.2$ sec IV) With the wind by II) the ball hits the ground before 380 ft so it certainly is not a home run. Without the wind the ball is only at $y \approx 8.5$ ft when $x = 380.985$ ft so it is still not a home run. By trial and error we find that we need a wind gust speed of about 12 ft/sec (8.182 mi/h) *in the direction of the flight of the ball* for the hit to be a home run.

21.

k	y_{max}	Time for y_{max}	Flight Distance	Flight Time
0.01	44.77 ft	1.6 sec	463.66 ft	3.3 sec
0.02	44.34	1.6	456.13	3.3
0.05	43.05	1.6	422.38	3.2
0.1	41.15	1.5	391.15	3.2
0.15	39.39	1.5	354.10	3.1
0.20	37.85	1.4	322.22	3.0
0.25	36.41	1.4	299.66	3.0

c) As the air density diminishes to 0, the air resistance to the motion of the projectile diminishes to 0, as was assumed in Eq. (6).

22. a) $t_f \approx 1.9$ sec.   b) $r_f \approx 149.11$ ft   c) $t_f = 1.9154$ sec   d) $r_f = \frac{2v_0^2(\sin(\alpha-\beta))\cos\alpha}{g\cos^2\beta}$ $(= 149.21$ ft in the specified case$)$.

24. In the second part v_0 should again bisect the angle between the hill and the vertical.

12.3 DIRECTED DISTANCE AND THE UNIT TANGENT VECTOR T

1. $T = -\frac{2}{3}\sin t i + \frac{2}{3}\cos t j + \frac{\sqrt{5}}{3}k.$ $L = 3\pi.$

2. $T = (12/13)\cos 2t i - (12/13)\sin 2t j + (5/13)k.$ $L = 13\pi.$

3. $T = \frac{1}{\sqrt{1+t}}i + \sqrt{\frac{t}{1+t}}k.$ $L = \frac{52}{3}.$

4. $T = -|\cos t|\frac{\sin t}{|\sin t|}j + |\sin t|\frac{\cos t}{|\cos t|}k.$ $L = \frac{3}{2}.$

5. $T = \frac{1}{\sqrt{3}}(i - j + k).$ $L = 3\sqrt{3}.$

6. $T = \frac{1}{7}(6i - 2j - 3k).$ $L = 14.$

7. $T = \left(\frac{\cos t - t\sin t}{t+1}\right)i + \left(\frac{\sin t + t\cos t}{t+1}\right)j + \left(\frac{\sqrt{2t}}{t+1}\right)k.$ $L = \frac{\pi^2}{2} + \pi.$

8. For $t \geq 0,$ $T = \cos t i - \sin t j.$ $L = 1.$

9. $s(t) = 5(t - t_0).$ $L = \frac{5\pi}{2}.$

10. $s(t) = \frac{1}{2}(t|t| - t_0|t_0|).$ Length of section $= \frac{3\pi^2}{8}.$

11. $s(t) = \sqrt{3}(e^t - e^{t_0})$. $L = 3\sqrt{3}$.

12. $s(t) = 7(t - t_0)$. $L = 7$.

13. $\sqrt{2} + \ln(1 + \sqrt{2})$.

12.4 CURVATURE, TORSION, AND THE TNB FRAME

1. $T = \cos i - \sin t j$, $N = -\sin t i - \cos t j$, $\kappa = \cos t$

2. $T = \sin t i + \cos t j$, $N = \cos t i - \sin t j$, $\kappa = \cos t$

3. $T = \frac{i - t j}{\sqrt{1+t^2}}$, $N = -\frac{t}{\sqrt{1+t^2}} i - \frac{1}{\sqrt{1+t^2}} j$, $\kappa = \frac{1}{2(1+t^2)^{3/2}}$

4. $T = \cos t i + \sin t j$, $N = -\sin t i + \cos t j$, $\kappa = \frac{1}{t}$ for $t > 0$

5. $T = \frac{3}{5}\cos t i - \frac{3}{5}\sin t j + \frac{4}{5}k$, $N = -\sin t i - \cos t j$, $B = \frac{4}{5}\cos t i - \frac{4}{5}\sin t j - \frac{3}{5}k$, $\kappa = \frac{3}{25}$, $\tau = \frac{4}{25}$

6. For $t > 0$, $T = \cos t i + \sin t j$, $N = -\sin t i + \cos t j$, $\kappa = \frac{1}{t}$, $B = k$, $\tau = 0$

7. $T = \left(\frac{\cos t - \sin t}{\sqrt{2}}\right)i + \left(\frac{\cos t + \sin t}{\sqrt{2}}\right)j$, $N = -\left(\frac{\sin t + \cos t}{\sqrt{2}}\right)i + \left(\frac{\cos t - \sin t}{\sqrt{2}}\right)j$, $B = k$, $\kappa = \frac{1}{\sqrt{2}e^t}$, $\tau = 0$

8. $T = \frac{12}{13}\cos 2t i - \frac{12}{13}\sin 2t j + \frac{5}{13}k$, $N = -\sin 2t i - \cos 2t j$, $B = \frac{5}{13}\cos 2t i - \frac{5}{13}\sin 2t j - \frac{12}{13}k$, $\kappa = \frac{24}{169}$, $\tau = \frac{10}{169}$

9. $a = \frac{2t}{\sqrt{1+t^2}}T + \frac{2}{\sqrt{1+t^2}}N$ 10. $a = \frac{2}{t^2+1}N$ 11. aN, assuming $a > 0$

12. $a = 0T + 0N$ 13. $a = \frac{4}{3}T + \frac{2\sqrt{5}}{3}N$ 14. $a(0) = 2\sqrt{2}N$

15. $a = 2N$ 16. $a(0) = 2T(0) + \sqrt{2}N(0)$

17. At $t = \frac{\pi}{4}$, $r = \frac{\sqrt{2}}{2}i + \frac{\sqrt{2}}{2}j - k$, $T = -\frac{\sqrt{2}}{2}i + \frac{\sqrt{2}}{2}j$, $N = -\frac{\sqrt{2}}{2}i - \frac{\sqrt{2}}{2}j$, $B = k$. Osculating plane: $z = -1$. Normal plane: $y = x$. Rectifying plane: $y = -x$.

18. At $t = 0$, $r = i$, $T = \frac{1}{\sqrt{2}}j + \frac{1}{\sqrt{2}}k$, $N = -i$, $B = -\frac{1}{\sqrt{2}}j + \frac{1}{\sqrt{2}}k$. Osculating plane: $z = y$. Normal plane: $z = -y$. Rectifying plane: $x = 1$.

20. b) $\kappa = \cos x$ c) Graph $x_1 = t$, $y_1 = \kappa = \cos t$, $x_2 = t$, $y_2 = \ln\cos t$, $-\pi/2 < t < \pi/2$ in $[-\frac{\pi}{2}, \frac{\pi}{2}]$ by $[-3, 1]$. At the endpoints of the interval where $\kappa \to 0$, the angle ϕ between T and i is changing at a slower and slower rate. It is changing fastest at $x = 0$ where κ is maximal.

21. $(x - \pi/2)^2 + y^2 = 1$. Graph $x_1(t) = t$, $y_1(t) = \sin t$ and $x_2(t) = \frac{\pi}{2} + \cos t$, $y_2(t) = \sin t$, $-2\pi \leq t \leq 2\pi$, tstep $= 0.1$ in $[-2\pi, 2\pi]$ by $[-4.2, 3.2]$.

22. $x^2 + (y + 4)^2 = 4$. Graph $x_1(t) = 2\ln t$, $y_1(t) = -(t + \frac{1}{t})$ and $x_2(t) = 2\cos t$, $y_2(t) = -4 + 2\sin t$, $0 \leq t \leq 3\pi$, tstep $= 0.1$ in $[-9.3, 9.3]$ by $[-10, 1]$.

24. $\frac{1}{2}$ 25. $\frac{1}{2b}$

12.5 PLANETARY MOTION AND SATELLITES

1. 93.17 min. compared to 93.11 min. in the Table   2. 30297 m/sec

3. 6763 km compared with 6765 km   4. a) 21890 km   b) 6481 km

5. 1655 min   6. 42167 km   7. 20427 km

8. 376800 km   9. $(1.9966 \times 10^7)/\sqrt{r}$ m/sec

10. In $\sec^2/m^3$: 2.97×10^{-19}, 9.903×10^{-14}, 8.046×10^{-12}.

11. Circle: $v_0 = \sqrt{\frac{GM}{r_0}}$. Ellipse: $\sqrt{\frac{GM}{r_0}} < v_0 < \sqrt{\frac{2GM}{r_0}}$. Hyperbola: $v_0 > \sqrt{\frac{2GM}{r_0}}$.

PRACTICE EXERCISES, CHAPTER 12

1.

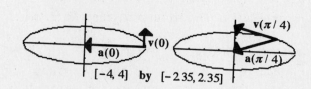

2.

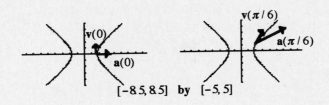

$[-8.5, 8.5]$ **by** $[-5, 5]$

3. $6i + 8j$

4. $3i + (\ln 2)j + k$

5. $r = (\cos t - 1)i + (\sin t + 1)j + tk$

6. $r = \tan^{-1} ti + (1 - \sin^{-1} t)j + \sqrt{t^2 + 1}k$.

7. $r = i + t^2 j + tk$

8. $r = (6t - t^2 - 2)i + (4t - 2t^2 + 1)j$

9. $\frac{\pi\sqrt{16+\pi^2}}{16} + \ln\left(\frac{\pi+\sqrt{16+\pi^2}}{4}\right) = 1.7199\ldots$

10. 14

11. At $t = 0: T = \frac{2}{3}i - \frac{2}{3}j + \frac{1}{3}k$, $N = (i+j)/\sqrt{2}$, $B = -\frac{1}{3\sqrt{2}}i + \frac{1}{3\sqrt{2}}j + \frac{4}{3\sqrt{2}}k$, $\kappa = \sqrt{2}/3$, $\tau = \frac{1}{6}$.

12. $T = \frac{1}{\sqrt{2}}\cos ti - \sin tj + \frac{1}{\sqrt{2}}\cos tk$, $N = -\frac{1}{\sqrt{2}}\sin ti - \cos tj - \frac{1}{\sqrt{2}}\sin tk$, $B = \frac{i-k}{\sqrt{2}}$, $\kappa = \frac{1}{\sqrt{2}}$, $\tau = 0$

13. $a(0) = 10T(0) + 6N(0)$

14. $a(0) = 2\sqrt{2}T + 2\sqrt{3}N$

15. 1

16. $\frac{\pi}{2}$

17. $t = 0, \frac{\pi}{2}, \pi$

18. $t = \frac{\pi}{3}$

19. $x = 66\sqrt{2}$ ft, $y = -42.66$ ft so it must be on the level ground.

20. 57 ft

21. 644.36 ft/sec and 675.42 ft/sec

22. 59.19 ft/sec

23. a) $x = (155\cos 18°)t - (176/15)t$, $y = 4 + (155\sin 18°)t - 16t^2$ and with the same $x, y, r = xi + yj$ b) Graph x, y in a), $0 \leq t \leq 4$, tstep $= 0.05$ in $[0, 500]$ by $[0, 100]$. Also include LINE$(380, 0, 380, 10)$.   c) With the set up in b) we use the TRACE function. (c-i) $y_{max} = 39.85$ ft at $t = 1.5$ sec (c-ii) $y = 0$ at about $t = 3.1$ sec and $x = 420.61$ ft (c-iii) $y = 25$ ft at about $t = 0.55$ sec and $t = 2.45$ sec, when $x = 74.62$ ft and 332.42 ft, respectively. (c-iv) Yes.

24. a) $y_{max} = 36.92$ ft at $t = 1.4$ sec   b) $y = 30$ ft at about $t = 0.75$ sec and $t = 2.05$ sec, 98.11 ft and 251.91 ft from home plate, respectively.   c) $y = 0$ at about $t = 2.95$ sec when x is about 347.32 ft   d) No, since by c) the ball hits the ground short of the fence. It is a home run if $k = 0.01$.

25. $x = 1 + t, y = t, z = -t$ **26.** $x = 1 - 5, y = 1 + t, z = \frac{\pi}{4} + t$

27. $\frac{1}{5}$ **28.** $x + y + z = \frac{8}{3}$

29. $\tau = b/(a^2 + b^2)$ has maximum value $1/(2a)$ for a given value of $a > 0$.

30. $\kappa = \cos t$

31. a) 5971 km   b) $VA = (5.2188 \times 10^6)\pi$ km^2 c) 3.21%

33. b) 1.49870113352. Graph f in the window $[-2, 3]$ by $[-2, 2]$.